Brief Contents

Detailed Contents

Chapter 2   *Finding the Main Idea*   61

Chapter 6   *PRO and Study-Outlining*   *190*

Chapter 9   *Drawing Inferences   301*

Appendix *355*

Preview Your Text

Before you begin any course, get familiar with your textbook. You can practice by examining this workbook. Then examine your other textbooks to make them seem less like foreign objects and more like a necessary part of your courses. Plus, you will be more likely to find the correct page quickly in class.

The title obviously stresses two important skills in reading: *speed* and *comprehension*. Make a personal connection. List at least three ways that improving these skills will help you outside school.

_____

_____

_____

How much importance do these skills have in the course that requires this book? Check your course outline or ask your instructor. How will these skills help you in other courses? Make another list.

_____

_____

You may be wondering *why the lists*? Writing them keeps you actively involved in the reading process. It forces you to clarify your thinking. Writing lists also helps prepare you for making study notes and for outlining.

Examine information you usually skip. What are the authors' names? _____ and _____ What is the edition number? ____ When was the book published? ____ (How current is it?) Check the front and back covers for the publisher's claims, if any, or comments from reviewers. (Notice what is special about the book.)

Now *look over the Table of Contents*. How many chapters does this book have? ____ What is the name of the section in the back where the Homework Lessons are located? _____

Look at each chapter's organization more closely. How many parts is each chapter divided into? (Clue: Look at the Roman numerals.) ____ In which of those parts is the Study Unit always found (except for Chapter 7)? ____ In which chapter will the Study Unit cover "Finding the Main Idea"? ____ "Skimming and Scanning"? ____ "Drawing Inferences"? ____ In which part of each chapter (except Chapter 7) do you always find the Timed Readings? ____

Examine the Appendix more closely. On which page do the Answer Keys for this book begin? ____ On which page do you find the Progress Chart for the Timed Readings? ____

Note: Your instructor may ask you to turn in this page.

Preview Your Reading Habits*

Choose the answer that fits your reading habits at this point in the course. On the line next to each item, write A for always, U for usually, S for sometimes, R for rarely.

_____ 1. Before I start to read, I preview the reading material for title, author, thesis, logic patterns, headings, lists, and other graphic aids.

_____ 2. In an article or chapter, I can tell where the introduction ends, the body begins and ends, and the conclusion begins.

_____ 3. I look first in the introduction of an article or chapter for the thesis or main idea for the whole piece.

_____ 4. Each time I read a paragraph, I am looking for a sentence that states the main idea for that paragraph.

_____ 5. If I do not see a topic sentence in a paragraph, I try to infer the main idea.

_____ 6. I try to determine the logic pattern for each paragraph and tell first-level details from second-level and third-level details.

_____ 7. I look for transitional words or phrases that writers use as signposts to guide the reader from one idea to the next.

_____ 8. I do not regress when reading easy material.

_____ 9. I read phrases at one glance instead of pausing on each word, and I avoid margin reading.

_____ 10. I use a different method when reading difficult material or for study purposes than when reading for pleasure.

_____ 11. When I finish studying or reading difficult material, I tell myself in my own words what I have just read.

_____ 12. I determine whether an author's purpose is to inform, persuade, or entertain.

_____ 13. I am aware of an author's tone. In other words, I can tell when a writer is being sarcastic, bitter, gentle, playful, or ironic.

_____ 14. I make a constant effort to learn the meaning of new words from their context and from word analysis.

_____ 15. I have made a commitment to read something every day for pleasure.

Look again at the items where you have answered "sometimes" or "rarely." Start now to change your habits so that you "usually" or "always" practice the good reading habits.

*Partly based on the *Leedy Reading Habits Inventory*.

Score: _____

A Note to the Instructor

A Whole Course in One Book

Each of the two graded workbooks in the **Reading Faster and Understanding More** series has been redesigned as a *whole course in one book*. Comprehension is the main focus of the books, but vocabulary has been expanded so that no additional books should be necessary for students to build their skills (although lab work with some of the excellent new programs on the market is recommended). Rate-building strategies are also presented as another means of improving comprehension.

The two books are intended for the young adult or mature adult reader whose vocabulary, comprehension, and reading rate are at the developmental level. The readings in Book One range through Levels E/F, G, and H* and in Book Two through Levels H/I, J, and K. Because both books follow the same progression of skills, they can be used concurrently in the same classroom with students of widely different reading levels. The examples used in each book differ and are appropriate to the reading level of the students of that book.

The fifth edition includes the following features:

1. The *Preview Your Text* exercise is continued to introduce students not only to the book, but also to the essential previewing skill early in the semester. To help students assess the changes in their reading habits, the exercise *Preview Your Reading Habits* **now** appears before the Pretests and again in the last chapter as a review.

2. The *Pretests* have been improved, and the *Posttests* are **now** placed in the **Instructor's Manual** to give the instructor more options over how they are given.

   (a) The *Vocabulary Pretest* has been expanded from 50 items to 100 items. The words in Part 1 are taken from *Vocabulary Previews*, and the words and word parts in Part 2 are taken from *Homework Lessons*.

   (b) The *Comprehension and Rate Pretest* **now** has a Percentage Chart and more objective questions, for easier scoring.

3. The **new** *Vocabulary Previews* are now more conveniently located before each chapter, instead of being combined with the *Homework Lessons* in the back of the book.

   (a) They continue to show the student how to look for context clues for 279 words taken from the readings in the chapters.

   (b) Each "Words in Context" section **now** has an Exercise with the words used in the context of a second sentence and easy-to-score multiple-choice answers.

---

*Based on the Flesch–Kincaid and the Fry readability formulas.

4. Each chapter has ***now*** been reorganized to follow more naturally the order in which items would be taught in the classroom and contains additional practice.

   (a) The *How to Understand More* section continues to emphasize logic strategies:
   - instruction advancing from main idea and details through logic patterns, study-reading, skimming and scanning, and critical reading to interpreting literature
   - a Study Unit with ***new***, additional Practice exercises and improved Study Notes to take the student from simple note-taking in a list to outlining
   - three untimed Paragraph exercises with questions reinforcing the logic skills

   (b) The *How to Read Faster* section, continuing to reinforce logic skills, gives rate-building tips and provides timed practice through phrase-reading and longer articles. The longer Timed Readings continue a topic introduced in the untimed Paragraph Practice exercises.

5. At the end of each chapter are two ***new*** review quizzes (with keys in the *Instructor's Manual*), designed so they can be torn out and turned in.

   (a) The *Vocabulary Review* has twenty words taken from the *Vocabulary Preview*, in an easy-to-score format with four types of questions.

   (b) The *Comprehension Review*, based on the Study Unit, includes at least one paragraph exercise and provides practice in thinking, test-taking, and writing.

6. Following the last chapter is the improved *Homework Lessons* section:

   (a) It has been shortened by moving the "Words in Context" to the front of each chapter.

   (b) It begins with a "How to Use the Dictionary" exercise followed by instruction on "How to Build a Vocabulary File"—segments that equip students to work their way through the remaining Homework Lessons as well as the Vocabulary Previews.

   (c) The charts for the roots, prefixes, and suffixes have been simplified to contain two easier sample words and only one new vocabulary word for each word part.

7. In addition to the *Homework Lessons*, the *Appendix* ***now*** includes the following:

   (a) Two lists of new words from the *Vocabulary Previews*: one list organized by chapter and one alphabetized list

   (b) Two lists from the *Homework Lessons*: an alphabetized list of roots, prefixes, and suffixes and an alphabetized list of new words introduced in the charts

   (c) *Answer Keys* including most of the exercises for each chapter are ***now*** combined at the back of the book for easy collection by the instructor

   (d) *Progress Charts* for recording scores from the Pretests and Posttests (***now*** including Chapter Reviews and Unit Tests) and from the Timed Readings

8. The *Instructor's Manual* (ISBN 0-321-04589-0) is ***now*** bound separately and includes the following:

   (a) Answers to Pretests, Posttests, Chapter Reviews, and Exercises for Vocabulary Previews and Homework Lessons

(b) Copyable model outlines for Study Notes, for paragraph exercises in Chapter 5, and for the extended outline in Chapter 6

(c) Suggestions for teaching each of the ten chapters

(d) Copyable Vocabulary Unit Tests, Study Unit Tests, Homework Lesson Reviews, Vocabulary Posttest, and Comprehension and Rate Posttest (plus keys for each)

(e) Copyable perceptual drills and word, phrase, and sentence practice

(f) *New* list of computer software, compiled by Dr. Diane Gross at El Camino College

(g) *New* percentage charts for convenience in scoring

We recommend that students work through each of the ten chapters in numeric order, particularly in the first six chapters, because each chapter has been carefully designed as a building block to later chapters.

The Longman Developmental Reading Package

In addition to the **Instructor's Manual/Test Bank** discussed above, a series of other skills-based supplements is available for both instructors and students. All of these supplements are available either free or at greatly reduced prices.

For Additional Reading and Reference

The Dictionary Deal. Two dictionaries can be shrinkwrapped with this text at a nominal fee. *The New American Webster Handy College Dictionary* is a paperback reference text with more than 100,000 entries. *Merriam Webster's Collegiate Dictionary,* tenth edition, is a hardback reference with a citation file of more than 14.5 million examples of English words drawn from actual use. For more information on how to shrinkwrap a dictionary with this text, please contact your Addison Wesley Longman sales representative.

Penguin Quality Paperback Titles. A series of Penguin paperbacks is available at a significant discount when shrinkwrapped with this title. Some titles available are: Toni Morrison's *Beloved,* Julia Alvarez's *How the Garcia Girls Lost Their Accents,* Mark Twain's *Huckleberry Finn, Narrative of the Life of Frederick Douglass,* Harriet Beecher Stowe's *Uncle Tom's Cabin,* Dr. Martin Luther King, Jr.'s *Why We Can't Wait,* and plays by Shakespeare, Miller, and Albee. For a complete list of titles or more information, please contact your Addison Wesley Longman sales consultant.

The Longman Textbook Reader. This supplement, for use in developmental reading courses, offers five complete chapters from AWL textbooks: computer science, biology, psychology, communications, and business. Each chapter includes additional comprehension quizzes, critical thinking questions, and group activities. Available FREE with the adoption of *Reading Faster and Understanding More.* Ask your Addison Wesley Longman sales consultant for more information.

The Pocket Reader, First Edition, and The Brief Pocket Reader, First Edition. These inexpensive volumes contain 80 or 50 brief readings respectively (1–3 pages each) on a variety of themes: writers on writing, nature, women and men, customs and habits, politics, rights and obligations, and coming of age. Also included is an alternate rhetorical table of contents. *The Pocket Reader:* 0-321-07668-0. *The Brief Pocket Reader:* 0-321-07699-9

***Newsweek* Alliance.** Instructors may choose to shrinkwrap a 12-week subscription to *Newsweek* with any Longman text. The price of the subscription is 57 cents per issue (a total of $6.84 for the subscription). Available with the subscription is a free "Interactive Guide to *Newsweek*"—a workbook for students who are using the text. In addition, *Newsweek* provides a wide variety of instructor supplements free to teachers, including maps, Skills Builders, and weekly quizzes. For more information on the *Newsweek* program, please contact your Addison Wesley Longman sales consultant.

Electronic and Online Offerings

Longman *Reading Road Trip* Multimedia Software, Version 2.0. This innovative and exciting multimedia reading software is available either in CD-ROM format or as a site license. The package takes students on a tour of 15 cities and landmarks throughout the United States. Each of the 15 modules corresponds to a reading or study skill (for example, finding the main idea, understanding patterns of organization, and thinking critically). All modules contain a tour of the location, instruction and tutorial, exercises, interactive feedback, and mastery tests. This second release includes a more streamlined and flexible navigation, along with hundreds of new readings, exercises, and tests. To shrinkwrap *Reading Road Trip* free with your text, please contact your Addison Wesley Longman sales consultant.

***Researching Online,* Fourth Edition.** A perfect companion for a new age, this indispensable new supplement helps students navigate the Internet. Adapted from *Teaching Online,* the instructor's Internet guide, *Researching Online* speaks directly to students, giving them detailed, step-by-step instructions for performing electronic searches. Available free when shrinkwrapped with this text. For more information, please contact your Addison Wesley Longman sales representative.

The Longman English Pages Web Site. Both students and instructors can visit our free content-rich Web site for additional reading selections and writing exercises. From the Longman English Pages, visitors can conduct a simulated Web search, learn how to write a resume and cover letter, or try their hand at poetry writing. Stop by and visit us at **http://www.awl.com/englishpages**.

The Longman Electronic Newsletter. Twice a month during the spring and fall, instructors who have subscribed receive a free copy of the Longman Developmental English Newsletter in their e-mailbox. Written by experienced classroom instructors, the newsletter offers teaching tips, classroom activities, book reviews, and more. To subscribe, visit the Longman Basic Skills Web site at **http://www.awl.com/basicskills**, or send an e-mail to **Basic Skills@awl.com**.

For Instructors

Electronic Test Bank for Reading. Available in December 2000, this electronic test bank offers more than 3,000 questions in all areas of reading, including vocabulary, main idea, supporting details, patterns of organization, language, critical thinking, analytical reasoning, inference, point of view, visual aids, and textbook reading. With this easy-to-use CD-ROM, instructors simply choose questions from the electronic test bank, then print out the completed test for distribution. 0-321-08179-X

CLAST Test Package, Fourth Edition. These two 40-item objective tests evaluate students' readiness for the CLAST exams. Strategies for teaching CLAST preparedness are included. Free with any Longman English title. Reproducible sheets: 0-321-01950-4 Computerized IBM version: 0-321-01982-2 Computerized Mac version: 0-321-01983-0

TASP Test Package, Third Edition. These 12 practice pretests and post-tests assess the same reading and writing skills covered in the TASP examination. Free with any Longman English title. Reproducible sheets: 0-321-01959-8 Computerized IBM version: 0-321-01985-7 Computerized Mac version: 0-321-01984-9

Teaching Online: Internet Research, Conversation, and Composition, Third Edition. Ideal for instructors who have never surfed the Net, this easy-to-follow guide offers basic definitions, numerous examples, and step-by-step information about finding and using Internet sources. Free to adopters. 0-321-07760-1

***Reading Critically: Texts, Charts, and Graphs*, Second Edition.** For instructors who would like to emphasize critical thinking in their courses, this brief book (65 pages) provides additional critical thinking material to supplement coverage in the text. Free to instructors. 0-673-97365-4

A Word of Appreciation

We wish to thank a number of instructors who made suggestions for this fifth edition of ***Reading Faster and Understanding More***:

1. The reading instructors at El Camino College, and, in particular, Phyllis West, who contributed lists of errors and flaws in the fourth edition; and Dr. Diane Gross, who compiled the list of computer software

2. The reading instructors at Santa Monica College, and, in particular, Gary Todd and Elisha Shapiro

3. The instructors who reviewed the manuscript: Jennifer Dolin, Illinois Central College; Linda Edwards, Chattanooga State Community College; Dorothy Fancher, Alpena Community College; Kristy Gorenz, Illinois Central College; Cecelia Guinee, Portland Community College; Alex Immerblum, East Los Angeles College; Karen Harell, Illinois Central College; Christine Phillips, Pueblo Community College; Carolyn Prusak, Illinois Central College; Donna Richardson, Mercer County Community College; Linda Robinett, Oklahoma City College; Patricia Rottmund, Harrisburg Area Community College; Kerry Segel, Saginaw Valley State University; Elisha Shapiro, Santa Monica College; Katie Smith, Riverside Community College; Sharon Stevens, Oklahoma City Community College; Barbara Sussman, Miami-Dade Community College; Carolyn Thomas, Illinois Central College; and Susan Wickham, Des Moines Area Community College

4. Angela O'Brien, who revised most of the vocabulary in Books 1 and 2, and Susana Orozco, faithful typist and Girl Friday

5. Dr. Ken Nies, Salvador Orozco, and Dr. David Wilczynski, who were on call for much needed help and advice with our new computers

6. Doris Flood Ladd and Anne Dye Phillips, who helped coauthor the original 1976 text of **Reading Faster and Understanding More**, from which the series evolved

WANDA MAUREEN MILLER

SHARON STEEBER DE OROZCO

A Note to the Instructor

Pretests

Vocabulary Pretest

This test has two parts. Part 1 contains words from the Vocabulary Previews—words taken from the readings in each chapter. Part 2 contains words and word parts from the Homework Lessons (a study of roots, prefixes, and suffixes) found in the back of this book. Since you have not yet begun to study these vocabulary words, you will not know as many as when you take the Posttest (in the Instructor's Manual), given at the end of the course. At that time you should be able to get a much higher score.

Note: *Write the letter of your answer in the short lines to the left of the numbers. Or your instructor may ask you to use a separate answer sheet.*

Part 1: Words from "Vocabulary Previews"

Match the vocabulary word on the left with its definition on the right. Match each group separately.

_____ 1. **elite**   (a) guessed

_____ 2. **carcinogens**   (b) allowing too much

_____ 3. **surmised**   (c) upper class

_____ 4. **permissive**   (d) starved

_____ 5. **emaciated**   (e) cancer-causing agents

_____ 6. **writhing**   (a) continues

_____ 7. **celibate**   (b) half-hearted

_____ 8. **harassment**   (c) twisting

_____ 9. **desultory**   (d) bad treatment

_____ 10. **perpetuates**   (e) without sex

*Choose the best definition for each **boldfaced** vocabulary word as it is used in its context.*

_____ 11. a **frugal** shopper
   (a) thrifty   (b) wasteful   (c) hurried

_____ 12. the **prolific** writer
   (a) talented   (b) mystery   (c) productive

_____ 13. a **delusive** idea
   (a) great   (b) unrealistic   (c) well–planned

_____ 14. a lengthy **repertoire**
   (a) grocery list   (b) performance list   (c) "to do" list

_____ 15. **diminished** his pain

(a) lessened   (b) checked   (c) increased

_____ 16. being **facetious**

(a) humorous   (b) tiresome   (c) tardy

_____ 17. an **insatiable** appetite

(a) easily satisfied   (b) satisfactory   (c) unable to be satisfied

_____ 18. the **empathy** she felt

(a) pain   (b) happiness   (c) understanding

_____ 19. a **paltry** price

(a) unfair   (b) insignificant   (c) too expensive

_____ 20. sudden **proliferation** of new bills

(a) disappearance   (b) increase in number   (c) decrease in number

_____ 21. the pain of **unrequited** love

(a) not returned   (b) immature   (c) crazy

_____ 22. a **pathetic** excuse

(a) reasonable   (b) believable   (c) pitiful

_____ 23. those clever **quipsters**

(a) jokers   (b) carpenters   (c) children

_____ 24. his **alleged** crimes

(a) murderous   (b) supposed   (c) earlier

_____ 25. full of **invective**

(a) poetry   (b) insults   (c) sugar

_____ 26. the **distraught** mother

(a) overworked   (b) very sleepy   (c) very upset

_____ 27. **subversion** of plans

(a) destruction   (b) support   (c) interpretation

_____ 28. **dynamic** between them

(a) bond   (b) force   (c) message

_____ 29. **transcended** her troubles

(a) transferred   (b) accepted   (c) rose above

_____ 30. her **filial** responsibility

(a) financially hard   (b) due to parents   (c) unwanted

Complete the following sentences by choosing the correct word from the box above each group of five sentences.

(a) **rigorous**	(b) **diversified**	(c) **implacable**
(d) **belittled**	(e) **correlation**	

31. Maurice has been _____ by his so-called friends one time too many, so he said goodbye and found some more supportive friends.

32. Molly saw a strong _____ between partying all night and flunking tests the next day.

33. After being teased about his dull gray clothes, Sam _____ his wardrobe.

34. The clerk at the department store gave her a(n) _____ stare when she tried to return the soiled silk blouse a year after she bought it.

35. Donna went on a _____ diet after gaining ten pounds over the holidays.

(a) **refute** (b) **tranquil** (c) **flourish** (d) **soliciting** (e) **fawn**

36. Maria felt _____ after a hot bath and a long massage.

37. The candidate for the school board spent the day knocking on doors and _____ votes from his neighbors.

38. I am forced to _____ your accusation that I insulted you.

39. The ballet dancer finished her routine with a bow and a small _____ with her hand.

40. After he won the lottery, even his casual acquaintances began to seek him out and _____ over him.

*Decide if the statement is true or false. Look for the correct usage of the **bold-faced** word in its context, rather than for facts.*

a = True   b = False

_____ 41. On her first trip to New York City, the unsophisticated, small-town girl **gawked** at the tall buildings and fast-moving traffic.

_____ 42. The lawyer earned a great deal of money because he took the case **quid pro quo**.

_____ 43. His **sardonic** smile expressed his cheerful nature and open heart.

_____ 44. An **erroneous** decision by a drug company could have serious consequences for its customers.

_____ 45. Peter was given a Congressional Medal of Honor for his **reprehensible** act.

_____ 46. Marlene's **tenuous** grasp of reality made her a great candidate for chief of staff at the hospital.

_____ 47. For those parents of small children, it was a relief to be at a party with their **contemporaries**—and without the children.

_____ 48. Susan wrote a **parody** of her mother's death that pleased and touched her entire family.

_____ 49. A **cynical** attitude is probably not the best qualification for a preschool teacher.

_____ 50. Her attempts at teaching her children to read before they learned to walk were **futile**.

% Correct _____

Vocabulary Pretest

Part 2: Words and Word Parts from "Homework Lessons"

Match the word part on the left with its definition on the right. Match each group separately.

	roots	definitions
_____ 1.	**homo**	(a) body
_____ 2.	**lus, luc**	(b) time
_____ 3.	**corpus**	(c) same
_____ 4.	**mor**	(d) light
_____ 5.	**chron**	(e) dead

	roots	definitions
_____ 6.	**derm**	(a) water
_____ 7.	**terra**	(b) skin
_____ 8.	**hydra**	(c) earth
_____ 9.	**manu**	(d) hold
_____ 10.	**tain, ten**	(e) hand

	prefixes	definitions
_____ 11.	**retro-**	(a) around
_____ 12.	**mal-**	(b) half
_____ 13.	**intra-**	(c) back
_____ 14.	**semi-**	(d) inside, within
_____ 15.	**circum-**	(e) bad

	suffixes	definitions
_____ 16.	**-ward** (adj.)	(a) in a certain manner
_____ 17.	**-ee** (n.)	(b) little
_____ 18.	**-ette** (n.)	(c) direction
_____ 19.	**-ly** (adv.)	(d) killing
_____ 20.	**-cide** (n.)	(e) one who receives an action

*Choose the best definition for each **boldfaced** vocabulary word.*

_____ 21. her unfortunate **incarceration**

    (a) time in the army   (b) wild youth   (c) time in jail

_____ 22. his impressive **elocution**

    (a) manners   (b) formal speech   (c) posture

_____ 23. tricked by a **charlatan**

    (a) imposter   (b) card dealer   (c) woman

_____ 24. an unfortunate **misnomer**

    (a) mistake   (b) blind date   (c) unsuitable name

_____ 25. **interred** the body

    (a) burned   (b) buried   (c) cleaned

_____ 26. **intractable** about the issue

    (a) stubborn   (b) informed   (c) open-minded

_____ 27. a visit to the **podiatrist**

    (a) financial expert   (b) foot specialist   (c) tree doctor

_____ 28. a **misanthropic** act

    (a) warm and generous   (b) selfish   (c) hating mankind

_____ 29. gave her report **semiannually**

    (a) twice a year   (b) twice a month   (c) twice a week

_____ 30. practiced **polytheism**

    (a) belief in many gods   (b) belief in one god   (c) belief in no god

Complete the following sentences by choosing the correct word from the box above each group of five sentences.

(a) **hydrated**   (b) **connoisseur**   (c) **formative**
(d) **convene**   (e) **monopolize**

31. The child tended to _____ all of Sheri's time, leaving little time for anyone or anything else.

32. The board of directors will _____ early for their annual budget review.

33. The young woman became _____ during the cross-country race because she didn't bring enough water.

34. Jake was a _____ of olives; he could determine their age and country of origin simply by smelling the open container.

35. Carol's character was set during her _____; she was taught morality long before she began kindergarten.

(a) **abdicate**   (b) **concession**   (c) **subjugate**
(d) **skittish**   (e) **extraneous**

36. The horse was _____ about jumping the wide ditch.

37. The old-fashioned boss continuously tried to _____ his employees, making them feel like children.

38. The king was forced to _____ his throne because of misconduct and scandal.

39. Mrs. Jackson felt that Shannon had too much _____ information on her application; she suggested that Shannon just stick to the facts.

40. Mrs. Gross was willing to make only one _____ regarding the upcoming holiday: students could mail their late papers to her over vacation.

*Decide if the statement is true or false. Look for the correct usage of the **bold-faced** word in its context, rather than for facts.*

a = True   b = False

_____ 41. A **pachyderm** is a hairy animal, like a lion, a tiger, or a bear.

_____ 42. Margo was the **antithesis** of calm; she remained peaceful and serene throughout her ordeal.

_____ 43. The three-times divorcée was worried that she would be a **spinster** all her life.

_____ 44. The factory workers wished they could return to an **agrarian** time when they could live off what they grew on their own land.

_____ 45. The crab had such a **tenacious** hold on Joshua's swimsuit that we needed a screwdriver to pry it loose.

_____ 46. The **audiophile** so hated electronic sound equipment that he forced the car dealer to remove the stereo and speakers from his new car.

_____ 47. The **pedophile** was convicted for crimes against children.

_____ 48. The loud party next door created an **auspicious** occasion for studying.

_____ 49. A person who is **photophobic** loves the light.

_____ 50. The **pyromaniac** was obsessed with fire and could not resist starting small fires in the neighborhood.

% Correct _____

Comprehension and Rate Pretest

Read the following article as rapidly as you can but with good comprehension.
Note: *This reading should be timed. As soon as you finish reading the article, look up and your instructor will indicate your reading time in minutes and seconds. (Or your instructor may instead ask you to time yourself with a stopwatch.) Then find the number closest to your reading time in the "min:sec" column of numbers at the end of the reading. Circle that number.*

Immediately answer the ten comprehension questions that follow. Remember, this is a pretest, and you may not know the answers to all the questions.

Wait for a signal from your instructor before you begin reading.

Secrets of Straight-A Students

Edwin Kiester, Jr., and Sally Valente Kiester

Everyone knows about straight-A students. We see them frequently in TV sitcoms and in movies like *Revenge of the Nerds.* They get high grades, all right, but only by becoming dull grinds, their noses always stuck in a book. They're klutzes at sports and dweebs when it comes to the opposite sex.

How, then, do we account for Paul Melendres?

The Kind of Student Who Gets A's

Melendres, now a freshman at the University of New Mexico, was student-body president at Valley High School in Albuquerque. He played varsity soccer and junior-varsity basketball, exhibited at the science fair, was chosen for the National Honor Society and National Association of Student Councils and did student commentaries on a local television station. Valedictorian of his class, he achieved a GAP of 4.4–straight A's in his regular classes, plus bonus points for A's in two college-level honors courses.

How do super-achievers like Melendres do it? Brains aren't the only answer. "Top grades don't always go to the brightest students," declares Herbert Walberg, professor of education at the University of Illinois at Chicago, who has conducted major studies of super-achieving students. "Knowing how to make the most of your innate abilities counts for more. Infinitely more."

In fact, Walberg says, students with high I.Q.s sometimes don't do as well as classmates with lower I.Q.s. For them, learning comes too easily and they never find out how to buckle down.

Hard work isn't the whole story, either. "It's not how long you sit there with the books open," said one of the many A students we interviewed. "It's what you do while you're sitting. Indeed, some of these students actually put in fewer hours of homework time than their lower-scoring classmates.

Ten Techniques for Getting A's

The kids at the top of the class get there by mastering a few basic techniques that others can readily learn. Here, according to education experts and students themselves, are the secrets to straight-A students.

1. ***Set priorities***. Top students brook no intrusions on study time. Once the books are open or the computer is booted up, phone calls go

unanswered, TV shows unwatched, snacks ignored. Study is business; business comes before recreation.

2. **_Study anywhere—or everywhere_**. Claude Olney, an Arizona State University business professor assigned to tutor failing college athletes, recalls a cross-country runner who worked out every day. Olney persuaded him to use the time to memorize biology terms. Another student posted a vocabulary list by the medicine cabinet. He learned a new word every day while brushing his teeth.

Among the students we interviewed, study times were strictly a matter of personal preference. Some worked late at night when the house was quiet. Others awoke early. Still others studied as soon as they came home from school when the work was fresh in their minds. All agreed, however, on the need for consistency. "Whatever I was doing, I maintained a slot every day for studying," says Ian McCray, a Middlebury College student from New Jersey.

3. **_Get organized_**. In high school, McCray ran track, played rugby and was in the band and orchestra. "I was so busy, I couldn't waste time looking for a pencil or missing paper. I kept everything right where I could put my hands on it," he says.

Paul Melendres maintains two folders—one for the day's assignments, another for papers completed and graded. Traci Tsuchiguchi, a top student at Clovis West High School in Fresno, California, has another system. She immediately files the day's papers in color-coded folders by subject so they'll be available for review at exam time.

Even students who don't have a private study area remain organized. A backpack or drawer keeps essential supplies together and cuts down on time-wasting searches.

4. **_Learn how to read_**. "The best class I ever took," says Christopher Campbell, who graduated from Moore (Okla.) High School last spring, "was speed-reading. I not only increased my words per minute but also learned to look at a book's table of contents, graphs and pictures first. Then, when I began to read, I had a sense of the material, and I retained a lot more."

In his book _Getting Straight A's_, Gordon W. Green, Jr., says the secret of good reading is to be "an active reader—one who continually asks questions that lead to a full understanding of the author's message."

5. **_Schedule your time_**. When a teacher assigns a long paper, Domenica Roman, of Fairmont (W. Va.) Senior High School, draws up a timetable, dividing the project into small pieces so it isn't so overwhelming. "It's like eating a steak," she says. "You chew it one bite at a time."

Melendres researches and outlines a report first, then tries to complete the writing in one long push over a weekend. "I like to get it down on paper early, so I have time to polish and review."

Of course even the best students procrastinate sometimes. But when that happens, they face up to it. "Sometimes it comes down to late nights," admits Christi Anderson, an athlete, student-council member and top student at Lyman High School in Presho, South Dakota. "Still, if you want A's, you make sure to hit the deadline."

6. *Take good notes*—and use them. "Reading the textbook is important," says Melendres, "but the teacher is going to test you on what he or she emphasized. That's what you find in your notes."

   The top students also take notes while reading the text assignment. In fact, David Cieri of Holy Cross High School in Delran, New Jersey, uses "my homemade" system in which he draws a line down the center of a notebook, writes notes from the text on one side and those from the teacher's lecture on the other. Then he is able to review both aspects of the assignment at once.

   Just before the bell rings, most students close their books, put away papers to rush out. Anderson uses those few minutes to write a two- or three-sentence summary of the lesson's principal points, which she scans before the next day's class.

7. *Clean up your act*. Neat papers are likely to get higher grades than sloppy ones. "The student who turns in a neat paper," says Professor Olney, "is already on the way to an A. It's like being served a cheeseburger. No matter how good it really is, you can't believe it tastes good if it's presented on a messy plate."

8. *Speak up*. "If I don't understand the principle my teacher is explaining in economics, I ask him to repeat it," says Christopher Campbell. Class participation goes beyond merely asking questions, though. It's a matter of showing intellectual curiosity.

   In a lecture on capitalism and socialism, for example, Melendres asked the teacher how the Chinese economy could be both socialist and market-driven, without incurring some of the problems that befell the former Soviet Union. "I don't want to memorize information for tests only," says Melendres. "Better grades come from better understanding."

9. *Study together*. The value of hitting the books together was demonstrated in an experiment at the University of California at Berkeley. While a graduate student there, Uri Treisman observed a freshman calculus class in which Asian-Americans, on average, scored higher than other minority students from similar academic backgrounds. Treisman found that the Asian-Americans discussed homework problems together, tried different approaches, and explained their solutions to one another.

   The others, by contrast, studied alone, spent most of their time reading and rereading the text, and tried the same approach time after time even if it was unsuccessful. On the basis of his findings, Treisman suggested teaching group-study methods in the course. Once that was done, the groups performed equally well.

10. *Test yourself*. As part of her note-taking, Domenica Roman highlights points she thinks may be covered during exams. Later she frames tentative test questions based on those points and gives herself a written examination before test day. "If I can't answer the question satisfactorily, I go back and review," she says.

Experts confirm what Roman has figured out for herself. Students who make up possible test questions often find many of the same questions on the real exam and thus score higher.

The most important "secret" of the super-achievers is not so secret. You always do more than you're asked. If her math teacher assigns five problems, Christi Anderson does ten. If the world-history teacher assigns eight pages of reading, she reads twelve. "Part of learning is practicing," says Anderson. "And the more you practice, the more you learn." . . .

TIMING CHART	
min:sec	**wpm**
9:01	160
8:01	180
7:13	200
6:33	220
6:01	240
5:33	260
5:09	280
4:48	300
4:30	320
4:14	340
4:00	360
3:48	380
3:36	400
3:26	420
3:17	440
3:08	460
3:00	480
2:53	500
2:46	520
2:40	540
2:35	560
2:29	580
2:24	600
2:20	620
2:15	640
2:11	660
2:07	680
2:04	700
2:00	720
1:57	740
1:54	760
1:51	780
1:48	800

Answer the following questions without referring to the article.

1. Which of the following is more important in getting A's?
   (a) hard work   (b) long study time   (c) how study time is spent

2. How many techniques are listed in the article? _____

3. Which of the following is a *minor* point (given in a less important subheading)?
   (a) the kind of student who gets A's
   (b) schedule your time
   (c) techniques for getting A's

4. What techniques did the Asian-Americans at the University of California at Berkeley use that helped them score higher in freshman calculus? _____
   _____

5. One of the techniques emphasizes neatness.   (a) true   (b) false

6. Give one more technique forgetting A's, one that is listed in the article and not already mentioned in these questions. _____

7. The *major* logic pattern in this article is its
   (a) example   (b) time sequence   (c) addition

8. Contrast is a supporting logic pattern. What are the two main things being contrasted?
   _____ vs _____

9. The author's purpose in this article is mostly to
   (a) inform   (b) entertain   (c) persuade

10. Choose the sentence that best states the main idea (thesis) of this article.
    (a) Students who study harder and longer get better grades.
    (b) The smartest students are generally the ones who get better grades.
    (c) Students who get better grades are those who use good study techniques.
    (d) Students who get better grades are those who know how to set priorities.

Check your answers with your instructor. To get your Words per Minutes (WPM) for this reading selection, look back at the reading time you circled. The number in the column to the right of your circled number is your Words per Minute. Refer to the percentage chart below for percent comprehension. Record your WPM and your percent comprehension below and on the Progress Chart on page 441.

Words per Minute _____

Percent Comprehension _____

PERCENTAGE CHART											
number of errors	0	1	2	3	4	5	6	7	8	9	10
percent correct	100	90	80	70	60	50	40	30	20	10	0

VOCABULARY PREVIEW for Chapter 1

You just learned the importance of preparing to read in ***Preview Your Text***. One way to prepare to read difficult material is to build your vocabulary. As you know, if a reading passage is filled with words you don't know, your understanding and speed will be affected. Learn the words and you will read faster and understand more.

At the beginning of each chapter this section presents words that may be new to you. They will appear in the reading selections in that chapter. You will first learn them through context and dictionary use. Then you will reinforce your understanding of the words in an ***Exercise***.*

Learning through Context

The most natural way to learn new words is from their context. As children, we acquired all our new words this way. As adults, we still rely mostly on context, what we read or hear, to decide what new words mean. So improving our awareness of a word's context is well worth the effort.

We often use the word *context* in daily life to refer to the situation or circumstances that normally surround a person or act. Suppose you meet your dentist jogging along the beach. It takes you a moment to recognize him, and you say, "Oh! I didn't recognize you out of context." You mean you didn't recognize him out of the white coat and dental office that "define" him for you.

Similarly, we can misinterpret a familiar word in a different context. The same word can mean different things in different settings. For example, consider the word *tramp* in these three sentences:

(a) The ***tramp*** went into the woods with his bedroll and all his belongings.

(b) The ***tramp***, her lipstick smeared, staggered home at sunrise.

(c) The children ***tramp*** through the woods, crushing the fallen leaves.

In sentences (a) and (b), *tramp* is a noun, a person [in (a), a homeless person; in (b), an immoral woman]. In sentence (c), *tramp* is a verb, an action (walk heavily). You probably know all three meanings and had no trouble with the different contexts.

Often, however, a word you know in only one context will confuse you when you see it in a less common context. What do you think of when you see the word *cashier*?

_____

Did you think of a *cashier* in a grocery store or a bank taking your money?

Now consider the same word in a sentence taken from a Timed Reading in this chapter:

_____

*Your instructor may give you these words in a ***Vocabulary Review*** after you finish the chapter, then again in a ***Vocabulary Unit Test*** after you finish every two or three chapters, and once more in a ***Vocabulary Posttest***. You may recognize some words from the ***Vocabulary Pretest***.

Once, when [President Abraham] Lincoln fired a cabinet member, senators pressed him to **cashier** the whole cabinet.

Guess at a definition for *cashier* in this setting: _____

The word clearly means something different in this context. *Cashier*, in this sentence, does not mean a person who handles money; it refers to an action. You probably guessed it means to "fire" or to "terminate the employment" of someone. You may have picked out the word "fired," used early in the sentence. In this context, then, *cashier* means to fire all the people in Lincoln's cabinet.

Learning the meaning of new words through their context is not an exact science. Usually you are making an educated guess about a word's possible meaning. As you continue to see the word in various contexts, you may have to revise the meaning you reasoned for that word. This is also a part of learning through context.

If you recognize parts of speech, or the way a word functions in a sentence, you will make an even better educated guess. If you recognized that *cashier* is a verb (or verbal) in the sentence about Lincoln, instead of a noun in the context of a grocery store, you have a big advantage. This recognition is like a flag that waves you in the right direction.

Using Your Dictionary

Sometimes you may see a word so unfamiliar that you have never heard of it. Maybe you have never seen it before. The context may not give a clear clue to its meaning. In that case, you will need to use your dictionary.

Homework Lesson 1, beginning on page 358, gives you a complete review on *How to Use the Dictionary*. For a more complete understanding of a word, so that you are able to use it in your speaking and writing, you may want to make a flash card. You will find these flash cards convenient for reviewing for the chapter and unit tests. You will also find them useful in learning difficult terms in your other classes. **Homework Lesson 2** teaches a flash card technique that will help you continue to build your vocabulary for the rest of your life.

WORDS IN CONTEXT for Chapter 1

Directions: *The key word or phrase, taken from a reading passage in this chapter, is in* **boldface** *print. It is followed by its pronunciation symbols and part of speech to the right. The sentence, just below the key word, shows the word or phrase as it appears in the sentence from the reading selection. Some sentences may have more than one vocabulary word. When this occurs, the sentence is not repeated for the other word(s).*

1. Study the context of the sentence carefully. (The sentence in the following exercise will give an additional, often clearer, context clue.)
2. Write your best guess at what the word means on the first blank line.
3. Then look up the word in your dictionary. Notice that most words have several definitions (as well as other forms and pronunciations).
4. Pick the definition that best fits the context, and write it on the second blank line. (See the sample filled in for you on #1 below.)

To add the word to your writing vocabulary, notice the part of speech and how it is used in the sentence. To add the word to your speaking vocabulary, practice its pronunciation. For any symbols you don't know, check the pronunciation guide.

a	cat	ā	made	ä	bar	k	cot, quit		adore
e	pet	ē	these	â	care	s	cent		travel
i	sit	ī	ride	ė	term	z	beds	ə	horrify
o	rot	ō	note	ô	order	j	giant		pardon
u	nut	o͞o	rude	o͝o	foot	Th	thank		circus
u̇	put	yo͞o	use	o͞o	food	TH	this		

from Paragraph 1B (p. 33)

1. **stricken**   (strik' ən)   *verbal (used as adjective)*

   Add to that list a dead child and an unfaithful husband who became **stricken** with polio.

   Your best guess: hit with something bad, maybe died from it

   Best dictionary definition: afflicted or overcome, as in illness or grief

   [Note: Your dictionary may list other definitions like "deleted," as in "*stricken* from a line," but "deleted" would not fit the context of "*stricken* with polio." Also, if *stricken* is not in your dictionary, look for *strike*, the present tense of the verb.]

2. **rigorous**   (rig' ər əs)   *adjective*

   She [Eleanor Roosevelt] used these experiences, the way she used her **rigorous** disciplines of ***calisthenics*** and ice-cold showers, to make herself stronger.

   Your best guess: _____

   Best dictionary definition: _____

   [Note: Do not hesitate to shorten or paraphrase definitions; just do not leave out important words that complete the explanation of the word.]

3. **calisthenics**   (kal' is then' iks)   *noun*

   Your best guess: _____

   Best dictionary definition: _____

   [Note: See sentence #2 for context clue to **calisthenics**.]

4. **lynch**   (linch)   *verb (used as adjective)*

   She supported civil rights in the days when an anti-**lynch** law was highly controversial with southern Democrats.

   Your best guess: _____

   Best dictionary definition: _____

5. **disparaged**   (dis par' ijd)   *verb*

   She promoted women in government when others **disparaged** them.

   Your best guess: _____

   Best dictionary definition: _____

---

from Paragraph 1C (p. 34)

6. **celibate** (sel′ ə bət)   *adjective*

   She [Jocelyn Elders] accused abortion foes of being part of "a **celibate**, male-dominated church."

   Your best guess: _____

   Best dictionary definition: _____

7. **uterus** (yo͞o′ tər əs)   *noun*

   [She added,] "Some of them love little babies so long as they're in somebody else's **uterus**."

   Your best guess: _____

   Best dictionary definition: _____

8. **fetuses** (fe′ təs iz)   *noun*

   "Be better if they got over their love affair with **fetuses** and started supporting children."

   Your best guess: _____

   Best dictionary definition: _____

from Timed Reading 1F (p. 42)

9. **evanescent** (ev′ ə nes′ ənt)   *adjective*

   Abraham Lincoln is the most written about figure in American history and the most mysterious, the most familiar of faces and the most **evanescent** in spirit.

   Your best guess: _____

   Best dictionary definition: _____

10. **quipster** (kwip′ stər)   *noun*

    The commander-in-chief was also the storyteller-in-chief, the **quipster**-in-chief, a country ham that couldn't be cured.

    Your best guess: _____

    Best dictionary definition: _____

    [Clue: You may have to look up "quip" and the suffix "-er" separately.]

11. **melancholy** (mel′ ən kol′ ē)   *noun (often an adjective)*

    Jokes drove the demons of **melancholy** back into the hidy-holes of his mind.

    Your best guess: _____

    Best dictionary definition: _____

12. **suit of mail**   (so͞ot′ əv māl′)   *noun phrase*

Yet Lincoln's wit was more than a **suit of mail** against despair.

Your best guess: _____

Best dictionary definition: _____

13. **lance**   (lans)   *noun*

One minute it [his wit] was a feather duster tickling friends, another minute a velvet-tipped **lance** pricking foes.

Your best guess: _____

Best dictionary definition: _____

14. **lathe**   (lāth)   *noun*

Lines like that [witty remarks] smacked of the **lathe**.

Your best guess: _____

Best dictionary definition: _____

15. **transom**   (tran′ səm)   *noun*

Hearing that a senator's brother-in-law was in trouble for peeping over a **transom** at a disrobing mademoiselle, Lincoln ***averred*** that the ***cad*** "should be elevated to the ***peerage***."

Your best guess: _____

Best dictionary definition: _____

[Note: See sentence #15 for context clues to **averred**, **cad**, and **peerage**.]

16. **averred**   (ə vėrd′)   *verb*

Your best guess: _____

Best dictionary definition: _____

17. **cad**   (kad)   *noun*

Your best guess: _____

Best dictionary definition: _____

18. **peerage**   (pir′ ij)   *noun*

Your best guess: _____

Best dictionary definition: _____

19. **gusto**   (gus′ tō)   *noun*

He would recite his stories with **gusto**, scratching his elbows and ***guffawing*** loudly as the punch lines neared.

Your best guess: _____

Best dictionary definition: _____

20. **guffawing** (gu fô′ ing)   *verb*

Your best guess: _____

Best dictionary definition: _____

[Note: See sentence #19 for context clues to **guffawing**.]

21. **taxing** (taks′ ing)   *verbal*

    They had never managed to bring up the topic **taxing** their minds.

Your best guess: _____

Best dictionary definition: _____

[Clue: This word has nothing to do with "income taxes." Look beyond the most common definition.]

22. **cashier** (ka shir′)   *verbal*

    Once, when Lincoln fired a cabinet member, some senators pressed him to **cashier** the whole cabinet.

Your best guess: _____

Best dictionary definition: _____

from Timed Reading 1G (p. 44)

23. **insatiable** (in sā′ shə bəl)   *adjective*

    After 30 years the literature of [President] John Kennedy is dominated by tortured accounts of assassination conspiracies and an **insatiable** sexual appetite.

Your best guess: _____

Best dictionary definition: _____

24. **luster** (lus′ tər)   *noun*

    Above all else there was his humor, the trait that helped lift him on the way up and gave him special **luster** when he got to the top.

Your best guess: _____

Best dictionary definition: _____

25. **chintzy** (chint′ sē)   *adjective*

    "Leave a tip," he instructed. Ten percent plunked down. "Pretty **chintzy**," he said.

Your best guess: _____

Best dictionary definition: _____

26. **scruffy**   (skruf′ ē)   *adjective*

Once when he was courting delegates in a **scruffy** hotel, the prospects were lined up and run through his suite.

Your best guess: _____

Best dictionary definition: _____

27. **sinister**   (sin′ ə stər)   *adjective*

All of us were aware of Kennedy's fascination with women, but when sex surfaced, it seemed more naughty than **sinister**.

Your best guess: _____

Best dictionary definition: _____

28. **sardonic**   (sär don′ ik)   *adjective*

One **sardonic** Kennedy scene still ***intrigues***.

Your best guess: _____

Best dictionary definition: _____

29. **intrigues**   (in trēgz′)   *verb*

Your best guess: _____

Best dictionary definition: _____

[Note: See sentence #28 for context clues to **intrigues**.]

30. **incredulous**   (in krej′ ə ləs)   *adjective*

"You know that they [the Russians] have an atomic bomb in the attic of the Soviet Union embassy on 16th Street?" His guests looked **incredulous**.

Your best guess: _____

Best dictionary definition: _____

Exercise, Vocabulary Preview, Chapter 1

Directions: *Choose the best definition for each **boldfaced** word or phrase as it is used in its context. Remember: A word may have more than one meaning.*

b   1. The child, **stricken** with guilt at breaking the cookie jar, handed the cookie to her mother and said, "I'll never eat another cookie in my life."
(a) caught (b) overcome (c) pretending

a   2. The study group planned a **rigorous** routine of meeting at six a.m., three mornings a week, to study for two hours before class.
(a) tough (b) regular (c) impossible

a   3. Already in good physical condition and disliking machines, she signed up for the most advanced **calisthenics** class at her gym.
(a) physical exercise (b) paperwork (c) study of the body

b   4. The angry ranchers were ready to **lynch** the cattle thief when the sheriff and his posse arrived just in time.
(a) put in jail (b) hang till dead (c) legally kill

b   5. Young John refused to be discouraged from learning to skateboard, even though the older boys laughed and **disparaged** him whenever he fell.
(a) knocked him down (b) belittled (c) encouraged

b   6. After two decades of sexual freedom and in an age of AIDS, many couples are deciding to remain **celibate** until after marriage.
(a) careful about sex (b) without sex (c) religious

c   7. She was unable to conceive a child until she had a surgical procedure to unblock her **uterus**.
(a) emotions (b) fat cells (c) womb

a   8. At the heart of the abortion debate lies the controversial question: "When does a **fetus** become a human being?"
(a) unborn young (b) advanced robot (c) live sperm

c   9. The poet who said, "Gather ye rosebuds while ye may," and the farmer who said, "Stack the hay while the sun shines," both knew that time is **evanescent**.
(a) forever (b) made for working (c) fleeting

a 10. Before Jay Leno and David Letterman, Johnny Carson reigned over late-night television as the king of **quipsters**.
(a) joke-tellers (b) funny remarks (c) actors

a 11. Clarissa could not shake the heavy **melancholy** that descended upon her when she entered the graveyard on those dark, foggy nights to visit her lover's grave.
(a) gloomy (b) suicidal (c) vengeful thoughts

_b_ 12. Many politicians today believe they need a **suit of mail** to protect them from the verbal slings and arrows thrown at them by the media.

(a) legal correspondence   (b) protective armor   (c) armed lawyers

_a_ 13. Sir Lancelot hurled his sharp **lance** at the evil heart of the villain dragging Lady Guinevere toward the moat filled with crocodiles.

(a) long spear   (b) short sword   (c) arrow

_c_ 14. The skilled craftsman carefully held the beautiful stick of mahogany against the **lathe** until it was transformed into the shape he had pictured.

(a) antique chair   (b) other craftsman   (c) tool for shaping

_b_ 15. Interested in her neighbor's loud argument, Linda stood on a stool and watched through the **transom** until a crisscross pattern was imbedded in her forehead.

(a) mail slot   (b) cross-barred window   (c) cracked door

_a_ 16. When Professor Sutch accused Cassandra of turning in a research paper that was not her own work, Cassandra **averred** that she had bought the essay with her own money.

(a) declared   (b) shouted   (c) whimpered

_b_ 17. "Begone, you **cad**!" shouted Diane. "You've broken my poor heart and drunk my fine wine for the very last time."

(a) criminal   (b) rascal   (c) wasteful man

_c_ 18. Respected British actors, like Sir Laurence Olivier and Sir Anthony Hopkins, are sometimes knighted by the queen of England, thus becoming instant members of the **peerage**.

(a) equal group   (b) secret society   (c) nobility

_c_ 19. The condemned man found it difficult to eat his last meal with **gusto**, even though the finest chefs of Europe had prepared his favorite dishes.

(a) good manners   (b) small bites   (c) enthusiasm

_a_ 20. Mike annoyed his wife by **guffawing** inappropriately at all the tender, romantic scenes in the movie.

(a) laughing loudly   (b) snoring loudly   (c) talking loudly

_a_ 21. The twins continued to argue over who could crack whose knuckles more loudly, finally **taxing** their mother's already strained patience, until she gave their knuckles the loudest crack of all.

(a) exhausting   (b) paying a fine   (c) uplifting

____ 22. Tim decided to **cashier** his receptionist when he discovered she had been taping his private conversations.

(a) take money from   (b) fire   (c) forgive

____ 23. Lorelei's appetite for chocolate is **insatiable**; after eating three fudge bars, she retrieved the candy wrappers and licked the inside of the paper.

(a) unhealthy   (b) easily satisfied   (c) greedy

_____ 24. Tired of her dull, limp hair, Carol shampooed it twice, conditioned it with mayonnaise, and dried it in the sun—giving it a rich **luster** that kept her tossing her head.

(a) dull look   (b) shine   (c) curl

_____ 25. The student was too **chintzy** to buy his own paper and pencils; he borrowed from other students in every class.

(a) cheap   (b) poor   (c) smart

_____ 26. Instead of bathing, shaving, and changing his clothes, Beavis appeared for his job interview looking so **scruffy** he was turned away at the door.

(a) neatly dressed   (b) bad-tempered   (c) shabby

_____ 27. When the villain foreclosed on the heroine's home mortgage and tied her to the railroad tracks, his motives were **sinister**.

(a) evil   (b) illegal   (c) mostly kind

_____ 28. "Here," said Professor Miller, with a **sardonic** smile, "let me put the waste basket next to your desk so you won't have to strain your arm when you throw balls of trash across the room."

(a) sarcastic   (b) helpful   (c) angry

_____ 29. Centuries after being painted, Mona Lisa's mysterious smile still **intrigues** art lovers; it seems to follow them around the room.

(a) frightens   (b) fascinates   (c) bores

_____ 30. Jim was **incredulous** when he learned that his wife had cut off his ponytail while he slept; he had always thought she liked his long hair.

(a) furious   (b) unbelievable   (c) unbelieving

Number of Errors _____

Chapter 1
Preparing to Read

I. How to Understand More

STUDY UNIT: *Preparing to Read*

         Practice the *Preview* Method

         Find the *Topic*

         Expand Topics into *Main Ideas*

PARAGRAPH PRACTICE: *Looking Closer at Famous People*

II. How to Read Faster

RATE-BUILDING TIPS:

         Make Three Changes

         Check Your Reading Rate

PHRASE PRACTICE

TIMED READINGS: *Looking Closer at Famous People*

         Who was Lincoln?

         A Sly and Wry Humor

I. How to Understand More

Note: *The Study Unit section in each chapter will serve two purposes. One, it will teach you useful reading (and logic) techniques that you will be able to practice immediately and that you should be able to use the rest of your life. Two, it will provide short, but focused, practice in how to study-read, take notes, and take tests. To motivate you and reinforce what you learn, your instructor may give you a Chapter Review Test on this material, plus a Unit Test, after every two chapters.*

STUDY UNIT

Preparing to Read

If you began this article by reading this sentence, perhaps even before reading the title, you have omitted the most important step to understanding what you read. That step is to *Preview* (or *survey* or *preread*) what you are about to study-read. It is the step you may have just learned in "Preview Your Text" (see page xv). It is the step that gives you the *topic* before you actually read the material. It gives you an overview. Think of it as loosening your muscles before a sports activity. It's a type of warm-up before the main event. Or think of it as looking over a map before you plan the route for a cross-country drive. When you preview, you see the whole before you examine the parts.

Without a preview, without thinking about the topic, you are less likely to understand what you read. You will read *passively*, cold, the material having no meaning for you. You will be less likely to focus and maintain concentration. We all have had the experience of passing our eyes over a passage, recognizing words, but getting no meaning from the words. Then we either give up or force ourselves to start over and reread, or *regress*. We get in a habit of regressing because we are in a habit of tuning out the first time we read a passage.

With a preview, you will actually save time because you will understand what you read the first time you read it. You will read *actively*, already knowing something about the material. You will begin with an investment in the process.

The authors and publisher have given you clues to meaning. Take advantage of those clues and stop wasting your valuable time!

Practice the Preview Method

First, ***preview this article as if for the first time***. Read the title again, "Preparing to Read"; it obviously tells you what this article is about. Read the introduction (first four paragraphs underneath the title, not the italicized "Note"). This introduction is an attempt to convince you of the importance of the previewing and to explain how it helps you find the topic. As most introductions do, it also gives you the *main idea* for the article. ("Main idea," or its variation, is a term you will see in this book many times.)

Look at the *subheadings* (or "undertitles"), like "Practice the Preview Method." These sentences or phrases might be in a different color or position on the page. They might be in boldface print or italics, or both. Remember, they provide visual clues to the authors' most important points. They also help you see how ideas fit together. These are all skills you will be practicing in this book.

These subheadings help you tell the difference between important and less important, between general and less general, and between whole and part. Making these distinctions is a basic logic skill. Without this skill, readers are lost. To them, reading is like trying to put together a jigsaw puzzle without ever having seen the picture on the box. If they haven't seen that picture, how can they fit the puzzle pieces together without long hours of frustrating trial and error?

Which subheadings are more important in this article?

(a) those in boldface, like **Practice the Preview Method**

(b) those in boldface italics, like ***preview this article as if for the first time***.

If you correctly answered (a), you may have used the additional clue of the more important heading being in a prominent position, set apart and flush with the left margin. If you picked (a) because you realized it was more general than (b), which is a supporting step for (a), then give yourself a pat on the back. You automatically grasped a basic logic skill.

Next, look over any terms that are italicized. Some italicized words, like *actively* and *passively*, are just words that are being emphasized in a sentence. But others, like *preview* and *regress*, are terms you need to know, terms you will see again in this book.

As a last step (or sub-substep) to previewing, skip ahead to the conclusion. In this article, the conclusion is the last paragraph on page 31. In longer articles, the conclusion may be several paragraphs. In textbook chapters, the conclusion may be several pages.

Most textbook authors and publishers deliberately provide important clues in the title, introduction, subheadings, italicized terms, and conclusion. Experienced readers *preview* to take advantage of them. (Note that this paragraph is like a mini-conclusion for the section under "Preview this article as if for the first time.")

Second, ***digest what you have previewed and start to take notes***. By now, even before actually reading the entire article, you know not only the "topic" and "main idea," but also the direction of the article. You also have an idea of what comes next. Before continuing to read, get some ideas down on paper. Without looking back and in your own words, write what you remember from your preview in the blanks below.

(a) Preview an article or chapter by reading five parts:

_____   _____

_____   _____

_____

(b) Regress, in reading, means _____

(c) Write a question that you think will be answered in the remainder of the article: _____

Throughout this book, you will practice the *preview* method on articles and short stories before you read them. In each chapter you will expand the technique and reinforce it by taking better and more organized notes. By Chapter 6, you will be ready to put those skills together into a study technique, called PRO (Prepare-Read-Organize), that will help you understand textbooks better. For now, you will be asked to use a short form of that technique: Preview-Read-Outline (or make lists).

Find the Topic

The first goal in previewing is to help you with the most essential skill in reading: finding the *topic*, or subject. Whether it is in a paragraph, an essay, an article (like this one), a chapter, or a book—you have to understand what the reading material is about in general. This ability to see the whole before you get lost in the parts is a logic skill that overlaps the other three communication skills—listening, writing, and speaking. You will be able to understand a lecture better, and you will be able to present a more logical whole, with "point-supporting details," when you write or speak.

Think about the logic in the following pairs of words, and do Practices 1, 2, and 3. Then check your answers with the key at the end of the chapter.

general and *specific* = *sports* and *football*
whole and *part*   = *apple* and *core*
abstract and *concrete* = *romance* and *roses*

Practice 1 Supply the missing words in the blanks below.

general and *specific*   =   *school* and _____

whole and *part*   =   *tree* and _____

abstract and *concrete* =   *death* and _____

Practice 2 Circle the general word below that covers (or includes) the other, more specific words.

bananas   pears   apples   fruit   grapes

Practice 3 In the blank below, write a general heading that covers the five specific words.

_____

carburetor   radiator   tires   dashboard   steering wheel

This kind of practice is easy because most of the items are concrete and familiar. The connections are clear in these short exercises, but seeing the logic becomes a little more challenging in a paragraph.

Practice 4 Read the untitled paragraph below and, on the blank line, write what you think the topic is. (In general, what is the paragraph about?)

_____
[topic]

In 1955, Rosa Parks triggered a civil revolution that resulted in the Civil Rights Act of 1964. It was not her intention to make history. It is commonly believed and written that she simply was too tired to move after a long day of work as a seamstress. But she said, "The only thing on my mind was that I didn't want to be treated that way any more." Instead of giving up her seat on the bus to

(Practice 4 continued on next page)

(Practice 4 continued from previous page)

a white man as demanded, she politely refused and was arrested. News of her arrest spread, and black leaders like Martin Luther King, Jr., organized a bus boycott that lasted 382 days. The protest was not just against buses in Montgomery, Alabama, but against all segregation laws. Rosa Parks is sometimes called the "mother of the civil rights movement." On June 15, 1999, she was awarded the Congressional Medal of Honor by President Bill Clinton.

Expand Topics into Main Ideas

Most previews will reveal the *main idea* as well as the topic. The *main idea* is the major point made about the topic, or a direction taken to develop the topic. Think of a title expanded, stretched out with more words, into a complete sentence, but still general enough to cover all the supporting details.

This process is simple when the topic is given in a clear title, as it is in this article (and in most textbook chapters). Thus, "Preparing to Read" can be expanded to this main idea sentence:

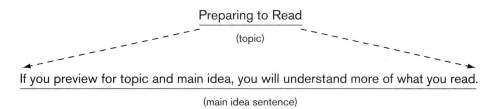

Preparing to Read
(topic)

If you preview for topic and main idea, you will understand more of what you read.
(main idea sentence)

Try expanding another topic that is often in the news: "Violence in Television." How many ways can you think of to expand it into a main sentence, besides those given below?

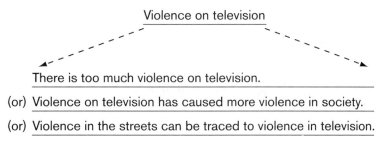

Violence on television

There is too much violence on television.

(or) Violence on television has caused more violence in society.

(or) Violence in the streets can be traced to violence in television.

Here is another example of expanding a different topic, "colon cancer." If you were reading an article on colon cancer, you would try to get a clearer focus on the topic. What point is the writer making about colon cancer? Is it about causes, or cures, or symptoms? Or is the focus more on prevention? Or on diet? Or on both prevention and diet? The main idea might be something like "A diet high in fiber may help prevent colon cancer." The general has become less general. And the phrase has become a complete sentence. You have stretched a topic into an idea.

Practice 5   On the line, write a more focused *topic,* or title, for the main idea statement below it. Try to write a short phrase, with fewer words than in the sentence.

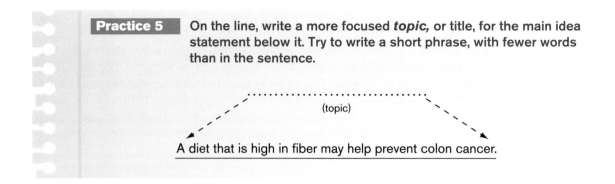

(topic)

A diet that is high in fiber may help prevent colon cancer.

Practice 6   Examine each of the following pairs. Mark the item in the pair that could be a *topic* with *T*. Mark the one that makes a point and could be a *main idea* with *M*.

Example: __M__ You can change a tire with five simple steps.
　　　　　 __T__ Instructions on how to change a tire.

_____ 1. Puff Daddy continues to be a popular rapper.
_____   The ongoing popularity of the rapper Puff Daddy.

_____ 2. The high rate of breast cancer in the United States.
_____   There is a high rate of breast cancer in the U.S.

_____ 3. What handling your anger well can do for you.
_____   Learning to handle your anger well can decrease stress.

_____ 4. It's important to teach children how to save money from a young age.
_____   Teaching children how to save money.

_____ 5. The medicinal use of marijuana.
_____   I am against legalizing street drugs.

Practice 7   Expand the following topic, or title, into a *main idea* statement. Using the words in the topic, try to write a complete sentence.

Noise Pollution

Practice 8   Look back at Practice 4 and reread the paragraph on Rosa Parks. Then, on the first dotted line, write an improved version of your topic. On the second dotted line, stretch out that topic into a main idea sentence.

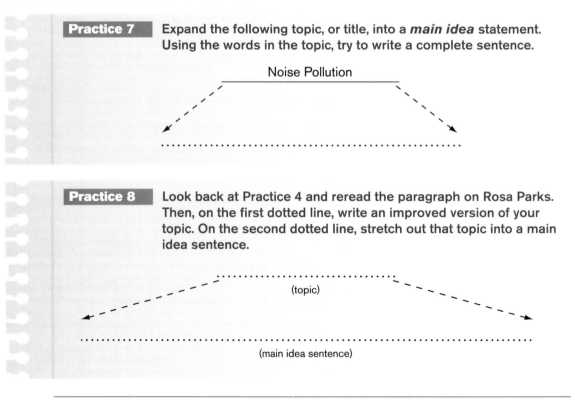

(topic)

(main idea sentence)

A *topic*, a *main idea*, and *supporting details*—one, two, three—are basics in any nonfiction you read, from a paragraph to an entire chapter. Finding those basics and connecting them logically will improve with preparation, like *previewing*. Preparing is as important in reading as it is in most activities. If you start reading cold (like putting that jigsaw puzzle together without looking at the picture on the box), you will waste a lot of time with poor results. Chances are you will give up in frustration and have little enthusiasm for reading your next assignment. Preparing before you read will improve your reading skills immediately and give you more confidence.

Study Notes

To reinforce what you have just previewed and read, and to prepare you for the chapter and unit tests, fill in the blanks below. Save these notes, add to them, and use them for review.

1. *Why* do you preview an article or chapter before reading it?

   _____

2. List at least five items you preview in an article or chapter. (Use accurate terms.)

   _____   _____

   _____   _____

   _____

3. The PRO method is used for _____ .

4. The *topic* is usually found in what part of an article or chapter? _____

5. Make a list of italicized terms and definitions (using your own words):

   _____

   _____

   _____

   _____

[Note: Your instructor may ask you to turn this page in.]

Looking Closer at Famous People

All the readings (three paragraphs and two timed articles) in most chapters are on a common theme to help improve concentration. You will focus better if you don't have to switch gears with each reading.

Directions: *Read the following three paragraphs carefully. The "preview" technique is more effectively practiced on longer articles, but you can apply it briefly to these paragraphs. Quickly glance at the paragraph to find "who" it's about. That should give you a very general topic. Then look for the "what," or the "what about the who." That should help you see the author's main idea about the topic. After answering the questions for each paragraph, check with the key on page 415.*

Exercise 1A: Paragraph

With a little luck, good or bad, any bozo can have fifteen minutes of fame, but it takes an extraordinary person to become and remain a public figure. That has been especially true for women in the twentieth century. Some women become famous by chance and grow into their fame. In the first half of the last century, Eleanor Roosevelt, a shy woman, born to wealth, was thrust into the spotlight by her husband's position as President of the United States. She forced herself to speak out on controversial issues like civil rights and women's rights. She believed in these causes long before they were even considered acceptable by most people. For that matter, before a woman speaking out on anything was acceptable. Other women, like the outspoken Jocelyn Elders, overcome obstacles to reach high positions of their own. Elders began life as the eldest of eight children of a poor Arkansas sharecropper. She worked her way through medical school and became Director of the Arkansas Department of Health in 1987. She too spoke out on unpopular causes, like birth control and abortion. From September 1993 to December 1994, Elders served in her highest position, as Surgeon-General of the United States. She was the first African-American woman to hold that position and the first to be fired from it. Born a half century apart, the two women had in common a social conscience.

1. Choose the phrase that best expresses the general *topic* of the paragraph. (Or which phrase would make the best title?)
   (a) Ambitious Women
   (b) Two Famous Women
   (c) Difficulties of Being a Public Figure
   (d) Eleanor Roosevelt, a Reluctant Heroine

2. Choose the sentence that best expresses the *main idea* of the paragraph. (Which idea is best supported by the details in the paragraph?)
   (a) Some women, like Eleanor Roosevelt, become famous because their husbands are famous.
   (b) Jocelyn Elders worked harder to become famous than Eleanor Roosevelt did.

    (c) Eleanor Roosevelt and Jocelyn Elders, famous women from different times, are both known for controversy.

    (d) Women need luck to become famous and courage to stay famous.

3. Briefly list examples of the two women's differences.

	Roosevelt	*Elders*
differences:	_____	_____
	_____	_____
	_____	_____

Exercise 1B: Paragraph

    Eleanor Roosevelt became a great lady, not because she was a first lady, but because she was able through tremendous will to turn her pain into strength. It was as if her backbone had been permanently strengthened by the brace she wore in childhood. We know that by all accounts, including her own, she had a miserable childhood. Regarded coolly by her mother, who called her "Granny," she was told that, "In a family that had great beauty, you are the ugly duckling of that family." We know, too, that she worshiped—and struggled to please—her father long after that attractive, self-destructive, and unreliable man was gone. From the time she was ten and an orphan, she spent a neglected childhood with her grandmother in a dark, gloomy house where, as a cousin recalled, "We ate our suppers silently." The facts, just the facts, of her life might have defeated any of us. Add to that list a dead child and an unfaithful husband who became stricken with polio. But she used these experiences, the way she used her rigorous disciplines of calisthenics and ice-cold showers, to make herself stronger. With this gutsiness, she cared about the poor even when the press accused her of interfering. She supported civil rights in the days when an anti-lynch law was highly controversial with southern Democrats. She promoted women in government when others disparaged them. And, as a widow, she worked for human rights in the world and the United Nations when others grew resigned.

—ELLEN GOODMAN, FROM KNOWING ELEANOR ROOSEVELT

1. What is the general topic of the paragraph? (Consider the topic like a title; write a short phrase. Remember, in a title, capitalize the first letter of the first word and of all important words.)

    _____

2. Choose the sentence that best states the main idea of this paragraph.

    (a) Eleanor Roosevelt was a great first lady to the President of the United States.

    (b) Eleanor Roosevelt was a great first lady because she turned hardships into positive acts.

    (c) Eleanor Roosevelt was a loyal wife and daughter, even though she was treated badly.

    (d) Eleanor Roosevelt was one of the first women to speak out for human rights.

3. List details, or examples, in the blanks below that support the two headings:

negative experiences   positive acts

_____   _____

_____   _____

_____   _____

_____   _____

Exercise 1C: Paragraph

Jocelyn Elders, America's first female Surgeon General under President Clinton, called herself a "lightening rod." She even wore a symbolic lapel pin shaped like a lightening bolt. This former Arkansas sharecropper's daughter drew fire whenever she spoke her mind. Even before her first year as Surgeon General had ended, there were already calls for her resignation. Why? She had suggested a study to legalize drugs as a solution to drug-related crimes. Her outspoken opinions were no surprise to the people of Arkansas, where she served as director of the Health Department. "You sold our children to the tobacco industry," she bluntly told Arkansas lawmakers after they rejected a cigarette tax. She shocked conservatives on the subject of abortion. She accused abortion foes of being part of "a celibate, male-dominated church, a male-dominated legislature and a male-dominated medical profession." Then she added fuel to the fire. "Some of them love little babies so long as they're in somebody's else's uterus. Be better if they got over their love affair with fetuses and started supporting children." She continued to speak her mind right up until she was fired for speaking out on masturbation as a method of safe sex.

1. What is the general topic of the paragraph? (Consider the topic like a title; write a short phrase. Remember, in a title, capitalize the first letter of the first word and of all important words.)

   _____

2. Write a complete sentence that states the main idea of this paragraph.

   _____

   _____
   [who?   in what position?   had what character traits?]

3. List all the words or phrases that mean the same as that trait.

   _____

   _____

   List five examples of that trait:

   _____

   _____

   _____

   _____

   _____

II. How to Read Faster

Note: *This section at the end of each chapter will give tips and practice in increasing your reading speed. The readings may be timed, to emphasize speed, while continuing to practice comprehension. Or they may be used, without timing, to concentrate more on comprehension. Both sections, the earlier "How to Understand More" and this "How to Read Faster," overlap because each skill reinforces the other.*

You know, of course, the value of reading—and not just in college. Modern life calls upon you to read everything from your driver's license test, to tax return forms, to instructions for new products, to your computer screen. And then there are your textbooks and exams. As an educated person, you will be expected to be well-read. Reading—reading *well*—is a necessity these days. Sometimes, on some types of material, reading faster is actually more efficient. Often, because of too much to do and too little time to do it, reading *faster* is also a necessity.

No doubt about it, everyone would like to be able to read faster. Slow readers not only have less time for other things; even worse, their understanding of what they read is usually lower. These alone are two good reasons to work on improving your reading rate: more time and better understanding.

Reading faster does not mean you must always speed-read and fly down the page in a blur. Reading faster is pointless if it does not lead to better understanding. In each chapter of this book, you will apply speed techniques that have worked for others. You will also develop different methods and speeds that fit the kind of material you are reading.

Make Three Changes

To read well, you need to make several changes. First, **you must develop an open, positive attitude**. That means you must be willing to break some old habits like tuning out. This leads to the bad habit of *regressing*, introduced earlier in this chapter. You must be willing to try new methods like tuning in through *previewing*. You must be willing to be uncomfortable at times as you get used to reading faster and more actively. You must be willing to see your comprehension drop at first in the speed-reading practice.

You may have taken a typing class in which you were pushed to force your speed faster. You were asked not to look at the keys as you typed. At first you made so many errors you may have wanted to slow down. The hunt-and-peck method looked pretty good to you. But, a mysterious thing happened. As you practiced and got used to the faster speed, you stopped making so many errors. Then you were asked to push your speed even faster. You repeated the process:

Push faster + make more errors + practice + make fewer errors + more practice
= SUCCESS.

You will be asked to try a similar process in this book. You have nothing to lose by trying it; you will not even lose your slow reading speed. You can still choose to read slowly when you need to on difficult material. It is the choice of reading "fast" that many students do not have. You must believe that you have the ability to read faster and understand more. And be open to practice, practice, practice.

Second, **you need to commit yourself to this course of study**. For the length of this term, you will give your best effort. This decision will help you through frustrating moments as you start to practice new techniques that will make you a better reader. You must be patient, especially toward yourself. You are learning, and learning occurs step-by-step, not instantly.

Third, **you must read a lot**. Read every day for pleasure, even if only for fifteen minutes. Get into the reading habit. Instead of watching television or movies for entertainment—*read*. Get your news from the newspaper instead of from television. Above all, read what interests you. Otherwise, you will give up and reach for the remote control.

Stop now and think of three subjects that interest you (besides the subjects in your textbooks):

1. _____

2. _____

3. _____

These subjects, no matter what they are, have been written about. Use your college or public library to find a newspaper, magazine, or book about one of your interests. Or buy yourself a paperback book, not for studying but for daily, free-time reading. Carry the newspaper or magazine or book with you—in your backpack, in your purse, in your car. If you have dead time, waiting in line or waiting in a doctor's office, *read*. If you read a lot, you will begin to love it, the way all good readers do. And all your reading skills—speed, vocabulary, and comprehension—will improve, naturally, as they have with all good readers.

Check Your Reading Rate

To increase your speed, it is important to know your reading rate, or WPM (Words per Minute), on different kinds of material. You already know your WPM on the "Comprehension and Rate Pretest," which is an easy, informative article. Now, get your WPM on an article *you* might choose to read.

Try a newspaper or magazine article. Ask a friend to time you for a minute. (Or set a timer or tape recorder for a minute.) Then, begin reading the article and read at whatever seems to be natural for you. You are reading for general, not perfect, comprehension. At the end of the minute, mark where you stopped reading. To get WPM, you need to *divide reading time into total words read*. (With one minute, of course, that is easy.)

total words read ___?___ ÷ reading time <u>1 min.</u> = WPM

To get the "total words read," you can either count all the words or you can take a shortcut. Get the average words on a line. (Count the words on three full lines and divide by three.) Then count the lines you read during the minute, and multiply by the average words per line.

You might also get your WPM in one of your textbooks. Is your WPM on the textbook similar to your WPM on the earlier article? How do your two speeds compare with your WPM on the "Comprehension and Rate Pretest"? Are they all within 100 WPM of each other? You may find that you have a narrow range of speeds. Doesn't it seem like a waste of time to read an easy newspaper or magazine article at the same speed that you read a textbook?

Estimate how much time you will need to read your textbook assignments. For example, if you read a half a page in a minute, you will need an hour to read an average textbook chapter of thirty pages. If you read the magazine article at the same rate, how much time will you spend on this pleasure reading?

If your WPM is lower than 200 to 250, you are reading word-for-word. You are focusing on every word on every line. This means you are reading for separate words instead of for ideas. It means you are reading at about one-half to one-third of your potential reading speed. You may also be reading at one-half to one-third your comprehension potential, even though you are reading slowly.

This slow WPM means you are stuck at the same speed you developed when you read out loud in elementary speed—one word at a time. Many people who do not read a lot for pleasure, or who have not had any speed-reading training, are stuck at that slow speed. The good news is that you do not need to stay stuck there.

Do not use your textbooks to practice speed-reading. Instead, use the timed exercises at the end of each chapter to take chances on speed. Do not worry too much at first about losing comprehension. That loss is natural, at first. Do not consider the questions at the end of the timed readings to be a test. As you get used to reading faster, your comprehension will gradually increase. You may eventually find that your understanding is better at the faster speed than at the old slow speed. You may even find a modest carryover in speed when you study-read.

Becoming a better reader is similar to getting better at a sport or a musical instrument. With new techniques and practice, you can bring all the related skills together and perform at a higher level.

These next two exercises further prepare you to read in phrases. They ask you to see the phrase as a *whole* instead of individual words. They encourage you to widen your eye span and get used to longer units of print.

Directions: *These exercises have a key phrase on the left, followed by three phrases on the right. The key phrase is repeated once among the three phrases on the right. Find the same phrase as quickly as you can. Then cross it out, as in the following example.*

Key Phrase

bed rest   red vest   best vest   ~~bed rest~~

Continue until you finish all twenty items. Look up and your instructor will indicate your time in seconds.

Check your work for errors. Then write your time and number of errors after the exercise.

Tips on How to Improve Phrase Exercises

1. If you find yourself reading each word in a phrase separately, try focusing on the dots above each phrase. You should be able to see the entire phrase through your peripheral vision, without pausing on each word.
2. React to the size and shape of the whole phrase, not to individual letters or words.
3. Relax and let your eyes do the work. *See* the whole phrase; do not repeat the separate words in the phrase under your breath. Remember, you are not *learning* the phrases, just *recognizing* them.
4. As soon as you find the identical phrase, immediately go to the next key phrase. Trust your judgment.

Exercise 1D: Phrases

Make a slash through the phrase identical to the key phrase. **Note:** *All phrases are adjective-noun combinations, a common structure in sentences.*

Key Phrase

1.	old rake	gold rock	old rake	rare oak
2.	brown grass	grown lass	brown grass	green grass
3.	hot sun	hot sun	new home	hog sound
4.	water tap	wooden top	water pipe	water tap
5.	spring bud	spring bud	singing buddy	spring fever
6.	wild river	ill diver	vile rival	wild river
7.	dry bush	dry bush	day bed	high brush
8.	tall tree	tall tree	late treat	tea time
9.	cold wind	wild colt	cold wind	old window
10.	orange moon	orange moon	arranged room	orchid moon
11.	swift stream	stiff swing	some string	swift stream
12.	small trail	tall sail	small trail	short trail
13.	rain cloud	rain cloud	loud train	clear train
14.	open sky	shy poet	open sky	open season
15.	wooden fence	warm face	wooden fence	wood lot
16.	rough rock	rude shock	tough cork	rough rock
17.	bright star	right start	bright star	light year
18.	broken gate	broken gate	grown gal	garden gate
19.	thick mud	muddy stick	sick maid	thick mud
20.	bare hill	rare bill	ill bear	bare hill

Time _____

Number of Errors _____

Exercise 1E: Phrases

Make a slash through the phrase identical to the key phrase. **Note:** *All phrases are adjective-noun combinations.*

Key Phrase

1.	red rug	bed bug	rude hug	red rug
2.	dirty wall	thirty balls	dirty wall	flirty gal
3.	light bulb	mighty bull	slight flub	light bulb
4.	clean sink	pink cream	mean wink	clean sink
5.	long hall	long hall	long sash	lame hand
6.	sharp knife	short knave	nice harp	sharp knife
7.	bread box	black bed	dread lox	bread box
8.	old chair	cold choir	bold cheer	old chair
9.	bright fire	bright fire	light briar	fair fight
10.	soft couch	slight slouch	soft couch	some grouch
11.	new broom	new broom	rude broom	nude brute
12.	wide porch	poor wife	dire scorch	wide porch
13.	table leg	labeled egg	maple peg	table leg
14.	small dish	silly dash	all fish	small dish
15.	green glass	last queen	green glass	genial lass
16.	glowing lamp	rolling land	glowing lamp	bowling hand
17.	cracked cup	cocker pup	cracked cup	crated rake
18.	dinner bell	inner dell	ill winner	dinner bell
19.	flower vase	flower vase	forward pace	lower base
20.	hot toaster	low loafer	hot toaster	late boaster

Time _____

Number of Errors _____

Looking Closer at Famous People

Directions: *To help you improve your concentration and speed, the next two readings are timed.*

1. *Preview each article* by following the directions above the title.

2. *When your instructor gives you the signal to begin, read each article from the beginning.*

3. *As soon as your finish, check your reading time.* Use a stopwatch, or your instructor may prefer to indicate the minutes and seconds for you.

4. *Find your words per minute (WPM).* Notice the two columns of numbers at the end of the article. The first column gives possible reading times, and the second column gives WPM. Circle your reading time and find your WPM right beside it.

5. *Answer the comprehension questions that follow each article.* Some of the questions will be strictly recall. (Answer these without looking back at the article.) Other questions require more interpretation. You may look back at the article to answer those. The last question, marked with a circle, is about the main idea (also called the thesis). Use the preceding questions to help you make your judgment about this most important question. Questions marked with a triangle require drawing an inference (or reading between the lines).

6. *Check your answers with the key at the end of the chapter.*

7. *Record your two scores (WPM and percent comprehension) twice*—below the questions and on your Progress Chart on page 442.

Although most of the Timed Readings were selected to build speed, they will also provide practice in comprehension. Don't worry if your comprehension score on the recall questions drops as you push your speed faster. Remember what happens in a typing class. When you push for faster speeds, at first you make more mistakes. Then, when you get accustomed to the speed, you make fewer mistakes. You will have a similar experience in speed-reading. Most of the Timed Readings are for speed practice, not for study-reading. Their content will not appear on a Chapter Review or Unit Test. So loosen up and experiment with higher rates of speed.

This selection is an excerpt from a magazine article about the sixteenth President of the United States (1861–1865). Remind yourself of what you already know about him and his role in the Civil War. Try to picture his face, the face you have seen in most of your history texts. Then ask yourself questions about his personality. How did a man who suffered from deep depressions keep a sense of humor while in such a difficult job and during such a turbulent time in U.S. history?

Preview: *Take twenty seconds (or less) to survey the title, all of the first paragraph, and the first sentence of the second paragraph. Write here what you think the*

main idea might be: _____

_____

Now wait for a signal from your instructor before you begin reading. Try to finish in a minute if you can. (Your instructor may tell you when a minute has passed.) Be sure to read the entire article from the beginning.

Circle your reading time as soon as you finish. Immediately find your WPM *in the column next to the time closest to your reading time. Then answer the comprehension questions.*

Who Was Lincoln?

Gerald Parshall and Michael Barone

Every new generation of Americans needs to get in touch with Abraham Lincoln. He is the most written about figure in American history and the most mysterious; the most familiar of faces and the most evanescent in spirit. . . .

The commander-in-chief was also the storyteller-in-chief, the quipster-in-chief, a country ham that couldn't be cured. Lincoln joked more than any president before or since and did it at a time when statesmen were expected to be as solemn as churchwardens. "I laugh because I must not weep—that's all, that's all," he once said. Indeed, jokes drove the demons of melancholy back into the hidy-holes of his mind. Yet Lincoln's wit was more than a suit of mail against despair. One minute it was a feather duster tickling friends, another minute a velvet-tipped lance pricking foes, as when he pronounced Stephen A. Douglas's arguments as thin as a homeopathic soup "made by boiling the shadow of a pigeon that had starved to death."

Lines like that smacked of the lathe. Others sprang from his lips in an inspired instant. Hearing that a senator's brother-in-law was in trouble for peeping over a transom at a disrobing mademoiselle, Lincoln averred that the cad "should be elevated to the peerage." . . . As another might walk a dog for recreation, Lincoln walked his wit.

Not least, the 16th president of the United States, who wrote the book on the political uses of humor, uses jokes as exercises in evasion. Delegations often came to the White House with demands or questions Lincoln had no wish to hear. He would recite his stories with gusto, scratching his elbows and guffawing loudly as the punch lines neared. Soon the visitors were out the door of the White House, still laughing at good old Abe, happy to have seen him even if somehow they had never managed to bring up the topic taxing their minds.

Once, when Lincoln fired a cabinet member, some senators pressed him to cashier the whole cabinet. That reminded the president of a farmer who con-

TIMING CHART

min:sec	wpm
2:23	160
2:07	180
1:54	200
1:44	220
1:35	240
1:28	260
1:21	280
1:16	300
1:11	320
1:07	340
1:03	360
1:00	380
0:57	400
0:54	420
0:52	440
0:50	460
0:48	480
0:46	500
0:44	520
0:42	540
0:41	560
0:39	580
0:38	600
0:37	620
0:36	640
0:35	660
0:34	680
0:33	700
0:32	720
0:31	740
0:30	760
0:29	800

fronted seven skunks. "I took aim," the farmer said, "blazed away, killed one, and he raised such a fearful smell that I concluded it was best to let the other six go."

Answer the following three recall questions without referring to the article.

1. President Lincoln has been written about in history so much that he is easy to understand.　(a) true　(b) false

2. What was Lincoln's reaction to a senator's brother-in-law being caught as a "peeping Tom"?
   (a) stern disapproval　(b) amused approval　(c) pretense of ignorance

3. Lincoln once compared his cabinet members to
   (a) skunks　(b) foxes in a hen house　(c) buzzards

You may refer to the article to answer the following questions.

4. Explain Lincoln's insult to Douglas when he compares the other man's arguments to a homeopathic soup "made by boiling the shadow of a pigeon that had starved to death."

   _____

5. Choose the sentence that best expresses the *main idea* (or thesis) of this article.
   (a) Abraham Lincoln was the sixteenth President of the United States and served during the Civil War.
   (b) Abraham Lincoln was the most famous President, partly because of his sense of humor.
   (c) Abraham Lincoln made corny jokes to avoid firing his staff.
   (d) Abraham Lincoln used humor to avoid depression, to amuse friends and attack enemies, and to evade unwanted requests.

Check your answers with the key on page 416. Note on the percentage chart below that each comprehension question is worth 20 percent. Record your scores below and on the Progress Chart on page 442.

Words per Minute　_____

Percent Comprehension　_____

PERCENTAGE CHART

number of errors	0	1	2	3	4	5
percent correct	100	80	60	40	20	0

Exercise 1G: Timed Reading

The last reading in each chapter will usually be considerably longer than the first and will have more comprehension questions. This final reading, a newspaper essay, is about the thirty-fifth U.S. President, John F. Kennedy (1971–1963), who is well-known for his wit and style. Because of his familiarity, you should have little difficulty visualizing him as you read.

Preview: *Take 30 seconds or less and survey the title, author (national syndicated columnist), about half the first paragraph, and the last paragraph. Write here what you anticipate the author will say about how Kennedy used his humor.* _____

Wait for a signal from your instructor before you begin. Try to push your reading speed faster even though the article is longer. Remember, read for "ideas," not separate words. Circle your reading time when you have finished, and find your WPM.

A Sly and Wry Humor

Hugh Sidey

After 30 years the literature of John Kennedy is dominated by tortured accounts of assassination conspiracies and an insatiable sexual appetite. Some of these stories may be true. But often lost in this clamor is a calm and just view of the man, flawed, wondering, trying. Above all else there was his humor, the trait that helped lift him on the way up and gave him special luster when he got to the top. "I don't have any money on me, can you pay?" he asked me one campaign day in 1960 after offering lunch at a Milwaukee counter. O.K., I paid. "Leave a tip," he instructed, grin showing. Ten percent plunked down. Kennedy counted every coin with his forefinger. "Pretty chintzy," he said. "Leave some more." The grin grew, and he was up and on his way to Omaha, trailing a low chuckle.

Once when he was courting delegates in a scruffy hotel, the prospects were lined up and run through his suite. He stuck his head out of a door during a pause. "Just like a whorehouse," he called. "They bring them into the front parlor, send them into the bedroom with me, and they go out the back door. Satisfied, I hope."

After he won the presidency, he calmed down–sort of. He rarely roared with mirth but had a low, dry chuckle and a broad grin. His humor was sly and wry and almost never deserted him, no matter how grave the issue. Talking about the threat of nuclear war and his deep doubts about military technology, he once summed up his notion of the first nuclear exchange: "The Soviets will shoot off their missiles and hit Moscow and we will respond and take out Miami or Atlanta."

After Bobby had been proclaimed by the media as the second most powerful man in the free world, J.F.K. took a phone call at his desk, listened, muffled the receiver and told a guest, "I am talking to the second most powerful man in the free world. Do you want to tell him anything?" More conversation, and Kennedy broke into laughter. "Bobby wants to know who No. 1 is."

All of us were aware of Kennedy's fascination with women; but, when sex surfaced, it seemed more naughty than sinister. One holiday night in Palm

Beach, he put in a midnight call to a journalist, urged him to rush down to Worth Avenue the next day and do an article on an unknown fashion designer named Lilly Pulitzer, who had come up with a colorful gown for casual wear. "They're tearing them off the rack, they tell me," said Kennedy. "Off the women too."

One sardonic Kennedy scene still intrigues. After the summit meeting with Nikita Khrushchev in 1961, the weary President with an aching back had a few friends in for dinner in the old mansion where he stayed in Palm Beach. Frank Sinatra crooned from records in the background. There were daiquiris and pompano and deep talk about the Soviet menace. Kennedy weighed the Soviet leaders and their diplomats, then suddenly said, "You know that they have an atomic bomb in the attic of the Soviet Union embassy up on 16th Street? If war comes, they are going to trigger it and take out Washington." He had a kind of half-grin on his face. His guests looked incredulous. "That's what they tell me," insisted Kennedy. "The bomb was assembled from parts brought in in the diplomatic pouches. This thing goes up, and we all go." He never stopped grinning. I had always intended to ask him, You were kidding, right?

But a lot of other things got in the way, and then came Dallas.

TIMING CHART	
min:sec	wpm
3:27	180
3:06	200
2:49	220
2:35	240
2:23	260
2:13	280
2:04	300
1:56	320
1:49	340
1:43	360
1:37	380
1:33	400
1:29	420
1:25	440
1:21	460
1:18	480
1:14	500
1:12	520
1:09	540
1:06	560
1:04	580
1:02	600
0:58	640
0:56	660
0:55	680
0:53	700
0:52	720
0:50	740
0:49	760
0:48	780
0:47	800

Answer the following five recall questions without referring to the article.

1. This article is mostly about
   (a) his sexual adventures   (b) his sense of humor

2. Who left the tip in Milwaukee?   (a) the author   (b) Kennedy

3. During his campaign, Kennedy compared his potential delegates to
   (a) sheep being fleeced   (b) customers of a whorehouse
   (c) wealthy relatives

4. Who is *not* mentioned in the article?
   (a) Bobby Kennedy   (b) Frank Sinatra
   (c) Lyndon Johnson   (d) Nikita Khrushchev

5. Where did Kennedy say the Soviet leaders were keeping their atomic bomb during their visit in 1961?
   (a) in the attic of the Soviet embassy
   (b) in the basement of the White House
   (c) under his bed in Palm Beach

You may refer to the article to answer the following questions.

6. What is the author's attitude toward Kennedy's humor?
   (a) disapproval   (b) admiration   (c) fear of embarrassment

7. What is the author's attitude toward Kennedy's interest in sex?
   (a) disapproval   (b) admiration   (c) tolerance

8. What does Kennedy's version of the first nuclear exchange between the U.S. and the Soviet Union indicate?
   (a) that he took the nuclear threat lightly
   (b) that he was confident the U.S. would win
   (c) that he had doubts about both countries' competence

9. What does the anecdote about Kennedy's phone call with his brother suggest about the President's ego? _____

_____

10. Write a complete sentence that states the main idea of this article.

_____

_____

[who? used what? why?]

Check your answers with the key. Each question in the longer Timed Readings is worth 10 percent. Record your scores below and on the Progress Chart on page 442.

Words per Minute _____

Percent Comprehension _____

PERCENTAGE CHART	number of errors	0	1	2	3	4	5	6	7	8	9	10
	percent correct	100	90	80	70	60	50	40	30	20	10	0

How to Improve—Timed Readings

1. Always preview or survey for the title and topic. This habit helps you "tune in" and concentrate.
2. Read for ideas, not single words. This technique will also help you concentrate.
3. Don't regress or reread.
4. Don't move your lips. This bad habit (and reading word-by-word) will make it hard for you to read more than 200 to 250 WPM.

Writing and Discussion Activities

1. Certain key events or people in our lives have influenced who or what we've become. Many of these influences were positive, others negative or painful. Think back over your childhood and teenage years. Then make a list of some people and events that helped shape the kind of person you are today. After you make the list, choose one of these influences to explain or describe in more detail.
2. Start a reading journal. Choose one or more of the articles you just read. Write your reactions to the author's story.

Vocabulary Review, Chapter 1

Match the vocabulary word on the left with its definition on the right. Write the letter of the answer in the short blank to the left.

_c_ 1. **peerage**   (a) gloomy   buồn rầu

_d_ 2. **rigorous**   (b) rascal   côn đồ

_e_ 3. **disparaged**   (c) nobility   quý tộc

_a_ 4. **melancholy**   (d) tough   cứng rắn

_b_ 5. **cad**   (e) belittled   xem thg

Choose the best definition for each **boldfaced** vocabulary word as it is used in its context.

_b_ 6. The sheriff and his deputies began to **lynch** the cow thief.   nghị sĩ
  (a) put in jail   (b) illegally hang   (c) lawfully execute

_a_ 7. After drinking a glass of champagne at the party, Marta felt in an **evanescent** mood.
  (a) fleeting   (b) gloomy   (c) drug-induced

_c_ 8. I have always been serious, but my brother is the **quipster** in our family.
  (a) burglar   (b) boring person   (c) joker

_a b_ 9. The well-known thief **averred** his ignorance of the latest string of robberies.
  (a) pretended   (b) covered   (c) declared   Transáns1 lg tâm

_b_ 10. Horace was **stricken** by his conscience after he made his children cry.
  (a) attacked   (b) hardly bothered   (c) reminded

Mark each sentence to show whether the **boldfaced** word is used correctly.

a = True   b = False

_F_ 11. Tom ate his meal with **gusto**, barely eating anything on his plate.   thả thức

_T_ 12. Attending school and working full-time **exacted** too high a price on Mary's health.   ko thể thoả mãn

_T_ _A_ 13. The student had an **insatiable** thirst for knowledge; he studied every spare moment.

_F_ 14. The kindly old gentleman gave the little girl a **sardonic** smile to reassure her.   nhao báng   evil

(Continued)

T ___A___ 15. John was **intrigued** by his sophisticated date's air of mystery.

Choose the word from the box that fits the context of the following paragraph.
Write the letter of each choice on the blank lines to the left of the paragraph.

(a) **taxing**	(b) **cashier**	(c) **ludicrous**
(d) **sinister**	(e) **incredulous**	

___c___ 16. I told my assistant that if he was late for work one more time, he

___e___ 17. would be fired. Sure enough, the next morning he came drooping in

___d___ 18. two hours late with the __(16)__ excuse that our office building had

___b___ 19. been roped off by the police. I must have had a(n) __(17)__ look on my

___b___ 20. face, because he then told me about a(n) __(18)__ plot by a hostile for-

eign government to take over our company's international interests.

He was really __(19)__ my patience now, so I decided to __(20)__ him,

effectively immediately.

% Correct _____

Comprehension Review, Chapter 1

1. Define the term *regress*, as it relates to reading, and explain the reason for ~~and think about the topic~~
   regressing. ~~To preview~~ *start over* or reread it because we will understand ~~what~~
   we read clearly.

2. Good readers are more like to read   (a) passively   (b̶) actively.

3. Why should a reader *preview* a chapter before actually reading the chapter?
   It's a first step to give the readers the topic of the essay or
   overview of it
   What are three items (or parts) in a textbook chapter that a reader should
   preview before reading it? Give correct terms for the parts, *not* "the first
   paragraph" or "the first sentence."

   [Clue: Remember, this is for a *chapter*, not for a book.]

4. _____ Read the title _____

5. _____ Read the introduction _____

6. _____ Look at the subheadings _____

7. Circle the general word that covers or includes the other, more specific
   words.

   roof   basement   attic   (house)   rooms   porch

8. On the blank line, write a general heading that covers all the words below.

   In the Court Room   ~~closing argument~~   _Court/Legal Vocab._

   lawyers   defendant   closing arguments   witnesses   testimony
              bị cáo   làm chứng   chứ nhận/lời chứ

   Read the following paragraph and answer the questions about it.

   The media has made us aware of the dangers of second-hand cigarette smoke,
   but where is the outcry about second-hand snoring? Forty-five percent of men
   snore, causing their spouses to lose approximately an hour of sleep per night.
   Snoring is usually caused by sleep apnea, or not breathing for a short time
   because of an obstruction of the upper respiratory tract. In self-defense, sleepless
   spouses have been jabbing and shoving their oblivious partners to get them to
   turn over and breathe. The most drastic solution is surgery, correcting a deviated
   septum. Other solutions might be devices like face masks or nasal grippers. A
   cheaper solution is for the offending partner to avoid sleeping on his (or her)
   back, taking sleeping pills, or drinking alcoholic beverages—all of which can
   lead to snoring. Perhaps the easiest solution can be found at your local drug store:
   a type of super-adhesive band-aid to stick on the bridge of the nose and open the
   nasal passages.

   (Continued)

9. Which of the following is a more accurate topic, or title, for the above paragraph?
   (a) Causes of Snoring
   (b) Some Solutions to Snoring
   (c) Dangers of Second-hand Smoke

10. Expand the topic into a complete sentence that states the *main idea* of the paragraph.

   Some of

   (Some of The second hand snoring have complaint about their spouses snore, and they)

   % Correct _____

   Several causes

   The short article gives the readers several causes and solutions for pepeople who snore

VOCABULARY PREVIEW for Chapter 2

Context Clue #1: Look for Synonyms

Many times when writers use a word that might be difficult for a reader, they give clues to its meaning. A common clue that is used, often within the same sentence, is a *synonym*. A synonym is a word or phrase that means the same thing as the new word. Good readers learn to look for pointers that alert them to these synonym clues.

Helpful Wording. Examine the <u>underlined</u> words or phrases that link the *italicized* vocabulary words to their synonyms.

- Edgar was in a *melancholy*, <u>or</u> gloomy, mood when both his wife and his bird died.
- Marie had hoped her job responsibilities would not be so *rigorous*, <u>that is</u>, hard and demanding.

Practice Each sentence has a helpful word or phrase that signals a synonym for the vocabulary word in *italics*. Underline the word or phrase that points to the synonym for the italicized word.

1. Spotting her first gray hair, Joan realized for the first time that her beauty was *transient*, in other words, fleeting and temporary, and that she should consider returning to college.

2. Only the most *cynical*, or negative-thinking, observer would doubt that Elizabeth and Richard were truly in love.

[*Answers:* 1. in other words   2. or]

Helpful Punctuation. Sometimes writers provide a comma, a set of commas, a dash, a set of parentheses, or a colon, which point you to a synonym for the unknown word. Examine the punctuation clues in these sentences.

- Donald failed to tip the staff so many times that he became known as *chintzy*, cheap, and penny-pinching, throughout the luxury hotel.
- When Carla discovered her lover in the act of stealing her jewelry to give his other girlfriend, she called him a *cad* (a rascal and a scoundrel).

Practice Circle the punctuation in the following sentences that points you to the synonym for the *italicized* word.

1. After all his property was seized by the Internal Revenue Service, Jack's words, "I'm broke," were *unequivocal* (definite and absolute).

(Practice continued on next page)

(Practice continued from previous page)

2. Some people think that herbal remedies are a *panacea*–a cure-all–for any ailment.

[*Answers:* 1. parentheses   2. dashes]

WORDS IN CONTEXT for Chapter 2

Directions: *Study the **boldfaced** word, its pronunciation, and its part of speech. Then examine the word as it is used in the sentence, and write your best guess of the word's meaning on the first blank line. Last, look up the word in your dictionary and write the best definition for its context on the second blank line.*

*To add the words you do not know to your active vocabulary, make flash cards for them. Use the technique you learned in **Homework Lesson Two**.*

PRONUNCIATION KEY

a	cat	ā	made	ä	bar	k	cot, quit		adore
e	pet	ē	these	â	care	s	cent		travel
i	sit	ī	ride	ė	term	z	beds	ə	horrify
o	rot	ō	note	ô	order	j	giant		pardon
u	nut	o͞o	rude	o͝o	foot	th	thank		circus
u̇	put	yo͞o	use	o͞o	food	ŦH	this		

from Paragraph 2A (p. 68)

1. **acupuncture**   (ak′ u̇ pungk′ chər)   *noun*

   Others [people with back problems] try **acupuncture**.

   Your best guess: _____

   Best dictionary definition: _____

2. **cellulite**   (sel′ yə līt)   *noun*

   Those of us with cottage-cheese thighs are taking Cellasine to fight **cellulite**.

   Your best guess: _____

   Best dictionary definition: _____

from Paragraph 2B (p. 69)

3. **charred**   (chärd)   *verbal*

   Do you avoid them [chili peppers] because you think they blaze a trail of **charred** flesh throughout your digestive system?

   Your best guess: _____

   Best dictionary definition: _____

4. **hemorrhoids**   (hem′ ə roidz′)   *noun*

   According to current research, hot peppers do *not* cause **hemorrhoids** or ulcers.

   Your best guess: _____

   Best dictionary definition: _____

5. **carcinogens**   (kär sin′ ə jənz)   *noun*

It prevents the liver from turning some toxins into **carcinogens**.

Your best guess: _____

Best dictionary definition: _____

from Timed Reading 2F (p. 76)

6. **delusive** (di lōō′ siv)   *adjective*

When two people are under the influence of the most violent, most insane, most **delusive**, and most *transient* of passions, they are required to . . . remain in that . . . condition continuously until death do them part.

Your best guess: _____

Best dictionary definition: _____

7. **transient**   (tran′ shənt)   *adjective*

Your best guess: _____

Best dictionary definition: _____

[Clue: Pick the adjective, not the noun, definition that fits sentence #6.]

8. **cynical**   (sin′ ə kəl)   *adjective*

To scientists studying brain chemistry, Shaw's **cynical** appraisal of romantic love is more than just memorable prose.

Your best guess: _____

Best dictionary definition: _____

9. **expounded**   (ek spound′ id)   *verb*

[Chemist John] Bowers **expounded** on the latest scientific thinking on why we pair up, and why we have so much trouble staying paired up.

Your best guess: _____

Best dictionary definition: _____

10. **propagation**   (prop′ ə gā′ shən)   *noun*

The reason for this chemical come-on? **Propagation** of the species, of course.

Your best guess: _____

Best dictionary definition: _____

11. **monogamy**   (mə nog′ ə mē)   *noun*

"**Monogamy** is definitely not what nature intended man and woman to be doing," Bowers says. "The more genetic *diversity* we have, the better able the species will be to survive."

Your best guess: _____

Best dictionary definition: _____

12. **diversity**   (də vėr′ sə tē)   *noun*

   Your best guess: _____

   Best dictionary definition: _____

   [Note: See sentence #11.]

13. **hiatus**   (hī ā′ təs)   *noun*

   Researchers can even tell you approximately when your "luv" hormones will go on **hiatus**.

   Your best guess: _____

   Best dictionary definition: _____

14. **duration**   (dů rā′ shən)   *noun*

   "Perhaps it is no coincidence that the American divorce peak corresponds perfectly with the normal **duration** of *infatuation*."

   Your best guess: _____

   Best dictionary definition: _____

15. **infatuation**   (in fach′ ōō ā′ shən)   *noun*

   Your best guess: _____

   Best dictionary definition: _____
   [Note: See sentence #14.]

from Timed Reading 2G (p. 78)

16. **traumas**   (trô′ məz)   *noun*

   The act of writing can be an avenue to that interior place where, free of pain and doubt, we can confront **traumas** and put them to rest.

   Your best guess: _____

   Best dictionary definition: _____

17. **anonymous**   (ə non′ ə məs)   *adjective*

   And the last year or two have brought a distinctly '90s invention: 1-900 confession hot lines, where **anonymous** callers *recount* their sins.

   Your best guess: _____

   Best dictionary definition: _____

18. **recount**   (ri kount′)   *verb*

   Your best guess: _____

   Best dictionary definition: _____

19. **embarked**   (em bärkt')   *verb*

In the late 1970s I **embarked** on a large research project.

Your best guess: _____

Best dictionary definition: _____

20. **correlation**   (kôr' ə lā' shən)   *noun*

The data show a clear **correlation** between confessional writing and greater health.

Your best guess: _____

Best dictionary definition: _____

21. **vent**   (vent)   *verb*

Those who wrote about traumas would either **vent** their emotions or just write down the facts.

Your best guess: _____

Best dictionary definition: _____

[Clue: Pick the verb, not the noun, definition that fits the context of this sentence.]

22. **depicted**   (di pikt' id)   *verb*

Many of these stories **depicted** *profound* human tragedies.

Your best guess: _____

Best dictionary definition: _____

23. **profound**   (prə found')   *adjective*

Your best guess: _____

Best dictionary definition: _____

24. **unequivocal**   (un' i kwiv' ə kəl)   *adjective*

In the follow-up studies with researchers in the immune system, . . . the findings were **unequivocal**.

Your best guess: _____

Best dictionary definition: _____

[Clue: You may have to look up "equivocal" and the prefix "- un" separately.]

25. **immune**   (i myo͞on')   *adjective*

People who wrote thoughtfully and emotionally about traumatic experiences showed heightened **immune** function.

Your best guess: _____

Best dictionary definition: _____

26. **resolution**   (rez' ə lo͞o' shən)   *noun*

You may find a **resolution** to your conflicts in a way that works uniquely for you, not for anyone else.

Your best guess: _____

Best dictionary definition: _____

27. **distraught**   (dis trôt′)   *adjective*

If you become overly **distraught**, back off and approach the topic more gradually.

Your best guess: _____

Best dictionary definition: _____

28. **caveats**   (kav′ ē äts′)   *noun*

With these **caveats** in mind, here are some basic approaches to the writing method.

Your best guess: _____

Best dictionary definition: _____

29. **grapple**   (grap′ əl)   *verb*

Although many people write every day in journals, most of the entries don't **grapple** with fundamental psychological issues.

Your best guess: _____

Best dictionary definition: _____

30. **perspective**   (pər spek′ tiv)   *noun*

From a health **perspective**, you will be better off making yourself the only audience.

Your best guess: _____

Best dictionary definition: _____

31. **rationalize**   (rash′ ə nə līz)   *verb*

That way, you don't have to **rationalize** or justify yourself to suit another person's perspective.

Your best guess: _____

Best dictionary definition: _____

32. **dissipate**   (dis′ ə pāt)   *verb*

These feelings usually **dissipate** within an hour; in rare cases, they may last a day or two.

Your best guess: _____

Best dictionary definition: _____

33. **panacea**   (pan′ ə sē′ ə)   *noun*

I should point out that exploring your deepest thoughts and feelings on paper is not a **panacea**.

Your best guess: _____

Best dictionary definition: _____

Exercise, Vocabulary Preview, Chapter 2

Directions: *Choose the best definition for each **boldfaced** word as it is used in its context. Remember: A word may have more than one meaning.*

_b_ 1. Gavin lay on the table, his back aching and his nose dripping from allergies, as he nervously watched the acupuncturist open the package of fine **acupuncture** needles.

(a) drug therapy (b) therapy with needles (c) scream therapy

_a_ 2. Martha knew she would never be successful as a bathing-suit model if she did not change her diet and exercise to get rid of the **cellulite** on her thighs.

(a) fatty deposits (b) discoloration (c) tattoos

_c_ 3. Todd had drunk so much and was so nearsighted that, when he grilled the hot dogs on the high flame, his fingers looked as **charred** as the wieners.

(a) pink (b) hot (c) scorched

_b_ 4. Norm had to sit on a cushion at football games whenever his **hemorrhoids** bothered him.

(a) sore back (b) sore anus (c) nieces

_b_ 5. Many modern doctors are more interested in preventing cancer than healing it; they advise their patients that many food preservatives may act as **carcinogens** in some people.

(a) age-reducing agents (b) cancer-causing substances
(c) fat cells

_b_ 6. Dwayne's conviction that he would be hired as president of the company was **delusive**; after all, he was a high school dropout.

(a) realistic (b) unrealistic (c) understandable

_a_ 7. Janice considered loyalty to her friends to be a **transient** quality, not meant to be permanent enough to interfere with her career plans.

(a) quickly passing (b) see-through (c) truly honorable

_c_ 8. Maureen became so **cynical** about, and suspicious of, marriage that she carefully selected wedding gifts that her friends could continue to use after the divorce.

(a) hysterical (b) nervous (c) disillusioned

_a_ 9. Professor Miller **expounded** on the difference between a sentence and a fragment so long, that she put half her students to sleep.

(a) explained at length (b) explained briefly (c) hinted at

_b_ 10. The Nies family, after pressure from the whole neighborhood, finally consented to have their dog, Romeo, neutered. Romeo believed his mission in life was the **propagation** of golden retrievers.

(a) destruction (b) reproduction (c) education

_a_ 11. Many couples enter into marriage with a strong belief in **monogamy** and exit marriage with an even stronger belief in polygamy, having many spouses at once.

(a) having one spouse   (b) having no spouse

(c) having two spouses

_c_ 12. Angela likes meat and potatoes for every meal; but Dan, an accomplished chef, insists on more **diversity**.

(a) vegetables   (b) veal   (c) variety

_c_ 13. After attending college for six semesters without a rest, Joe decided to take a **hiatus** and travel.

(a) friend   (b) honeymoon   (c) break

_b_ 14. Mike was determined to bodysurf, skateboard, and hang glide for the **duration** of the summer so he could return to work in the fall refreshed and eager.

(a) time change   (b) time span   (c) time clock

_a_ 15. "It was just an **infatuation**," Nancy sang merrily to her new boyfriend, as her old boyfriend sadly played off-tune on the piano.

(a) foolish love   (b) lasting love   (c) serious commitment

_b_ 16. Liz never recovered from the **trauma** of seeing her younger brother, whom she was babysitting, shot while he played in their yard.

(a) emotional release   (b) emotional shock

(c) emotional outburst

_a_ 17. Too embarrassed to let anyone know he had written a sensitive love poem, Roger signed it, **"anonymous"** before he mailed it to Martha.

(a) unknown   (b) well-known   (c) another name

_a_ 18. What Mallory found hardest about confession was having to remember all her misdeeds for the week so she could **recount** them to the priest.

(a) lie about   (b) hide   (c) tell

_b_ 19. Sarah **embarked** on a long, dangerous trip through unmarked jungle trails.

(a) howled   (b) started   (c) matured

_b_ 20. Archie discovered a direct **correlation** between attending class and passing his classes.

(a) contradiction   (b) relationship   (c) benefit

_a_ 21. After being interrupted four times during dinner by telephone sales calls, Dave finally **vented** his frustration on the fifth caller, who unfortunately turned out to be his boss.

(a) let out   (b) withheld   (c) lost

_b_ 22. The animated movie *Beauty and the Beast* **depicted** the heroine, Belle, as a strong, modern woman.

(a) computerized   (b) represented   (c) misrepresented

_C_ 23. Beauty's love for the Beast in the movie had a **profound**, not a shallow, influence on humanizing his animal nature.

(a) superficial   (b) lengthy   (c) deep

_C_ 24. When Alan asked Miranda for a dinner date, after standing her up twice, she gave him an **unequivocal** answer: "No!"

(a) loud   (b) wishy-washy   (c) firm

_C_ 25. Lisa's long illness weakened her **immune** system and made her vulnerable to colds all winter.

(a) nervous   (b) muscular   (c) protection from disease

_C_ 26. The couple argued for weeks about where to go on their vacation until they finally reached a **resolution**—separate vacations.

(a) answer   (b) destination   (c) compromise

_C_ 27. Sharon became **distraught** when she saw five-year-old Chris start her car and begin to back out of the driveway.

(a) confused   (b) angry   (c) upset

_b_ 28. Calvin received several **caveats** before he tried to jump his motorcycle across the ravine, but he wished he had gotten one more— "Don't jump!"

(a) carrots   (b) warnings   (c) compliments

_a_ 29. Daniel **grappled** all night long with his private demons, only to lose the minute he reached for the rum bottle.

(a) struggled   (b) danced   (c) drank

_C_ 30. Sam needed a fresh **perspective** on life; he was so stressed out by work that he no longer looked forward to the future.

(a) someone's advice   (b) set of rules   (c) point of view

_b_ 31. Whenever Roland went to a party before a big test instead of studying, he **rationalized** that he would get up early the next morning to study, but he usually slept through the test instead.

(a) planned   (b) justified   (c) believed

_C_ 32. Her anger at her husband's snoring all night usually **dissipated** when he presented her with a rose on her breakfast tray.

(a) increased   (b) hardened   (c) disappeared

_a_ 33. We all want a **panacea** for our problems, but we soon find that there is no cure-all for them, that we just have to hunker down and solve them.

(a) remedy   (b) outlet   (c) diversion

Number of Errors _____

Chapter 2
Finding the Main Idea

I. How to Understand More

STUDY UNIT: *Finding the Main Idea*

> Think of an Umbrella
>
> Look for Topic Sentence in a Paragraph
>
> Look at Other Locations for Topic Sentence
>
> Look for Implied Main Idea

PARAGRAPH PRACTICE: *Feeling Good*

II. How to Read Faster

RATE-BUILDING TIPS:

> Read in Phrases, Not for Words

PHRASE PRACTICE

TIMED READINGS: *Feeling Good*

> *That Loving Feeling*
>
> *Writing Your Wrongs*

I. How to Understand More

Note: *Before you actually read this article, practice the preview technique you learned in Chapter 1. Read the title, introduction, subheadings, and conclusion. To help digest the preview, jot down a few notes at the end of the Study Unit.*

STUDY UNIT

Finding the Main Idea

After finding the topic, the next and most essential skill that will improve your reading is finding the *main idea*, or major point. Similar to previewing for the topic, looking for the main idea is an aid that will help you see the whole instead of getting lost in the parts. Also, seeing the main idea when you read will help you form a more effective main point when you write or speak.

If you are writing essays in a composition class, you too will want to make your main idea clear to your reader. The main idea sentence in the introduction to your essay is often called a *thesis* or *thesis statement*.

Remember that *the main idea expands the topic by making a point about it.* Most writers want us to know what their point is as soon as possible, so they make it easy for us. For the same reason they place the title at the top of the page, they state the main idea at the beginning, in the introduction, as the authors do in this article. The introduction might be one or two paragraphs in an article like this, or it might be two or three pages in a textbook chapter.

Look in a textbook from another class, such as history or science, and notice how long the introductions are. The introduction ends just before the first major subheading, which may be in larger or darker print, or in a different color ink. Some students skip the introduction because they think it does not include items that will appear later on a test. This is a mistake because they miss the whole. Instead, they study by trying to memorize parts that are meaningless to them.

Think of an Umbrella

When you think of finding the main idea, think of an umbrella. The cover, or fabric, of the umbrella is like the main idea statement. The spokes inside that hold up the umbrella are like the supporting details. The handle is like the topic, which you hold onto first. The main idea statement must cover, or include, all those spokes, or details. The details must all support or hold up the main idea. If not, the umbrella can't be very effective.

Look for Topic Sentence in a Paragraph

A supporting paragraph in an article or essay will also have its own main point. (Some short paragraphs may have a linking function, marking a switch from one idea to another.) A well-developed paragraph might have four sentences or ten sentences, but those sentences will be connected to the same point. The sentences will explain, define, or develop a dominant idea, a major idea, or a "main idea." A more general sentence in the paragraph that clearly states the main idea is a *topic sentence*, a term also used in writing classes.

Just as writers want you to find the main idea to an article, they want you to find the topic sentence in a paragraph. In an essay, you put your thesis in an introduction; in a paragraph, you put your topic sentence in the first few sentences. Whether you are reading a paragraph or a whole chapter, 70 to 90 percent of the time you will find the main idea(s) at the beginning. Occasionally, in a paragraph, writers will state their point at the end. Sometimes in longer paragraphs, writers will state the main idea in a topic sentence at the beginning, then repeat it in a concluding sentence at the end. Rarely do writers put their topic sentence in the middle of a paragraph. They do not want to make their readers search for their point.

> **Practice 1** Does the previous paragraph have a topic sentence? __y__
>
> If "yes," which sentence? __1st__
>
> Does it have a concluding sentence? __last one__

Reread the previous paragraph on "The Location of Topic Sentences" and compare it with the visual chart below. Examine the relationship between the main idea and its support details.

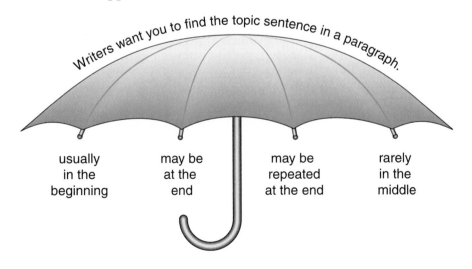

Read the following paragraph on "Education and Weight" and underline the topic sentence. It will be the sentence most closely related to the supporting details.

Are education and weight connected? According to The Harris Poll, the more degrees people have, the less likely they are to think they are overweight. Only 17% of people with college degrees think they are overweight. A big jump to 31% of high school graduates believe they are overweight. And a whopping 40% of people who did not finish high school describe themselves as being overweight.

Practice 2 Fill in the dotted lines on the chart, using information from the above paragraph on "Education and Weight."

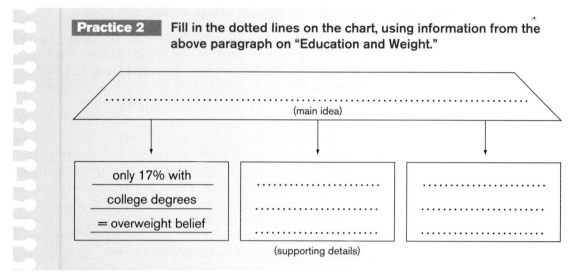

(main idea)

only 17% with
college degrees
= overweight belief

(supporting details)

Look at Other Locations for Topic Sentence

In longer, better-developed paragraphs, you must not assume that the topic sentence will be the first or even the second sentence. Similarly, in a long introduction to a chapter on evolution in a science textbook, you may read a long anecdote about a strange young man rolling around on the ground while hunting in South America. What has this weird young man to do with evolution, you may think (as you will in the long Timed Reading, page 206, in Chapter 6 of this book). It may be the second paragraph (or the second page) of the introduction before you find out that the strange young man is Charles Darwin, who first published the theory of evolution. The story about his odd hunting technique is to get your attention and to give an example of Darwin's willingness to be unconventional.

A careless reading of the next indented paragraph may lead you to think it is about Henry VIII instead of about "Diet and Colon Health." As you read the paragraph, note that Henry VIII is never mentioned again. Nor are his unfortunate wives, like the beheaded Anne Boleyn, or his bad eating habits ever mentioned. If the details do not support the sentence you have picked as the topic sentence, keep looking. Readjust your thinking or you will misread the paragraph. Also notice that, in a more-developed paragraph like this one, there are details about details. Or some details are more specific than others.

[1]Some new age historians say that Henry VIII would not have gotten rid of all those wives if his digestive system had been more efficient. [2]An inefficient colon can really put you in a bad mood. [3]A diet high in fiber may not only improve your digestion and your disposition, but it may also help prevent colon cancer. [4]So start your morning off with a high-grain, low-sugar cereal. Stay away from pop-up tarts. Include salads and vegetables with lunch and dinner. Avoid fast-food restaurants. For snacks, eat fruit and nuts, not potato chips and candy bars. As you get older, you may need to add a product containing psyllium husks to your morning or evening vitamin ritual. These habits should improve your colon health—and possibly your general mood.

Practice 3   Which sentence in the paragraph is the topic sentence?

(a) first   (b) second   (c) third   (d) fourth

Practice 4   Fill in the dotted lines in the chart, using information from the paragraph on "Diet and Colon Health." Try to paraphrase the topic sentence, or put it into your own words. Use the squares to represent the more important supporting details and the circles to represent the more specific details.

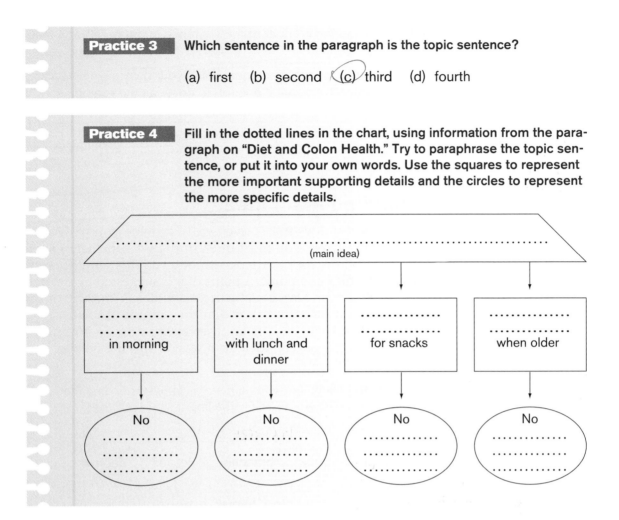

Read the next indented paragraph about "Self-hypnosis and its Benefits." If you assume that the first sentence is the topic sentence, you will misread the paragraph. If the first sentence were the topic sentence, the remainder of the paragraph would be examples of "Social Fears Helped by Self-hypnosis." This topic is too specific, too limited. It is only one example of several in the paragraph. Look beyond the first sentence for a more general sentence that covers all the examples.

[1]Self-hypnosis can decrease social fears such as excessive shyness, nervousness, and awkwardness and even fear of flying. [2]It not only helps people shed fat, but also can improve their eating habits and help them sleep more soundly. [3]It can also help cure more serious habits, such as smoking, alcoholism, and drug abuse. [4]Further, doctors have successfully used it as an anaesthesia for patients during dental work, childbirth, and certain operations during which the patient must remain conscious. [5]Self-hypnosis is indeed a powerful tool that has varied benefits and reminds us that mind and body are one.

Practice 5 What is the number of the sentence in the paragraph that is the topic sentence? _____

Paraphrase that sentence, using your own words. Make sure your sentence is general enough to cover all the examples.

_____

_____

Look for Implied Main Idea

Sometimes the writer does not conveniently provide you with a topic sentence. From the details given, you must infer, or draw a conclusion about, what the main idea is. Even if the topic sentence is not given in a sentence in the paragraph, the paragraph still has a point. A point that is suggested by the details, but not stated, is an *implied main idea*. Usually the main idea is implied, or suggested, when the details are so specific and clear that the point is obvious.

Finding the implied main idea is another exercise in determining general from specific, or forming a general idea from several specific details.

Practice 6 On the blank line, write a general, *implied* heading that covers all the specific words below the line.

_____Oak tree_____

roots   trunk   branches   leaves   acorns

Again, as in similar practice in Chapter 1, notice that forming the generalization becomes more challenging in a paragraph.

Practice 7 Read the following paragraph and, on the blank line, write what you think is the *implied main idea*. Make sure your sentence is general enough to cover all the specific details.

_____hot temper_____

If Harry's friends make even mildly negative comments to him, he lashes out at them with searing insults. If a teacher returns an essay with too many red marks, he slams his books together and stamps out of the classroom. If other drivers honk at him on the freeway, he speeds up and tries to ram into the backs of their cars. When he gets unwanted phone calls at home, he curses and bangs the telephone receiver against the wall.

Now check the sentences you wrote for the implied main idea. Every detail in the paragraph should be a specific example for your sentence. Is your sentence general enough to cover *all* the examples? Or is it too general? Did you write "Harry is a bad person" or "Harry is nuts"? These are close but not as focused as they could be. What personality trait is bad? Resulting in what? Look again at the supporting details, the examples, and improve your focus.

Harry's _____ *causes him to* _____.

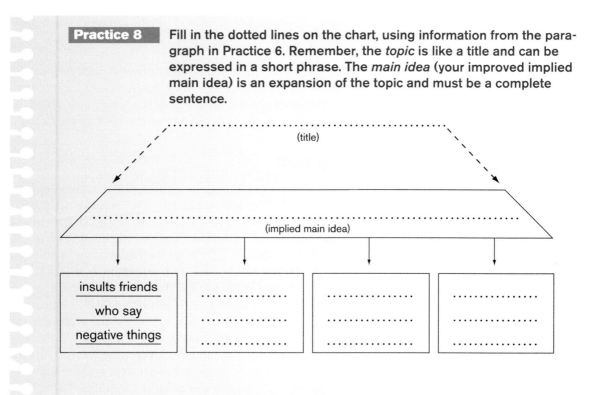

Practice 8 Fill in the dotted lines on the chart, using information from the paragraph in Practice 6. Remember, the *topic* is like a title and can be expressed in a short phrase. The *main idea* (your improved implied main idea) is an expansion of the topic and must be a complete sentence.

(title)

(implied main idea)

| insults friends who say negative things | | | |

Again, think of the paragraph as an expanding whole. The details are an expansion of the main idea, which is, in turn, an expansion of the topic. If we rank the three reading terms on a scale of general to specific, the main idea would fall in the middle—as it does in Practice 8.

most general → less general → specific
topic ⟶ *main idea* ⟶ *supporting details*

Study Notes

1. Write at least three important ideas from this study unit—ideas that you think you will be asked on the Chapter Review or the Unit Test.

   main idea / implied main idea.
   topic
   supporting ideas.

2. List three italicized terms and define them.

   implied main idea.
   thesis statement. / topic sentence

Note-Taking Tips

1. Be brief, no extra words.
2. Use your own words, not the authors'.
3. Make your notes visual: make charts or indent or label.
4. Review these notes (and those from Chapter 1 on page 31) for Comprehension Unit Test 1.

Feeling Good

Directions: *Carefully read the three paragraphs about health and continue to look for the* topic *and* main idea. *In particular, look for the main idea stated in a* topic sentence—*usually the most general sentence in the paragraph. After answering the questions for each paragraph, check with the key in the back of the book.*

Exercise 2A: Paragraph

¹More and more Americans recognize a connection between mental and physical illness. ²More of us are using that cause-effect relationship for healing. ³Two out of five Americans use some type of alternative medicine, according to the *Journal of the American Medical Association*. ⁴For decades, some of us have been trying to beat stress with free remedies like yoga, self-hypnosis, and meditation. ⁵Some people with back problems have tried chiropractors. ⁶Others try acupuncture. ⁷ The biggest trend has been toward herbal supplements. ⁸We are dosing ourselves in record numbers with cures that do not require a doctor's prescription or FDA approval. ⁹Aging athletes and armchair athletes alike are popping glucosamine for arthritic joints. ¹⁰We take echinacea to fight colds. ¹¹We take ginkgo to make us alert. ¹²We take ginseng for energy. ¹³We take kava to improve our memory. ¹⁴Instead of Prozac, we take St. John's wort and SAM-e for depression. ¹⁵Those of us with cottage-cheese thighs are taking Cellasine to fight cellulite. ¹⁶We are spending $15 billion a year for these alternative cures.

1. Choose the phrase that best expresses the general topic of the paragraph.
   (a) Money Spent on Alternative Treatments
   (b) Too Many Americans Going to Quacks
   (c) More Americans Using Alternative Medicine
   (d) How Americans Connect Mind and Body

2. Is the main idea stated in a *topic sentence*? (a) yes, sentence #_____   (b) no

3. Using your own words, write a complete sentence that states the main idea of the paragraph.

   _____

   _____

   [who?   and how many?   are doing what?]

4. List details, or examples, in the blanks below that support the two headings.

problem or illness	*alternative treatment*
_____	_____
_____	_____
_____	_____
_____	_____

Exercise 2B: Paragraph

[1]Do you love the sizzle that chili peppers add to your food? [2]Do you avoid them because you think they blaze a trail of charred flesh throughout your digestive system? [3]According to current research, hot peppers do *not* cause hemorrhoids or ulcers. [4]Even better news, these chili peppers are actually beneficial. [5]They add A and C vitamins to your diet but add no fat and few calories. [6]Because they "increase salivation and stimulate stomach activity," they improve digestion. [7]The chemical *capsaicin* that makes peppers hot also helps burn up to 25 percent more calories a day than usual. [8]Capsaicin may even protect against cancer. [9]It prevents the liver from turning some toxins, like *aflatoxin* in peanut butter, into carcinogens. [10]If you want to decrease the pepper's hotness, you can remove its seeds and the white ribs running down the sides and middle. [11]You may, however, be removing part of the pepper's benefits.

1. What is the general topic of the paragraph? (Consider the topic like a title; write a short phrase. Remember, in a title, capitalize the first letter of the first word and of all important words.)

    _____

2. Is the main idea stated in a *topic sentence?* (a) yes, sentence #___4___   (b) no

3. Using your own words, choose the sentence that best states the main idea of the paragraph.
    (a) Chili peppers are good for your health in several ways.
    (b) Chili peppers make food taste better.
    (c) Chili peppers are beneficial in some ways but cause hemorrhoids or ulcers.
    (d) It is the chemical *capsaicin* that causes chili peppers to be good for your health.

4. List the four most important details given to support the main idea.
    ___add A and C vitamin___   _____

    _____   _____

Exercise 2C: Paragraph

[1]Pay attention to your breathing. [2]How you breath can tell you how relaxed or how tense you are. [3]For example, when you are calm, your breathing is deep and steady. [4]Your breath comes from the stomach, not the chest. [5]But when you are nervous, excited, or under stress, your breathing changes. [6]It becomes shallow and ragged, almost like panting. [7]It comes from the chest or throat. [8]Sometimes, when upset, you may even catch yourself holding your breath without knowing it. [9]Or you may exhale more quickly than you inhale. [10]So whenever you want to calm down, try to breathe to a rhythm. [11]Inhale to the count of three; exhale to the count of four. [12]Then get in the habit of checking your breathing from time to time to make sure you stay relaxed and at your best.

1. What is the general topic of the paragraph? (Consider the topic like a title; write a short phrase. Remember, in a title, capitalize the first letter of the first word and of all important words.)

   _____Breathing and relaxtion_____

2. Is the main idea stated in a *topic sentence*?
   (a) yes, sentence #__2__   (b) no

3. Using your own words, write a complete sentence that states the main idea of the paragraph.

   _____

   _____

   [how you what?   affects what or what?]

4. Finish the lists of supporting details by briefly filling in the blanks in the right column. (The first answer has been supplied to get you started.)

state of relaxation	description of breathing
when calm	deep and steady—from stomach
when nervous	_____
when upset	_____
when you "want" to be calm	_____

II. How to Read Faster

Note: *Before you actually read this instruction, practice the preview technique you learned in Chapter 1.*

This section continues the training you began in Chapter 1 to improve your rate. (Remember, you should have already done the Vocabulary Preview for Chapter 2.) In this chapter, you will continue to practice reading whole phrases at a glance.

Read in Phrases, Not for Words

Here is a technique that can start to improve both your rate and your comprehension right away: read in phrases (units of thought) instead of stopping on individual words. Consider this example:

To / train / yourself / to / read / in / phrases, / use / the / natural / rhythm / of / the / language / to / help / you.

The slashes mark the places where many readers pause, whether they are aware of it or not. Too many students read word-by-word. The reader who pauses on every word in that sentence stops (or fixates) seventeen times. The person who reads in phrases, however, groups together chunks of words that make sense. That person pauses just once to read each chunk or phrase. A more effective reader might see the sentence this way:

To train yourself / to read in phrases, / use the natural rhythm / of the language / to guide you.

The slashes mark logical "bites" of meaning to take at one time. Did you notice how punctuation such as commas and periods also marks natural places to stop and read? The better reader would fixate only five times instead of seventeen times. This reader could be reading three times as fast—just because of reading in phrases instead of word-by-word.

The Phrase practice, Exercises 2D and 2E, on the next two pages will help you make the transition to phrase-reading.

> **Practice** Now take your first step toward practicing this concept. Mark phrases—groups of words—with slashes in the three sentences that follow. Pay attention to what the words say so you can see which words belong together.
>
> When you read, hold the book about sixteen inches from your face. Try to create a mental picture of what you're reading, and your concentration (and memory) will automatically improve. Look for the six *W's* that news reporters use: *W*ho and *W*hat, *W*here and *W*hen, *W*hy and How.

Now you are ready for the next step. In the rest of this chapter, remember to read in phrases (or for ideas) instead of word-by-word. To do this, pay attention to the sense of the sentence.

Then use this approach on all your easier reading. As you get more practice, you'll be able to digest longer phrases at a time, and reading in phrases will soon become natural. You will probably find that it carries over into more difficult material. Be aware, however, that even the best readers read difficult materials word-by-word some of the time. Many reading experts believe word-by-word reading in such cases can even help the learning process, especially for memorizing. So don't try to speed-read your textbooks by straining to read in phrases. Other techniques, such as previewing and vocabulary building, are more likely to increase your speed when you study-read.

Exercise 2D: Phrases

Make a slash through the phrase identical to the key phrase. Remember to focus on each dot above the phrase to reinforce phrase reading.

Key Phrase

1. to save gas	to have gas	two gas savers	to save gas
2. controls pollution	central pollution	controls pollution	controlled pullout
3. owning a car	owning cars	owning a car	the owner's car
4. slow driving	slow driver	slow driving	slow drive
5. a seat belt	a neat belt	a seat belt	a near belt
6. car pool	car pooling	car pool	careful pal
7. pedal travel	pedal travel	pedal traveled	pedal drag
8. careful driver	careful driver	careful diver	scared of driving
9. radial tires	radial tires	radial tire	radical tire
10. make and model	made a model	make and model	maker's model
11. a popular item	a populous item	a popular item	a popular mite
12. having overdrive	having overhang	having overdrive	having overdone
13. lower rpm	lower rim	lower rpm	slower rpm
14. air filter	air filter	fair filter	air flight
15. natural resource	national resource	nature's resource	natural resource
16. harmful emissions	harmful omissions	harmless emissions	harmful emissions
17. wasting energy	wasteful energy	wasting energy	wasting energies
18. used the brakes	abused the brakes	fused the brakes	used the brakes
19. road tested	toad rested	rod tested	road tested
20. camping trip	camping trip	camping tent	camper rip-off

Time ___40 sc___

Number of Errors ___3___

Exercise 2E: Phrases

Make a slash through the phrase identical to the key phrase.

Key Phrase

1.	six swimming swans	swats six swans	six sweet sins	six swimming swans
2.	this covered wagon	the costly wigs	this covered wagon	that wagging dog
3.	the dripping faucet	the file cabinet	the worst fault	the dripping faucet
4.	downfall of man	downfall of man	fall of women	many funny clowns
5.	a clean ashtray	a clean ashtray	clears an aisle	a betrayed clod
6.	gangster movie	big motorcycle gang	picture of mother	gangster movie
7.	smoke-filled lungs	smoke-filled lungs	dreadful smog	broken filling
8.	polka-dot bikini	yellow dotted bikini	polka-dot bikini	danced the polka
9.	down narrow streets	down narrow streets	marrow of bones	deft right turns
10.	danced a jig	danced a jig	a rigged dance	a fancy jig
11.	in slow motion	in slow motion	inside the track	an insolent action
12.	a crossword puzzle	a crossword puzzle	a jigsaw puzzle	a puzzling word
13.	handles with care	careful handling	handles with care	a hot handle
14.	puts to sleep	a sleazy slut	but not there	puts to sleep
15.	cooks your goose	cooks your goose	goose your crook	cupful of gin
16.	prays for peace	prays for peace	pans of pears	preys on people
17.	wins the war	war to win	wins the war	the won war
18.	the lost letter	a lost letter	the better lot	the lost letter
19.	treads on me	treads on me	reads this too	one dread night
20.	rips it across	crosses the rip	trips it across	rips it across

Time _____

Number of Errors _____

As you move from paragraphs to longer readings, like articles in magazines and newspapers, you will find the basic structure is the same. They all have a *main idea*. This controlling idea is like an umbrella for the whole article. It helps the author write about only the ideas that fit under that cover.

Since, because of your writing classes, you may be more familiar with the term *thesis*, we will use that term to refer to the main idea for an article made up of several paragraphs. Remember that an author usually states the thesis of an essay or article in the first or second paragraph, just as the main idea for a paragraph is often in the first or second sentence.

Examine the following diagram to see how similar a paragraph is to an essay, how the paragraph expands to an essay using the same structure. Then be aware of that structure as you read the Timed Readings.

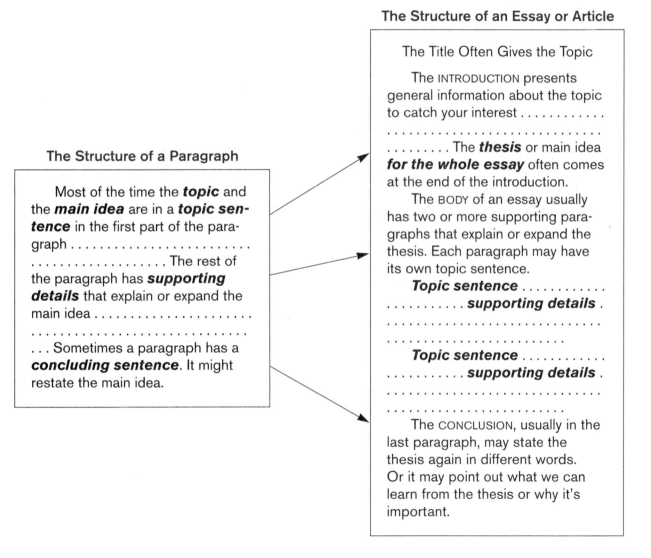

The Structure of an Essay or Article

The Title Often Gives the Topic

The INTRODUCTION presents general information about the topic to catch your interest . . . .
. . . .
. . . . The **thesis** or main idea *for the whole essay* often comes at the end of the introduction.

The BODY of an essay usually has two or more supporting paragraphs that explain or expand the thesis. Each paragraph may have its own topic sentence.
Topic sentence . . . .
. . . . *supporting details* .
. . . .
. . . .
Topic sentence . . . .
. . . . *supporting details* .
. . . .
. . . .

The CONCLUSION, usually in the last paragraph, may state the thesis again in different words. Or it may point out what we can learn from the thesis or why it's important.

The Structure of a Paragraph

Most of the time the **topic** and the **main idea** are in a **topic sentence** in the first part of the paragraph . . . .
. . . . The rest of the paragraph has **supporting details** that explain or expand the main idea . . . .
. . . .
. . . Sometimes a paragraph has a **concluding sentence**. It might restate the main idea.

The arrows between the two diagrams point to where the key parts of a paragraph are also present—in an expanded form—in an essay or article.

Exercise 2F: Timed Reading

503 words

This first selection is a light, breezy newspaper essay about love. It is a perfect article for practicing speed-reading. Use the slashes in the first two paragraphs to get a sense of natural phrases.

Preview: *In twenty seconds or less, preread the title, the first paragraph (the quotation), the second paragraph (the introduction), and the last paragraph (the conclusion). Write here what point (or thesis) you think the author is making about love:*

_____

 Wait for a signal from your instructor before you begin reading. Try to finish in one minute, if you can. Circle your reading time when finished, and find your WPM.

That Loving Feeling

Loraine O'Connell

> When two people / are under / the influence / of the most violent, / most insane, / most delusive, / and most transient / of passions, / they are required / to swear / that they / will remain / in that excited, / abnormal and exhausting / condition continuously / until death / do them part.
>
> —GEORGE BERNARD SHAW

To scientists / studying brain chemistry, / Shaw's cynical appraisal / of romantic love / is more than / just memorable prose. / It's an accurate description / of what's wrong / with our / boy-meets-girl / -marries-then-divorces / -and-remarries society. / "People need / to understand / that the feeling / (romantic love) / is going to fade, / and there's nothing / they can really do / about it / except deal / with it, / says Orlando, Florida, / chemist John Bowers.

Although technical director of a company, Orlando Laboratories, that analyzes water and soil pollution (a distinctly unromantic occupation), Bowers has a particular interest in brain chemistry and human behavior. Bowers expounded on the latest scientific thinking on why we pair up, and why we have so much trouble staying paired up to the same person for life.

His bottom line: It's all hormones.

When we meet someone we're attracted to, the hormones our brains churn out—serotonin, norepinephrine, and dopamine, among others—are what make us feel so great, he says. The reason for this chemical come-on? Propagation of the species, of course.

Think back several million years ago. Go on, you can do it. The idea was: Our hairier ancestors would be attracted to a mate, feel that rush of hormones and—under the influence of all those chemicals—reproduce. Nature knew what she was doing, Bowers says.

However, these chemicals are also biologically programmed to level off. The reason? Propagation of the species. Once the thrill was gone, our ancestors would move on to new mates and make whoopee again, thus ensuring the continued reproduction and evolution of the species.

"Monogamy is definitely not what nature intended man and woman to be doing," Bowers says. "The more genetic diversity we have, the better able the species will be to survive."

That was then; this is now. Propagation of the species and genetic diversity aren't pressing issues for *Homo sapiens* in 1993; however, our brain chemistry hasn't changed with the times, Bowers says.

TIMING CHART	
min:sec	wpm
2:48	180
2:31	200
2:17	220
2:07	240
1:56	260
1:48	280
1:41	300
1:34	320
1:29	340
1:24	360
1:19	380
1:15	400
1:12	420
1:09	440
1:06	460
1:03	480
1:00	500
0:58	520
0:56	540
0:54	560
0:52	580
0:50	600
0:49	620
0:47	640
0:46	660
0:44	680
0:43	700
0:42	720
0:41	740
0:40	760
0:39	780
0:38	800

Researchers can even tell you approximately when your "luv" hormones will go on hiatus. Quoting the work of various scientists, Helen E. Fisher, author of "Anatomy of Love: The Natural History of Monogamy, Adultery and Divorce," reports that the typical romantic high lasts 18 months to three years.

"Perhaps it is no coincidence that the American divorce peak corresponds perfectly with the normal duration of infatuation—two to three years," Fisher writes.

Thus, when the Righteous Brothers sang, "You've lost that lovin' feeling," what they really means was, "You've lost that hormonal rush."

As with any drug, once the effect wears off, the tendency is to want more, Bowers says. "Some people are attraction junkies," he says. "They can't handle it when the level drops off. They'll go looking for someone else who can get the level up fast."

Answer the following recall questions without referring to the article.

1. What bottom-line reason does chemist John Bowers give for people pairing up and splitting up? _____

2. Bowers thinks monogamy is essential for the survival of the species.
   (a) true   (b) false

3. According to Fisher, how long does the typical romance (and often marriage) last?
   (a) six months   (b) 18 months   (c) five years

You may refer to the article to answer the following questions.

4. What words from the quotation by George Bernard Shaw give the author the impression that Shaw is cynical about love? _____
_____

5. Choose the sentence that best expresses the *thesis* (or main idea) of this article.
   (a) Only fools fall in love.
   (b) True love conquers all.
   (c) Scientists in this article believe that only monogamy will overcome people's natural tendency to fall out of love.
   (d) Scientists in this article believe that love is temporary and that monogamy is unnatural.

Check your answers with the key. (Remember, each comprehension question is worth 20 percent.) Record your scores below and on the Progress Chart on page 442.

Words per Minute _____

Percent Comprehension _____

PERCENTAGE CHART						
number of errors	0	1	2	3	4	5
percent correct	100	80	60	40	20	0

Exercise 2G: Timed Reading

This last reading will provide a greater challenge, in both concentration and speed building, because of its length. It explores the benefits of journal writing to psychological health.

Preview: *Take one minute (at least) for a more thorough survey, not only because of the article's length, but also because it gives more visual clues. Quickly read the title, author's name (because of his title), first paragraph, first few sentences of the second paragraph (still a part of the introduction), all subheadings, and the last paragraph. Write here why or how the author is recommending journal writing:*

_____

_____

Wait for a signal from your instructor before you begin reading. Try to push your speed faster even though the article is longer. Use your awareness of "topic sentences" to help you focus. Then circle your reading time when finished, and find your WPM.

Writing Your Wrongs

James W. Pennebaker, Ph.D.

Gone are the days when we used to sit for hours writing long letters to friends and family. With pen and paper we took time to explore our feelings and express our deepest beliefs. The world we now inhabit is too hurried for that. But, while using the phone and the fax machine is a time-saver, have we lost something in the process?

[1]Recent research suggests that are distinct advantages to the old-fashioned method of communication. [2]The act of writing can be an avenue to that interior place where, free of pain and doubt, we can confront traumas and put them to rest—and heal both body and mind. [3]The words we write can have a healing power even if they're never read by another human being. [4]In our studies we've asked people to use an ancient form of writing: keeping a journal of their deepest thoughts and feelings, which they might not want to share even with close friends. [5]Using writing as a means of confession, we've found, can measurably improve physical and mental health. . . .

A growing number of Americans pay millions of dollars to therapists and self-help groups to share feelings they're afraid to tell the world. And the last year or two have brought a distinctly '90s invention: 1-900 confession hot lines, where anonymous callers recount their sins.

In the late 1970s, I embarked on a large research project to determine the extent to which it's healthy for us to express what's stored deep inside. Now, more than a decade later, the data show a clear correlation between confessional writing and greater health.

In September 1983, along with Sandra Beall, a graduate student at Southern Methodist University in Dallas, I asked a group of student volunteers to write about either *traumatic* experiences or *superficial* topics. As a further refinement, those who wrote about traumas would either:

1. just vent their emotions,

2. just write down the facts, or

3. write about facts and emotions at the same time.

They kept journals, writing fifteen minutes a day over four days. We planned to evaluate their health by counting the number of visits each person made to the student health center for illness in the five and a half months following the experiment compared with the two and a half months before.

For the students, the immediate impact of the study was far more powerful than we had even imagined. Several cried as they wrote. Many told us they found themselves dreaming about their writing topics over the fours days of the study. Essay after essay revealed people's most intimate feelings. Many of the stories depicted profound human tragedies.

One student recounted how his father took him into the back yard on a hot summer night and coolly announced his plans to divorce the boy's mother and move to another town. Although the boy was only nine years old at the time, he vividly remembers his father saying, "Son, the problem with me and your mother was having you kids in the first place. Things haven't been the same since you and your sister were born." . . .

Another student described being sexually abused by her grandfather when she was 13, and wrote about the terrible conflict she experienced. On one hand, she admitted the physical pleasure of his touching her and the love she felt for her grandfather. On the other, she suffered with the knowledge that what they were doing was wrong, that he was betraying her trust.

Other essays disclosed the torture of a woman not able to tell her parents she was gay, a young man's feeling of loss over the death of his dog, and the anger of three different people as they tried to cope with their parents' divorces. Family abuse, alcoholism, suicide attempts, and public humiliation were also frequent topics.

Boosting Mood and Health

While these accounts were very moving, we were discouraged to find that writing didn't help these students feel better initially—just the opposite. In fact, it seemed that we were inventing a new way to make people depressed.

But, when our volunteers completed additional questionnaires four months after the experiment, we found that their moods *had* improved. Writing about their deepest thoughts had started a process that resulted in a lighter mood and more positive outlook.

Almost six months after the experiment, the student health center was able to tell us the number of times each student had sought treatment for an illness. Those numbers brought good news too. People who wrote about their deepest thoughts and feelings about a traumatic event became healthier—they visited the health service for treatment much less often than other groups after the study.

In the months before the experiment, everyone had gone to the health center at the same rate. After the experiment, however, those who wrote detailed accounts of their traumatic experiences went fewer than 0.5 times a month on average—a 50 percent drop in the monthly visitation rate. To get this healing benefit, a complete accounting was necessary. People who wrote just about their emotions surrounding a trauma, or just about the facts, averaged almost 1.5 visits per person to the health center—the same rate as those who wrote about superficial topics and avoided difficult subjects entirely. . . .

In follow-up studies with researchers in the immune system, the students consented to having their blood drawn the day before they started writing, after the last writing session, and again six weeks later. The findings were unequivocal.

People who wrote thoughtfully and emotionally about traumatic experiences showed heightened immune function compared with those who wrote about superficial topics. Although this effect was most pronounced after the last day of writing, it tended to persist six weeks after the study. In addition, health center visits for illness dropped once again for the people who wrote about traumas compared with those who wrote on the trivial topics.

In the surveys we sent out several months after each experiment, we asked people to describe in their own words what long-term effects, if any, the writing process had on them. Everyone who had written about traumas described the study in positive terms. Rather than saying it felt good to get negative emotions off their chests, the students said they now understood themselves better. One said, "Although I have not talked with anyone about what I wrote, I was finally able to deal with it and work through the pain instead of trying to block it out. Now it doesn't hurt to think about it."

Observations like this are telling us in very concrete terms that our thought processes can be healed.

Putting It on Paper

How can you best confront the upsetting events in your past and free yourself from them? My recommendations are based not only on our experiments but also on my experiences. When writing about personal difficulties, be your own researcher. Try different topics and approaches. You may find a resolution to your conflicts in a way that works uniquely for you, not for anyone else. If you become overly distraught, back off and approach the topic more gradually. With these caveats in mind, here are some basic approaches to the writing method.

What should your writing topic be? It isn't necessary to write about the most traumatic experience of your life. If you find yourself dwelling on any event or experience too much of the time, writing about it can help resolve it in your mind. Similarly, if there is something you would like to tell others but can't for fear of embarrassment or punishment, express it on paper.

Whatever your topic, it's critical to explore both the objective experience and your feelings about it. Let go and express your deepest emotions: *what* you feel about it and *why* you feel that way. Write continuously; don't worry about grammar, spelling or sentence structure. If you run out of things to say or reach a mental block, just repeat what you have already written.

When and where should you write? Try to write for 15 minutes a day in a setting where you will not be interrupted. Although many people write every day in journals, most of the entries don't grapple with fundamental psychological issues—the goal of this approach.

Where you write depends on your circumstances. Our studies suggest that the more special the setting, the better. Find a unique, comfortable, isolated room where you will not be interrupted or bothered by unwanted sounds, sights, or smells.

What should you do with what you have written? Planning to show your journal to someone else can affect your mind-set while writing. From a health perspective, you will be better off making yourself the only audience. That way, you don't have to rationalize or justify yourself to suit another person's perspective.

What can you expect to feel during and after writing? You may feel sad or depressed immediately afterward. These feelings usually dissipate within an hour; in rare cases, they may last a day or two. Indeed, the vast majority of our volunteers report feeling a heightened sense of relief, happiness, and contentment that lasts up to six months after the writing studies are concluded.

I should point out that exploring your deepest thoughts and feelings on paper is not a panacea. If you're coping with death, divorce, or some other major trauma, you won't feel better instantly after writing. You should, however, have a clearer understanding of your feelings and emotions as well as your objective situation. In other words, writing should give you some distance and perspective on your life. And that can lead to positive changes in your physical and mental health.

TIMING CHART	
min:sec	wpm
9:05	180
8:11	200
7:26	220
6:49	240
6:17	260
5:50	280
5:27	300
5:07	320
4:49	340
4:33	360
4:16	380
4:05	400
3:54	420
3:43	440
3:33	460
3:24	480
3:16	500
3:09	520
3:02	540
2:55	560
2:49	580
2:44	600
2:38	620
2:33	640
2:29	660
2:24	680
2:20	700
2:26	720
2:13	750
2:09	760
2:06	780
2:03	800

Answer the following recall questions without referring to the article.

1. This article, in general, is more about (a) writing skills [or] (b) a method to help with psychological problems.

2. Six months after the 1970s research project, which group of students had visited the student health center "less" often for treatment?
   (a) Those who wrote about traumatic experiences
   (b) Those who wrote about superficial topics

3. Briefly list any one of the traumatic stories the students wrote in their journals. _____

   _____

4. At first, writing about their tragedies made the students more depressed.
   (a) true   (b) false

5. The author recommends that while you are journal writing you show what you have written to someone you trust.   (a) true   (b) false

You may refer to the article to answer the following questions.

6. Which of the five sentences in the second paragraph is too specific to be the thesis of the article? _____

   In your own words, list three tips from the article on "how" to explore your feelings in writing:

7. _____

8. _____

9. _____

10. In your words, write a complete sentence that states the *thesis* for this article. _____

   _____

[who recommends what?   why?]

Check your answers with the key, and record your scores below and on the Progress Chart. (Remember, each comprehension question is worth 10 percent.)

Words per Minute _____

Percent Comprehension _____

PERCENTAGE CHART	number of errors	0	1	2	3	4	5	6	7	8	9	10
	percent correct	100	90	80	70	60	50	40	30	20	10	0

How to Improve Getting the Thesis/Main Idea

As you apply the reading principles you are learning in this book to your outside reading, you may notice these things:

1. The thesis is not usually the first sentence in an article or essay. The author often starts with a little story (called an anecdote) to get your interest and introduce the topic. Or the author may start with some surprising facts or statistics. *The thesis may not be stated until the end of the first paragraph or even until the second paragraph.*

2. The thesis in writing for newspapers and magazines is often more general than the type of thesis you are learning to write for school assignments. It doesn't always list *all* the main ideas that the article will develop. Instead, it may just give the main point the author will expand on in the rest of the article.

3. Looking for the article's thesis and main ideas is a thinking skill. You cannot always spot the thesis of an article nor the main idea of a paragraph the first time you see it. Only when you *compare what a sentence is saying to what the other sentences are saying* can you tell which statement is the most general, the umbrella for the others.

Writing and Discussion Activities

1. Write a letter to your boss. In the letter, give your ideas about what your company or business could do to improve the well-being of the employees. You may wish to use some of the ideas from the articles you just read. But feel free to add other ideas that come to you. When you finish, your instructor may want you to break into small groups of three or four and discuss the ideas in each other's letters. (If you have no job, imagine the conditions you'd like to have once you start to work.)

2. Continue your reading journal. Give your feelings about one of the articles you just read. Start by summing up your feelings in a single sentence. This will be your topic sentence. In the rest of the paragraph, explain why you feel this way.

Vocabulary Review, Chapter 2

Match the vocabulary word on the left with its definition on the right. Write the letter of the answer in the short blank to the left.

_c_ 1. **charred**   (a) deep

_d_ 2. **delusive**   (b) unknown

_b_ 3. **anonymous**   (c) very scorched

_a_ 4. **profound**   (d) unrealistic

_e_ 5. **unequivocal**   (e) firm

*Choose the best definition for each **boldfaced** vocabulary word as it is used in its context.*

_c_ 6. Students in year-round schools go on **hiatus** about every two months.
     (a) field trips   (b) computer training   (c) break

_a_ 7. Ever since the Watergate scandal, Americans have become increasingly **cynical** about their politicians.
     (a) disillusioned   (b) trusting   (c) frightened

_c_ 8. It was amazing to the mother how her son **rationalized** going to play basketball instead of doing his homework.
     (a) planned   (b) enjoyed   (c) justified

_c_ 9. Having just built a greenhouse, Tiffany decided to take a course in plant **propagation**.
     (a) nutrition   (b) herbal medicine   (c) reproduction

_b_ 10. The judge **expounded** upon the meaning of the legal term "reasonable doubt."
     (a) invited questions   (b) explained at length   (c) summed up

*Mark each sentence to show whether the **boldfaced** word is used correctly.*

a = True   b = False

_F_ 11. As soon as Wanda took care of her problem with **hemorrhoids**, she found she could move her arms freely.

_T_ 12. Because the elementary school had such a **transient** population, the teacher knew that by the end of the school year, more than half of her students would have left.

_T_ 13. The mother became **distraught** upon finding her toddler lying at the bottom of the stairs.

(Continued)

_____✓ 14. The yearly parade was so popular that a big crowd **dissipated** along
the parade route hours before its scheduled start.

F ___I__ 15. The five-year-old kept silent as she **recounted** how she had stuck
her fingers in the freshly-baked pie.

Choose the word from the box that fits the context of the following paragraph.
Write the letter of each choice on the blank lines to the left of the paragraph.

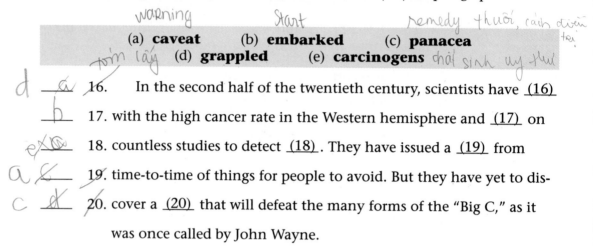

(a) **caveat**   (b) **embarked**   (c) **panacea**
(d) **grappled**   (e) **carcinogens**

d ___a__ 16.   In the second half of the twentieth century, scientists have __(16)__

___b__ 17. with the high cancer rate in the Western hemisphere and __(17)__ on

___e__ 18. countless studies to detect __(18)__ . They have issued a __(19)__ from

a ___e__ 19. time-to-time of things for people to avoid. But they have yet to dis-

c ___d__ 20. cover a __(20)__ that will defeat the many forms of the "Big C," as it

was once called by John Wayne.

% Correct _____

Comprehension Review, Chapter 2

1. A *topic* is more general than a *topic sentence*. (a) true (b) false

2. *Supporting details* are more specific than the *main idea*. (a) true (b) false

3. What is the term that is often used for the main idea statement in an essay? (a) topic sentence (b) thesis statement

4. In what position is the *topic sentence* more likely to be found?
   (a) beginning (b) middle (c) end

5. What is the term for a main idea that is not actually stated in a sentence in a paragraph, but is suggested by the supporting details?
   implied main idea / determine general from specific / form a general idea from several specific details

6. On the blank line, write a general heading that covers all the words below.
   _____ family _____
   baby   parents   brother   sister   grandparents   aunts and uncles

Read the following paragraph and answer the questions about it.

[1]Maria's insecurities cause her to try too hard to please the people she knows, even those who don't treat her well. [2]She is so afraid her friends won't like her that she apologizes when they make a mistake like stepping on her toe. [3]When Mr. Holyfold, her math teacher, made a twenty percent mistake in computing Maria's final-exam score, she accepted the lower score without protest. [4]She even has an after-school job so she can buy expensive presents for her parents, in spite of their careless neglect of her. [5]For example, they often forget her birthday. [6]Even worse, last Christmas, they went on a cruise without inviting Maria.

7. What is the general *topic* of this paragraph? (Write a short phrase, like a title; and use correct capitalization, as in a title.)
   _____ Maria's Insecurities _____

8. Is the main idea stated in a *topic sentence*? (a) yes, sentence #__1__ (b) no

9. In your own words, write a complete sentence that states the main idea.
   Maria always thinks and cares about the people around her more than her

10. Give one example that supports the main idea. Maria gives expensive works hard and to buy
   presents for her parents but they often forgot her birthday
   and didn't invite her care careless less her
   People around Maria doesn't care about her than she
   care about them.

% **Correct** _____

VOCABULARY PREVIEW for Chapter 3

Context Clue #2: Look for Antonyms

Antonyms are words or phrases that mean the opposite of another word. When writers include an antonym in a sentence, they are often giving their readers a clue to unlock the meaning to a difficult vocabulary word. Consider these examples:

- Mike want to impress his beautiful, intelligent date with *profound* ideas, <u>but</u> he was so nervous that he could only stammer silly, shallow remarks.

- Marsha felt *distraught* when she saw her new husband sneak a $20 bill from her purse; <u>however</u>, she became much calmer when she saw him replace it with a $100 bill.

The underlined words in the examples are helpful words that connect the new vocabulary word to its antonym. The common transition "but" and "however" signal contrast, or opposite. The word "but" signals that *profound* means the opposite of "silly, shallow." The word "however" signals that *distraught* means the opposite of "calm." Other transitions that point to antonym clues are *not, in contrast, except, although, on the other hand, instead, as opposed to.*

Now that you know the antonyms, you know that *profound* means _____ and that *distraught* means _____.

Practice   Each sentence has a helpful word, or transition, that signals an antonym for the word in *italics.* Underline the transition. Then, using the antonym as a clue to the meaning of the italicized word, write the word's meaning in the blank.

1. Claudia tearfully poured out her feelings to her husband, hoping for an openly sympathetic reaction in return, instead of his usual silence and *implacable* stare. _____

2. The mule *balked* at crossing the stream, as opposed to going forward willingly. _____

3. Most of the rats were *haphazardly* chosen for the experiment, except for Mickey, who was carefully picked because of his large brain. _____

[Answers: 1. *instead of*; hard-hearted and unyielding
            2. *as opposed to*; resisted or refused
            3. *except for*; randomly or without a plan]

Directions: *Examine the **boldfaced** word as it is used in the sentence and write your best guess of the word's meaning. Then look up the word in your dictionary and write the best definition for its context in the sentence. Continue to make flash cards for the words you don't know.*

PRONUNCIATION KEY										
a	cat	ā	made	ä	bar	k	cot, quit			adore
e	pet	ē	these	â	care	s	cent			travel
i	sit	ī	ride	ė	term	z	beds	ə	{	horrify
o	rot	ō	note	ô	order	j	giant			pardon
u	nut	o͞o	rude	o͝o	foot	th	thank			circus
ů	put	yo͞o	use	o͞o	food	ŦH	this			

from Paragraph 3A (p. 102)

1. **proliferation**   (prō lif′ ə rā′ shən)   *noun*

   One doubtful sign of progress is the **proliferation** of gadgets.

   Your best guess: _____

   Best dictionary definition: _a sudden increase in the amount or number of sth_

2. **chastise**   (chas′ tīz)   *verbal*

   The actor . . . stepped out of character to **chastise** a theatergoer whose cell phone kept ringing.

   Your best guess: _____

   Best dictionary definition: _to criticize someone severely_

3. **dubious**   (dyo͞o′ bē əs)   *adjective*

   Another **dubious** improvement is the increased use of polls.

   Your best guess: _____

   Best dictionary definition: _probably not honest, true._

from Paragraph 3B (p. 104)

4. **repertoire**   (rep′ ər twär′)   *noun*

   Finally, hold back some books and keep a **repertoire** of new games in your head for that last endless stretch of time.

   Your best guess: _____

   Best dictionary definition: _the total number of thing is able to do_

from Paragraph 3C (p. 105)

5. **spunky** (spung' kē)   *adjective*

   And their full-bosomed, flashing-eyed heroines are every bit their match—though these **spunky** women would make a modern feminist cringe at their tendency to turn to mush in their hero's manly arms.

   Your best guess: _____

   Best dictionary definition: _having a lot of energy_

6. **mired** (mīrd)   *verbal*

   Are we tired of being tame city dwellers, **mired** in routine?

   Your best guess: _____

   Best dictionary definition: _stuck in a bad situation_

from Timed Reading 3F (p. 109)

7. **implacable** (im pla' kə bəl)   *adjective*

   They [self-service gas station pumps] are as **implacable** as the cows I used to milk.

   Your best guess: _____

   Best dictionary definition: _very determined to continue opposing someone or sth_

8. **eke** (ēk)   *verb*

   Their hoses are as stubborn as the udders I pulled to **eke** out a small strain of milk.

   Your best guess: _____

   Best dictionary definition: _to make a small supply of sth such as food or money last longer by carefully using sm amount of it._

from Timed Reading 3G (p. 112)

9. **persona** (pər sō' nə)   *noun*

   Ever wonder what happens when a pet takes on a **persona**?

   Your best guess: _____

   Best dictionary definition: _the way you behave when you are with other people_

10. **haphazardly** (hap' haz' ərd lē)   *adverb*

    He was picked for the role quite **haphazardly**.

    Your best guess: _____

    Best dictionary definition: _____

11. **balked**   (bôkt)   *verb*

When I **balked** at the $60-a-year fee, the cheery telephone company representative suggested I list the number in one of my children's names.

Your best guess: _____

Best dictionary definition: _____

12. **touted**   (tout' id)   *verb*

"A remarkable new book about the Coppolas . . . and you, Ashley Coppola, are in it," **touted** one letter asking Ashley to send $10 right away for "this one-time offer."

Your best guess: _____

Best dictionary definition: _____

13. **bulk**   (bulk)   *noun*

Ashley received hundreds of pieces of mail, the **bulk** [of it] *soliciting* his money.

Your best guess: _____

Best dictionary definition: _____

14. **soliciting**   (sə lis' it ing)   *verbal*

Your best guess: _____

Best dictionary definition: _____

[Note: See sentence #13 for context clues to **soliciting**.]

15. **ironic**   (ī ron' ik)   *adjective*

The most **ironic** pitches for cash were from the SPCA and the Buffalo Zoo, a kind of animal-helping-animal *scenario*.

Your best guess: _____

Best dictionary definition: _____

16. **scenario**   (si ner' ē ō)   *noun*

Your best guess: _____

Best dictionary definition: _____

17. **canine**   (kā' nīn)   *noun*

And we wondered how the chief executive of a local cemetery might react if he knew he was asking a **canine** to buy a [burial] plot.

Your best guess: _____

Best dictionary definition: _____

18. **frivolity**   (fri vol′ ə tē)   *noun*

    My wife would have nothing of that **frivolity**, preferring to simply reply, "He's deceased."

Your best guess: _____

Best dictionary definition: _____

19. **tack**   (tak)   *noun*

    But that **tack** backfired on her one day when our youngest child took an almost pleading call from a survey-company employee looking for Ashley.

Your best guess: _____

Best dictionary definition: _____

20. **smitten**   (smit′ ən)   *verb*

    He was named by our daughter at the time she was reading *Gone With the Wind* and was **smitten** with Ashley Wilkes.

Your best guess: _____

Best dictionary definition: _____

[Clue: Look for the present tense form of the verb "smite."]

21. **calamity**   (kə lam′ ə tē)   *noun*

    You see, he broke several chain letters urging him to copy and send 20 others or risk some **calamity**.

Your best guess: _____

Best dictionary definition: _____

22. **scrutiny**   (skro͞ot′ ən ē)   *noun*

    Made us wonder about the **scrutiny** of the nation's credit-card industry.

Your best guess: _____

Best dictionary definition: _____

23. **solicitation**   (sə lis′ ə tā′ shən)   *noun*

    How else to explain the **solicitation** to Mr. Coppola Ashley that came all the way from Altamura, Italy . . .?

Your best guess: _____

Best dictionary definition: _____

[Clue: This word is the noun form of #14. Look up the suffix "-tion."]

24. **cherished**   (cher′ isht)   *verbal (adjective)*

    Then there was the offer to obtain his family's **cherished *crest**, "fash-ioned** hundreds of years ago in Italy."

Your best guess: _____

Best dictionary definition: _____

25. **crest** (krest)   *noun*

Your best guess: _____

Best dictionary definition: _____

26. **fashioned** (fash′ ənd)   *verbal*

Your best guess: _____

Best dictionary definition: _____

27. **registry** (rej′ ə strē)   *noun*
    [There was the offer to] . . . purchase the Coppola family **registry** that listed him along with all the other Coppolas in America.

Your best guess: _____

Best dictionary definition: _____

28. **saplings** (sap′ lingz)   *noun*
    Think of all the **saplings** that were sacrificed [by cutting them down] to try to squeeze money from a canine.

Your best guess: _____

Best dictionary definition: _____

29. **affixed** (ə fikst′)   *verb*
    Or the time, energy and money that were wasted each time a postage or bulk-mail stamp was **affixed** to an envelope being sent to a mutt.

Your best guess: _____

Best dictionary definition: _____

30. **initial** (i nish′ əl)   *adjective*
    We wondered if a local dentist really would have given Ashley a "complete **initial** consultation, exam and bitewing X-rays for ONLY THREE DOLLARS."

Your best guess: _____

Best dictionary definition: _____

[Clue: Look for the less common adjective, not the noun, definition of the word.]

31. **complimentary** (kom′ plə men′ tər ē)   *adjective*
    And what might have been the expression on the saleswoman's face if Ashley had shown up for his **complimentary** Mary Kay facial?

Your best guess: _____

Best dictionary definition: _____

Exercise, Vocabulary Preview, Chapter 3

Directions: *Choose the best definition for each **boldfaced** word as it is used in its context. Remember: A word may have more than one meaning.*

a 1. The **proliferation** of telemarketing companies in this country is very strange; surely the market isn't doing well enough to justify the increase.

(a) rapid increase   (b) rapid decline   (c) rapid elimination

a 2. Susan's mother would **chastise** her for wearing clothes that were too revealing, then shorten her own skirts to show off her slender legs.

(a) scold   (b) compliment   (c) question

c 3. Joe held the **dubious** distinction of being the first student in the history of the university to achieve a negative grade point average.

(a) grand   (b) famous   (c) questionable

b 4. At her first concert in twenty years, Barbra Streisand sang from her vast **repertoire** of popular songs.

(a) vocal power   (b) performance list   (c) audience support

c 5. On the old *Mary Tyler Moore* television show, when Mary stood up to her boss, he told her she was **spunky**—but that it was too bad he hated spunk; he much preferred wimpy women.

(a) lazy   (b) smart   (c) spirited

c 6. **Mired** in a sticky situation by his own lies, the student made his suspension from school even more likely by telling yet another obvious lie.

(a) shot down   (b) pulled down   (c) bogged down

b 7. The uncaring stranger behind the Complaint window gave me an **implacable** stare (even though her badge read "Service with a Smile") as I begged for a full refund on the defective toaster—one day after the warranty had expired.

(a) angry   (b) unyielding   (c) considerate

a 8. The Oklahoma farmers tried for many years to **eke** out a living from the dusty land before finally giving up and moving to California.

(a) strive with great effort   (b) accomplish easily   (c) find

b 9. The senator's stern public **persona** was quite different from the role he played at home—that of the easygoing, accessible daddy.

(a) clothing   (b) character   (c) speaking voice

c 10. Mary was chosen as the club treasurer rather **haphazardly**; usually the candidates go through a strict selection process.

(a) by choice   (b) by careful consideration   (c) by chance _a_ 11. Although Scout loved to go for walks, he **balked** at the leash, refusing to move more than a few inches; however, when unleashed he ran like the wind.

  (a) resisted   (b) howled   (c) lunged

_b_ 12. Governor Johnson's supporters **touted** his accomplishments at every opportunity, and I was reminded that this was an election year.

  (a) screamed shrilly   (b) praised excessively   (c) suggested quietly

_b_ 13. The great **bulk** of a mother's day seems to involve wiping things—spills, noses, hands, and bottoms of small children mostly.

  (a) smallest part   (b) major portion   (c) most rewarding

_a_ 14. The young man who called, **soliciting** used firearms, found a willing listener in Mrs. Danvers, whose husband had recently left her for another woman.

  (a) seeking business for   (b) shooting off   (c) leasing

_c_ 15. Some phone salespeople might find it **ironic** that I would be willing to spend large amounts of money to outlaw telemarketing in this country, but wouldn't pay the greatly reduced price for their merchandise.

  (a) ridiculous   (b) illegal   (c) contradictory

_a_ 16. In Peer Mediation, the students act out possible **scenarios** in order to practice how they could respond in difficult situations.

  (a) imaginary situations   (b) school plays   (c) emotional conflicts

_b_ 17. The **canine** officers of the police force don't have to wear uniforms; instead, they wear leashes and flea collars to work.

  (a) female   (b) dogs   (c) undercover

_a_ 18. Clarence's parents wanted him to be more serious, but he was interested only in **frivolity**.

  (a) laughter and good times   (b) making money   (c) sports

_c_ 19. One day my mother tried another **tack**; instead of constantly nagging me to brush my teeth, she simply stopped, until the feel and taste of my own mouth drove me to brush with enthusiasm.

  (a) threat   (b) bribe   (c) approach

_a_ 20. Joey tried to resist her charms, but he was **smitten** from the first time he saw her.

  (a) infatuated   (b) disgusted   (c) friendly

_b_ 21. Brad was always getting involved in some **calamity**; it was a miracle he had survived to the age of thirty-five.

  (a) illegal act   (b) misfortune   (c) romance

_a_ 22. Rufus squirmed under his teacher's **scrutiny** as he had no idea what he was supposed to be reading; he preferred to be ignored.

  (a) close inspection   (b) offhand manner   (c) heavy ruler

_c_ 23. Phone **solicitation** has got to be one of the most annoying aspects of modern life.

  (a) call-waiting   (b) bad manners   (c) earnest plea

_b_ 24. The gold ring was a **cherished** family treasure, passed down from generation to generation with great love and care, until it got to Tyler, who sold it without a second thought.

(a) hated   (b) beloved   (c) wasted

_a_ 25. The O'Brien family **crest** was sewn onto the children's backpacks to remind them of their heritage.

(a) symbol   (b) song   (c) name

_a_ 26. Buck **fashioned** his hat after his father's, folding and bending the brim until it was an exact match for his dad's old Stetson hat.

(a) formed   (b) bought   (c) sewed

_b_ 27. Before buying her cousin's wedding gift, Lois checked the bridal **registry** at the department store to see what color the couple had chosen for their sheets and towels.

(a) floral order   (b) record of items   (c) bridal suite

_b_ 28. Wanda planted thousands of tiny **saplings** on her father's land in Arkansas, then waited for a forest to grow.

(a) honey bees   (b) young trees   (c) wild strawberries

_c_ 29. Always be sure to **affix** the blame for any error on the person standing nearest the door, looking guilty and ready to leave work early.

(a) detach   (b) look for   (c) attach

_a_ 30. My **initial** thought was that I had dialed the wrong number, but then I realized that little Tommy was now a teenager and his voice was changing.

(a) first   (b) next   (c) last

_a_ 31. I am the world's biggest sucker for the marketing strategy of "**complimentary** gift with each purchase," even though I know that nothing is without cost.

(a) nice   (b) expensive   (c) free

Number of Errors _____

Chapter 3
Finding the Framework

I. How to Understand More

STUDY UNIT: *Finding the Framework*

How We Remember Details

Key Words

Four Logic Patterns

PARAGRAPH PRACTICE: *Problems with Progress*

II. How to Read Faster

RATE-BUILDING TIPS:

Avoid Margin Reading

Avoid Regressing

PHRASE PRACTICE

TIMED READINGS: *Problems with Progress*

Full Service

My Dead Dog May Already Be a Winner

I. How to Understand More

Note: *As always, preview this article before you read it. Approach the material as you would a textbook chapter. After you preview and as you read, quickly put a check-mark in the margin by the ideas you think are important enough to include in your notes later.*

STUDY UNIT

Finding the Framework

In Chapter 2, you learned the importance of finding the main idea so that the details would have meaning for you—or you learned to see the whole before you examined the parts. When we try to locate a friend's address on a map, we first find the general area, then the street, before we look for the house number.

Similarly, unless you understand the overall idea when you read, you will get lost in the details. They will float meaninglessly from the page, through your brain, and disappear without a trace. You began in Chapter 2 to see how the details connect to the main idea, or to see how the parts fit logically to the whole. The next step is to see how the details connect with each other, as well as to the main idea. All details are not equal; some are more important than others. Some minor details support and expand other major details.

The major details form a pattern, or *framework*, of a reading passage. They provide the logic of a passage, in the same way that beams provide the support for a building. Good writers use a clear framework when writing; good readers look for that framework when reading.

How We Remember Details

Details don't add up to anything by themselves, even if you memorize them perfectly. The human brain wants things to "add up." We resist understanding or remembering what does not "add up" for us.

For example, try to retain the following details as they are written:

> "Group 1: walk 4 minutes, jog 6 minutes, walk 3 minutes, jog 6 minutes. Group 2: walk 4 minutes, jog 15 minutes. Group 3: walk 2 minutes, jog 17 minutes. Group 4: jog 19 minutes."

The details seem meaningless, difficult to remember. They don't "add up." But suppose you had been reading a pamphlet about the physical fitness class at your local gym. You see that one of the main ideas in the pamphlet is that the class is divided up on the basis of "fitness" into four groups. You then see how the details fit the main idea. Group 1 is for beginners. Group 4 is for the most physically fit. Finally, you see how the details fit together into a pattern. The list of groups provides the *framework*: They are like the beams in the walls of a house. The details about walking and jogging are like the minor supporting details. They are like the boards that fill in the walls between the beams.

Group 1	Group 2	Group 3	Group 4
Walk 4 min.	Walk 4 min.	Walk 2 min.	
Jog 6 min.	Jog 15 min.	Jog 17 min.	Jog 19 min.
Walk 3 min.			
Jog 6 min.			

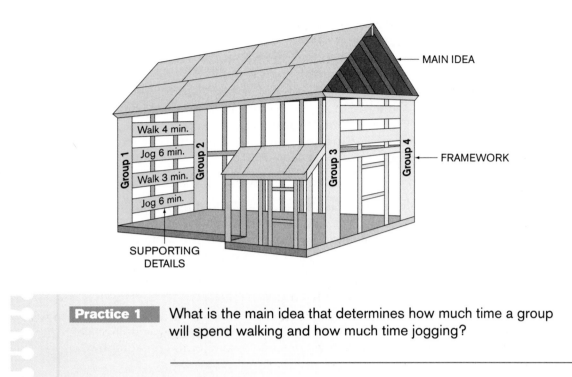

MAIN IDEA

Group 1
Walk 4 min.
Jog 6 min.
Walk 3 min.
Jog 6 min.

Group 2

Group 3

Group 4

FRAMEWORK

SUPPORTING
DETAILS

Practice 1   What is the main idea that determines how much time a group will spend walking and how much time jogging?

Now you will be more likely to remember the details because they have meaning for you. They are connected to a main idea. They are unified in a pattern. Forming patterns is a sign of intelligence. In reading (as well as writing, speaking, and listening), you will utilize your intelligence more if you consciously recognize the most common *logic patterns*, or thought connections.

Key Words

Important clues to the organization, or framework, of a reading passage are key words or phrases. These key words are usually found in the beginning of a passage: in the topic sentence of a paragraph and in the introduction of an article. Remember, authors want you to follow their logic, so they use obvious clues like "three growing problems" or "four important points" or "five easy steps." Organizing details by numbering or listing is a clear, easy way to help readers see the framework.

Note that in the first sentence of the next paragraph the authors of this textbook give the key words four of the common ways. The "four ways" refer to the "four logic patterns" covered in the next section. Therefore, the "four ways writers connect major details" sets up the framework for the next long section.

Four Logic Patterns   *transition work*

The rest of this chapter will focus on four of the common ways that writers logically connect major details to support the main idea. These logic patterns show how the *major* supporting details expand the main idea and how they connect to each other. Though the patterns may overlap and they may be minor details, they usually can be spotted as a *list*, providing the *framework*. If you can see how the items on the list fit together, you will be able to follow the logic of a reading passage.

Time Sequence and ***process*** are two logic patterns that are so similar they are often confused. They both use chronology—the order in which something

Ex: first, second

happens. They also use many of the same *transitions*, or clue words, like "first," "second," "then," and "last." The difference between the two logic patterns is that *time sequence* narrates or tells a story, whereas *process* explains how to do something or how something was done.

Time sequence is a sequence of *events:* "this happened, then that happened." Process is a sequence of *steps:* "do this, then do that." (Look back at the last Timed Reading, "Writing Your Wrongs," in Chapter 2. The section that relates the research project is time sequence; the section that explains how to write the journal is process.)

1. Model paragraph for **time sequence** (transitions are in *italics*):

> **The early years of Lisa's life were marked by wealth.** *First,* **she was born in 1965 to a family with vast land-holdings in Montana.** *Then,* **when Lisa was just one year old, her grandmother died suddenly, and left Lisa three office buildings in Beverly Hills. The rental income and value of these buildings increased rapidly every year.** *Finally,* **on Lisa's twenty-first birthday, still more riches came her way when she inherited a trust fund of $10 million.**

Practice 2   What are the two key words in Model Paragraph 1 that set up the *time sequence* framework for the paragraph?

_____

2. Model paragraph for **process** (transitions are in *italics*):

> **To get the classes you want in college, you must start early.** *First,* **get a college catalog and schedule of classes and read the directions.** *Second,* **fill in your application accurately and send it in, with tuition fees, right away.** *Third,* **see a counselor about which classes to take.** *Fourth,* **find out what time you are scheduled to register for classes.** *Fifth,* **arrive early, with identification and checkbook in hand and an alternative schedule in mind.** *Last,* **be prepared to wait.**

Practice 3   Explain the difference between the two types of sequences in Model Paragraphs 1 and 2. How are the items on the list different?

_____

Addition and **classification** are two other major logic patterns that often provide the framework for main ideas. They both involve lists, and they share the same transitions, usually numbers. They are different in the "basis," or foundation, for their lists. The nature of the items on the lists is different for the two patterns.

Addition, sometimes called "enumeration," involves a list of parallel (or similar types of) points: first one point, then a similar type point, then another. Addition can overlap or provide the framework for most of the other logic patterns. For example, notice that Model Paragraph 1 has a list of events in a time sequence. Model Paragraph 2 has a list of steps in a process. (In the next chapter, you will find that addition overlaps other logic patterns like *causes, effects,* and *examples.*)

The items in these lists are often written using *parallel* (similar or equal) phrasing because they are parallel in type and importance. Notice, for example, in Model Paragraph 2 how similarly the sentences are worded:

> get a   fill in   see a   find out   arrive early   be prepared

This repetition may seem monotonous, but it makes the logic connections easier to see.

3. Model paragraph for **addition** (transitions are in *italics*):

> The student council supported three solutions to the parking problems at El Camino College. The *first,* and most obvious, solution was to create more parking spaces, enough to accommodate the growing number of students with cars. A *second,* and harder to implement, solution was to encourage students to ride buses or bikes to school, rewarding them with priority registration or free football tickets. A *third* solution, and a favorite with students, was to remove all assigned spaces for faculty and administration in exchange for open parking—first come, first parked.

Practice 4

(a) What are the two key words in the first sentence that set up the list in this paragraph? _____

(b) In as few words as possible, make a list of the three parallel solutions:

_____

_____

_____

(c) Make your own list of parallel items on a completely different topic (problems or solutions, advantages or disadvantages). Use parallel phrasing, if you can.

_____

_____

_____

Classification is used to group what might otherwise be a shapeless, unmanageable mass of details into categories or "classes." Then characteristics (or minor supporting details) are given for each group, or class. You may find classification when you read about a broad topic that needs to be manageable. "College Students," for instance, is a massive, sprawling topic. Think of all the different kinds of college students you see.

The topic can be managed, or organized, if the students are classified according to *one* basis, or reason, for grouping them. In a longer essay, the college students might be classified according to their religion: that is, Catholic, Protestant, Jew, Moslem, Buddhist. Or in a shorter essay, they might be classified by marital status: married, single, divorced. A helpful tip: classification has at least three groups. If you find only two groups, like male and female, the logic pattern is usually comparison or contrast.

4. Model paragraph for **classification** (transitions are in *italics*):

Ken washed and displayed the produce from his garden in large baskets. He put the ripe fruit in the *first* and largest basket. It overflowed with oranges, apples, strawberries, and pears. In the *second* basket he arranged his vegetables. He mixed root vegetables like potatoes and onions with those from a vine like beans and squash. *Finally*, he placed the herbs in the smallest basket. The fragrance of thyme and dill mingled with that of sweet basil and cilantro.

Practice 5

(a) Finish the chart below by writing in items from the paragraph. Write in the general category on the top lines and the supporting examples on the indented lines.

 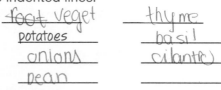

fruit	~~foot~~ veget	thyme
organes	potatoes	basil
apples	onions	cilantro
	bean	

(b) Classify your own choice of topics into three logical categories with examples of each. (possible topics: cars, coats, musical bands)

_____   _____   _____

_____   _____   _____

_____   _____   _____

Practice 6   Look back at all four model paragraphs.

(a) How many have topic sentences? _all of them_

(b) How many have topic sentences at the beginning? _____

Look for these common patterns in your other verbal activities—as you listen, talk and write. Look for them in ads, political speeches, course lectures. Look for them in sentences, as well as in paragraphs. Find them in conversations with friends and even in your own thoughts. They are simply logic patterns used by all logical thinkers to connect ideas.

Again, these four logic patterns (plus those in the next chapter) often combine and overlap. You can discover this for yourself if you try to think in any organized way, even about a seemingly simple, one-word topic such as "dogs." If you group them (*classification*), you may also list the types and subtypes (*addition*). Or you might say what the dogs look like (*description*) or give typical behavior (*example*) or tell anecdotes about them (*time sequence*). You will recognize this combining of patterns as you consciously look for patterns in the reading selections.

The advantage to recognizing the patterns is that you will begin to anticipate the author's thoughts. You will connect ideas and form thought patterns of your own, and you will remember these connected ideas longer. You will distinguish between major and minor, general and specific, whole and part. This skill is the difference between reading actively and reading passively. The result is you will *understand more* of what you read.

Study Notes

1. Define these terms as they relate to reading.

   (a) logic patterns: _____

   (b) framework: _____

   (c) transitions: _____

   (d) key words: _____

   (e) parallel: _____

2. List the four logic patterns and their definitions. (Explain how they are similar and how they are different from each other.)

   logic patterns   *definitions*

   (a) _____   _____

   _____

   (b) _____   _____

   _____

   (c) _____   _____

   _____

   (d) _____   _____

   _____

Problems with Progress

As you read the three paragraphs, look not only for the more general topic and main idea, but also look for the specifics. Examine the supporting details, and notice how they fit the main idea. Notice what logic pattern is used to connect the details with each other. After answering the questions for each paragraph, check the key.

Exercise 3A: Paragraph

[1]"Progress is a comfortable disease," writes the poet e. e. Cummings. [2]The contradiction in this line ("progress" and "comfortable" are positive words; "disease" is negative) reflects the conflict most of us feel about life at the end of the twentieth century. [3]Few of us would give up our televisions and cars, but we wonder whether some signs of progress have made our lives worse. [4]One doubtful sign of progress is the proliferation of gadgets. [5]Okay, maybe we need answering machines. [6]But does every person in the whole world need a cell phone? [7]Does a twelve-year-old need to talk on the phone while skateboarding? [8]Does a high-school student need to take a phone call during a timed final exam—a phone call saying that his ride will be late? [9]The actor Laurence Fishburne got a standing ovation in a play on Broadway when he stepped out of character to chastise a theatergoer whose cell phone kept ringing. [10]Another dubious improvement is the increased use of polls. [11]The President takes a poll to help him decide whether or not to tell the truth about sex. [12]And do we really need a poll to tell us that 3 percent of men wish they were allowed to work in the nude? [13]Finally, one of the most alarming changes is the increase in junk mail. [14]The Postal Service estimates our junk mail to be 4.6 million tons per family. [15]What makes this waste of paper even more disturbing is that we are cutting down trees at a faster rate than we are growing them. [16]The "good old days" are beginning to look better.

1. Choose the phrase that best expresses the general topic of the paragraph.
   (a) Too Much Technology
   (b) Negative Signs of Progress
   (c) Changes in Time and Money
   (d) Changes in the Twentieth Century

2. Is the main idea stated in a topic sentence?
   (a) yes, sentence #____   (b) no

3. Using your own words, write a complete sentence that states the main idea of the paragraph.

_____

_____

[what?   when?   are mostly how?]

4. Finish the chart by writing brief phrases in the blank lines. In the left column, fill in the signs of progress, or changes (not the examples). In the right column, fill in the transitions or key words that help you find the major changes.

signs of progress	transitions or key words
more gadgets	one doubtful sign
paper	Another
poll	Finally

5. Which *logic pattern* provides the *framework* for the paragraph?
   (a) time sequence   (b) process   (c) addition   (d) classification
   What are the four key words that set up the framework of this logic pattern?

   _____   _____   _____   _____

Exercise 3B: Paragraph

[1]Modern families spend so much time in their automobiles that they could potentially be in as much danger from each other as from other cars. [2]Head off the shouting, crying, and whining on family trips. [3]Carole Shakely-Parkman, in her handbook, *Learning All the Time*, gives parents some creative suggestions for using the travel time constructively. [4]First, prepare well before the trip. [5]Always keep pencils and pens, a book, a magazine, maps, and, if possible, a tape recorder in the car. [6]A recorder is a marvelous way to make up stories or conduct interviews with each other, since writing is more difficult in moving vehicles. [7]Second, get your children involved in the travel route from the beginning. [8]If your patience can stand it, appoint your children the map readers and path finders for the family. [9]Map-reading skills can become even more appealing when children are encouraged to draw their own maps of neighborhood areas or familiar routes. [10]Let them keep track of the car's gas mileage—terrific math practice. [11]Finally, hold back some books and keep a repertoire of new games in your head for that last endless stretch of time. [12]Asking children to read aloud to the driver is excellent language practice. [13]You can use license plates and billboards for a variety of games—like playing poker, making up words, finding the alphabet sequentially. [14]Some of these games can be carried over until the next long trip.

1. What is the general topic of the paragraph?

   _____

2. Is the main idea stated in a topic sentence?
   (a) yes, sentence #_____   (b) no

3. Choose the sentence that best states the main idea of the paragraph.
   (a) Ms. Shakely-Parkman gives parents creative suggestions for keeping kids occupied during a car trip.
   (b) Modern families spend so much time in their cars that they are in danger of their kids getting on their nerves.
   (c) The best tip for traveling with kids is to be prepared, says Ms. Shakely-Parkman.
   (d) The best travel suggestion is leave the kids at home until they are over ten.

4. Briefly list the three general tips. Use the transitions to help you find them.

   _____

   _____

   _____

5. *Addition*, *time sequence*, and *process* all overlap to provide the framework that holds the paragraph together in a list of three general tips.
   (a) What are the three key words that set up the framework for addition?

   _____   _____   _____

   (b) What are the three phrases that reinforce time sequence?

   _____

Exercise 3C: Paragraph

¹What's your girlfriend doing right now? ²Or your sister? ³Or your mother, for that matter? ⁴Chances are good that she's got her nose deep in a type of book that tops the list of best-sellers week after week. ⁵These women are reading the historical romance, a kind of novel that's really more romance than it is history. ⁶What's the big attraction? ⁷For one thing, it has characters larger than life. ⁸These handsome, brave, tight-lipped heroes make Clint Eastwood look like a wimp. ⁹And their full-bosomed, flashing-eyed heroines are every bit their match—though these spunky women would make a modern feminist cringe at their tendency to turn to mush in their hero's manly arms. ¹⁰Another appeal is the novels' dramatic action. ¹¹Pirates! ¹²Kidnapping! ¹³Close calls! ¹⁴Of course, these novels' special appeal is their exotic settings. ¹⁵They take place in exotic locations such as southern plantations, sultans' harems, kings' courts—during earlier, exciting times we've read about in history books. ¹⁶Could it be that these books—so popular with women—tell us something important about what we've lost? ¹⁷Are we tired of being tame city dwellers, mired in routine? ¹⁸Do we long for the brave deeds and bold kisses of a more romantic time gone by?

1. What is the general topic (or a possible title) of the paragraph?

   _____

2. The topic sentence is not stated in one clear cover sentence. What are the numbers of the two general sentences that give the main idea for the paragraph?

   _____   _____

3. In your own words, write a complete sentence that states the main idea.

   _____

   _____

   [who?   is doing what?   why?]

4. Finish the chart below by filling in, on the top lines, the general characteristics of the historical romance. On the lines indented underneath, fill in examples of those characteristics.

   larger-than-life characters _____   _____
      brave, handsome heroes   _____   _____

   _____   _____   _____

5. Which two of the four logic patterns are used to connect the supporting details?

   _____   _____

   Write your own key words to set up the framework. _____

   _____

II. How to Read Faster

Avoid Margin Reading

In Chapter 2, you learned the importance of reading in phrases of meaning instead of word-by-word. To do that, you have practiced *fixating* on a whole phrase at a single glance. You have learned to rely more on your *peripheral vision*. The next technique also asks you to use your peripheral vision.

This is the technique of not "reading" the blank margins. If you always start fixating right on the first word of each line, you are including in your line of vision the blank margin, which contains no information. You are *margin reading*.

How do you stop wasting part of your fixation on the margin? Simply said, you start and stop your point of fixation about a half-inch—two or three words—in from each side margin. With your peripheral vision, you still see the information to the left or right of your new fixation point. So you don't lose anything except the meaningless blank space in the margin.

You may wish to try this technique right now with the rest of this article.

As you continue to read this page, remember to start fixating at the vertical line on the left side of the page. Then, move your eyes horizontally along the line of print as usual. Take your attention off the line of print when you get to the vertical line on the right side of the page. With a little practice, you won't need to draw vertical lines because avoiding margin reading will have become automatic. You may want to start with the narrower columns in a newspaper, and draw your own lines.

Avoid Regressing

Do you *regress* often when you read? That is, do you reread phrases, sentences, or even whole paragraphs, sometimes whole pages? If you find that you have passed your eyes over a page, recognizing the words but remembering nothing, then you may be in the habit of regressing. You may have programmed your brain to regress. You start to read and a message in your subconscious lazily says: "Oh, don't bother to tune in yet. Think about something else. You know you're just going to reread this. Tune in on the second reading."

What an obvious waste of time! To break the habit, reprogram your subconscious. Tell yourself: "You may read this only once. You will not have the luxury of rereading. A big rock will fall on your head if you regress. You have only one chance. Tune in." Or try reading with an index card in your hand. Use the card like a camera shutter to cover the lines you just read.

Even if you backslide and tune out, keep reading. Try to pick up the train of thought without regressing; you will be more successful than you think. Once your subconscious knows you have taken away the crutch of regressing, you will regress less.

Remember, both these tips—avoid margin-reading and avoid regressing—involve some skipping. So try them on your practice reading, not on your study-reading.

Exercise 3D: Phrases

Make a slash through the phrase identical to the key phrase. **Note:** *All phrases are prepositional phrases.*

Key Phrase

1.	by the wharf	by the wharf	by the whale	by the wheel
2.	through the fog	through the frost	through the fog	for the thought
3.	to his racquet	to his request	to the rally	to his racquet
4.	beyond a doubt	beyond a doubter	beyond a cloud	beyond a doubt
5.	within a hair	within a harem	with a hare	within a hair
6.	to the seashore	to the sailboat	to the seashore	to the shells
7.	until the dusk	until the dusk	until the fuss	under the dust
8.	of her heart	in her hearing	of her heart	of her heartbeat
9.	down the path	down the path	for the down	down the lane
10.	behind his mask	behind her mask	behind his map	behind his mask
11.	for some time	for some time	for some truth	for their time
12.	between the rocks	behind the rocks	between the rocks	between the stocks
13.	of his idea	of his idea	to her idea	of his hide
14.	in our thoughts	into our thinking	for your thoughts	in our thoughts
15.	by my fence	by my feet	by my fender	by my fence
16.	in my opinion	in my opinion	in her opinions	in my opposite
17.	up his alley	up his alligator	up his alley	upon his alibi
18.	across our land	around the land	across our land	across our lake
19.	of your making	of your making	of his taking	of her baking
20.	around a post	across a path	around a boat	around a post

Time ___45"___

Number of Errors ___0___

Exercise 3E: Phrases

Make a slash through the phrase identical to the key phrase. **Note:** *All phrases are prepositional phrases.*

Key Phrase

1. about the job   over the job   about the blob   about the job
2. over the hill   over the hill   out of the sill   outside the hill
3. before night   before light   before night   between nights
4. behind him   behind him   beneath them   beside them
5. beyond roles   beyond roles   between roles   before roads
6. beside herself   besides her   beside herself   by his side
7. within bounds   in mounds   with sounds   within bounds
8. except them   through him   because of them   except them
9. in spite of us   instead of us   in spite of us   in front of us
10. off his feed   off his steed   off his feed   on her feet
11. in front of it   in for it   inside of it   in front of it
12. since the fall   since the bats   since the fall   beside the ball
13. during vacation   during vaccines   despite nations   during vacation
14. despite my vote   despite my vote   during my vote   beside my goat
15. outside the law   on the outs   out of the law   outside the law
16. until summer   until summer   after summer   until soon
17. after my turn   past my churn   after my turn   at my twin
18. toward home   toward home   toward Rome   toward houses
19. upon the step   up the steeple   upon the step   on the trip
20. since the rain   since the rain   since the drain   since noon

Time   40"

Number of Errors   0

Problems with Progress

The two longer readings explore the complexities of progress in more depth. As you read, continue to look for the topic and thesis, and try to anticipate the authors' logic patterns.

Exercise 3F: Timed Reading

795 words

This reading is a personal essay, in which the author reacts to the frustrations of mechanical objects. As you read, look for the logic pattern that provides the *framework* for the article.

Preview: *Quickly survey the title, author's name, first paragraph, the first sentence of a few paragraphs, and the last paragraph. Write here what you think the author wants besides "full-service" gasoline.* _____

_____

Wait for a signal from your instructor before you begin reading. Circle your reading time when you have finished, and find your WPM.

Full Service

Wanda Maureen Miller

I think I run out of gas sometimes because of so many self-service gas stations. Full-service gas stations are a faint memory of the past, but I still remember and long for them. I want full service. I deserve full service. I left the family farm and moved to a big city so I wouldn't have to do smelly manual labor. I educated myself so I could pay people to do things to my car. Self-service gas stations represent the worst of both worlds to me—manual labor of the farm and impersonal technology of the city. I've learned to operate my video recorder and my answering machine, even the automatic teller machine at the bank. Isn't that enough? I don't want to learn to operate one more machine. I want full service!

Most Monday mornings are an adventure for me. I drive to work and watch the red "Empty" light flashing. Sometimes it stops flashing, and I know I am really in trouble. There are no full-service gas stations on the route to the freeway, so I take the chance. I might just have enough gas left to make it.

I hate getting out of my car and reading a new set of instructions—each gas station has its own peculiar system. I hate trying to match the instructions on the pump with the right lever or nozzle. I hate struggling with the hose. And, if I'm successful, I hate the smell of gas on my hands. Sometimes I'm not successful, and I never get it right the first time.

I have to turn levers this way and that before the impersonal oblong containers yield their gas to me. They are as implacable as the cows I used to milk. Their hoses are as stubborn as the udders I pulled to eke out a small strain of milk. I remember my brother saying he hated the smell of milk on his hands all day at school. He said the smell never went away, no matter how many times he washes his hands. That's how I feel about the smell of the gas. Even perfume doesn't mask the smell.

I have to lean into the car, as I once did with the cows, with my weight on the hose to keep the nozzle intact and the gas coming. The hose fights me and tries to shake free as I fumble to replace the nozzle on its receptacle.

I see the other customers fill their cars competently, effortlessly; their eyes glance at me with uncaring amusement. I want to turn the gas hose on them and spray them.

Once, just outside of Palm Springs, after a particularly long struggle, I gave up on the damn gas and just got in my car, leaving the hose to dangle obscenely. A disembodied voice on a microphone said crisply from its glass case, "Please return the nozzle to its proper place." The voice rose in hysteria as I spun rubber in the gravel and drove away, in search of a full-service gas station.

Last week, I was once again unable to find a full-service station. The light on my gas gauge was an accusing, unblinking red. I stopped at a new self-service station, got out, put my glasses on and peered at the instructions: "Lift the. . . ." A big smudge covered the crucial direction. I felt the familiar frustration and helplessness rise in me. I felt like a hick in the big city. And really alone. Why wasn't there a man here to do this for me?

And a man appeared. A grizzled, brown old man in dirty work clothes walked over from a battered pickup truck and said kindly, "Push it that way," and pointed. I nearly cried in gratitude. I looked at his patient, respectful face and his shapeless, nonthreatening body and knew that I knew him.

Or I had known men just like him. I could have grown up with him. I could have been kin to him. He was like my uncle or cousin or grandpa. I wished he were my daddy. He was like the men who left their corn fields to help me change a flat tire or pull my car out of the mud with their mules or their tractors.

When I finished filling my car with gas, he appeared again. "Pull it up that way," he said, pointing again. I obeyed.

"Thank you," I said inadequately, wanting to ask him home to supper. But I turned away as he drove off in his pickup truck, the cab filled with other workmen.

I drove home to my efficient new condo, with its labor-saving gadgets—as different from the old farmhouse as I could make it.

Answer the following recall questions without referring to the article.

1. What does the author hate most about self-service gas stations?

   (a) the smell   (b) the work   (c) the directions

2. The author compares getting gas to what farm chore?

   (a) hosing down hogs   (b) milking cows   (c) picking cotton

3. What is the author's reaction to the old man who helps her?

   (a) tearful gratitude   (b) arrogant acceptance   (c) resentment

You may refer to the article to answer the following questions.

4. Of the four logic patterns, which two are used in the article?

   _____   _____

TIMING CHART	
min:sec	wpm
3:59	200
3:37	220
3:19	240
3:03	260
2:50	280
2:39	300
2:29	320
2:20	340
2:13	360
2:05	380
1:59	400
1:54	420
1:48	440
1:44	460
1:39	480
1:35	500
1:32	520
1:28	540
1:25	560
1:22	580
1:20	600
1:17	620
1:15	640
1:12	660
1:10	680
1:08	700
1:06	720
1:04	740
1:03	760
1:01	780
1:00	800

5. In your own words, write a complete sentence that states the *thesis* of the article. [Clue: Paraphrase the *thesis* from the first paragraph.]

_____

_____

Check your answers with the key, and record your scores below and on the Progress Chart.

Words per Minute _____

Percent Comprehension _____

The last reading, from *Newsweek* magazine, presents a more lighthearted approach to a modern frustration that is epidemic. As you read, look for the logic pattern that provides the *framework* for the article.

Preview: *Quickly survey the title, first paragraph, the first sentence of a few paragraphs, and the last paragraph. Write here what you think the author's complaint will be.*

_____

_____

Wait for a signal from your instructor before you begin reading. Circle your reading time when you have finished, and find your WPM.

My Dead Dog May Already Be a Winner

Lee Coppola

Ever wonder what happens when a pet takes on a persona? Ashley could have told you, if he could have talked. Ashley was the family mutt, an SPCA special, part beagle and part spaniel.

For years, most of them after he died, he also served as the family's representative in the local telephone book. He was picked for the role quite haphazardly one day when I tried to keep my number out of the book to avoid getting business calls at home. When I balked at the $60-a-year fee, the cheery telephone company representative suggested I list the number in one of my children's names.

I was munching on a sandwich at the time and Ashley followed me around the kitchen waiting for a crumb to fall. "Can I put the phone in any name?" I asked the rep as I sidestepped Ashley. "Certainly," she answered, and therein gave birth to 10 years of telephone calls and mail to a dog.

"A remarkable new book about the Coppolas since the Civil War is about to make history—and you, Ashley Coppola, are in it," touted one letter asking Ashley to send $10 right away for "this one-time offer." Ashley received hundreds of pieces of mail, the bulk soliciting his money.

The most ironic pitches for cash were from the SPCA and the Buffalo Zoo, a kind of animal-helping-animal scenario. And we wondered how the chief executive of a local cemetery might react if he knew he was asking a canine to buy a plot to give his family "peace of mind." Or a local lawn service's thoughts about asking a dog who daily messed the grass, "Is your lawn as attractive as it could be?" Then there was the letter offering Ashley "reliable electronic security to protect your home." One of the kids asked if that wasn't Ashley's job.

The kids soon got into the swing of having their dog receive mail and telephone calls. "He's sleeping under the dining-room table," one would tell telemarketers. "He's out in the backyard taking a whiz," was the favorite reply of another. My wife would have nothing of that frivolity, preferring to simply reply, "He's deceased."

But that tack backfired on her one day when our youngest child took an almost pleading call from a survey-company employee looking for Ashley. "I'm Ashley," the 17-year-old politely replied, taking pity on the caller. He dutifully gave his age and answered a few questions before he realized he was late for an appointment and hurriedly cut short the conversation. "Can I call you again?" the surveyor asked. "OK," our son said as he hung up.

Sure enough, the surveyor called again the next day and asked for Ashley. But this time Mom answered and gave her standard reply. "Oh my God," exclaimed the caller. "I'm so, so sorry." The surveyor's horrified grief puzzled my wife until our son explained how he had been a healthy teenage Ashley the day before.

It seemed direct mailers had a tough time figuring out Ashley's sex and marital status. He was named by our daughter at the time she was reading *Gone With the Wind* and was smitten with [the character] Ashley Wilkes. "Dear Mr. Coppola," his mail sometimes would begin. More often though, Ashley's mail came to Mrs. Coppola, or, on those politically correct occasions, to Ms. Coppola.

Sometimes we worried about our dog's fate. You see, he broke several chain letters urging him to copy and send 20 others or risk some calamity. After all, Ashley was warned, didn't one person die nine days after throwing out the letter?

Did I mention credit cards? Ashley paid his bills on time, judging from the $5,000 lines-of-credit for which he "automatically" qualified. Made us wonder about the scrutiny of the nation's credit-card industry.

Of course, Ashley was no ordinary dog. He was an *Italian* dog. How else to explain the solicitation to Mr. Coppola Ashley that came all the way from Altamura, Italy, and sough donations to an orphanage? Then there was the offer to obtain his family's cherished crest, "fashioned hundreds of years ago in Italy," and purchase the Coppola family registry that listed him along with the other Coppolas in America.

Is there some message to all this? Think of all the saplings that were sacrificed to try to squeeze money from a canine. Or the time, energy and money that were wasted each time a postage or bulk-mail stamp was affixed to an envelope being sent to a mutt. We did feel sheepish about the deception when the mail came from the self-employed trying make a buck. We wondered if a local dentist would have given Ashley a "complete initial consultation, exam and bitewing X-rays for ONLY THREE DOLLARS." And what might have been the expression on the saleswoman's face if Ashley had shown up for his complimentary Mary Kay facial?

Ashley did appreciate, however, the coupon for dog food.

Answer the following recall questions without referring to the article.

1. Why did the author list his home telephone number in his dog's name?
   (a) Listing it in his dog's name was cheaper than listing it in a family member's name.
   (b) He wanted to play a joke on telemarketers who called him at home.
   (c) He wanted to confuse people who might call him at home about business.
   (d) He wanted to avoid the extra fee for an unlisted number and randomly picked his dog's name.

TIMING CHART	
min:sec	wpm
04:36	200
04:11	220
03:50	240
03:32	260
03:17	280
03:04	300
02:53	320
02:42	340
02:33	360
02:25	380
02:18	400
02:11	420
02:05	440
02:00	460
01:55	480
01:50	500
01:46	520
01:42	540
01:39	560
01:35	580
01:32	600
01:29	620
01:26	640
01:24	660
01:21	680
01:19	700
01:17	720
01:15	740
01:13	760
01:11	780
01:09	800

2. What is the name of the author's dog? _____ And how did he get his name? _____

Give any two examples of inappropriate phone calls the dog received.

3. _____

4. _____

5. Which family member replied, "He's deceased," to phone calls for the dog?
   (a) the author   (b) his wife   (c) his 17-year-old son   (d) his daughter

   You may refer to the article to answer the following questions.

6. The *framework* of the article is *cause* and *effect*, which will be introduced in the next chapter. However, the supporting details are mostly anecdotes, or stories, which fit what logic pattern?
   (a) time sequence   (b) process   (c) addition   (d) classification

7. Explain how the reply, "He's deceased," backfired. _____
   _____

8. When the dog broke chain letters, how serious is the author when he says, "Sometimes we worried about our dog's fate"?
   (a) very serious   (b) moderately serious   (c) not at all serious

9. What is the author's target in this statement: "Ashley paid his bills on time, judging from the $5,000 lines-of-credit for which he 'automatically' qualified"?
   (a) wasteful dogs   (b) people with bad credit
   (c) businesses that offer easy credit

10. The thesis is suggested, but not clearly stated, in the next-to-last paragraph. In your own words, write a complete sentence that clearly states the thesis.
    _____
    _____

    [what results?   make what kind of point?   about what?]

Check your answers with the key, and record your scores below and on the Progress Chart.

Words per Minute _____

Percent Comprehension _____

Writing and Discussion Activities

1. After reading the articles, what time period would you choose to live in? Make a list of the reasons for your choice. Then use this list to compose a paragraph. (Use what you know about the main idea to form a topic sentence. The supporting details in your paragraph will be the reasons drawn from your list and put in sentence form.) When you are finished, exchange paragraphs with the person sitting next to you. On what do you agree? Disagree?

2. Have you had a bad experience with a "labor-saving" machine or a modern "time-saving" plan? Tell about your experience in a paragraph or two. Make a topic sentence (main idea statement) for each paragraph. Then give enough details so that a reader can understand why your experience was so frustrating. (If you are keeping a journal, your instructor may wish you to write your experience there.)

Vocabulary Review, Chapter 3

Match the vocabulary word on the left with its definition on the right.

_b_ 1. **dubious**   (a) beloved

_d_ 2. **tack**   (b) questionable

_a_ 3. **cherished**   (c) official symbol

_e_ 4. **complimentary**   (d) approach

_c_ 5. **crest**   (e) free

*Choose the definition for each **boldfaced** word as it is used in its context.*

_a_ 6. **chastised** the motorist for driving too fast
       (a) scolded   (b) educated   (c) followed

_c_ 7. concern over the **proliferation** of illegal gun sales
       (a) consequences   (b) untaxed earnings   (c) rapid increase

_c_ 8. the attitude of the **implacable** teacher
       (a) well-prepared   (b) uncertain   (c) unyielding

_a_ 9. became **mired** in forms to fill out
       (a) bogged down   (b) challenged   (c) moving quickly

_c_ 10. became an actor **haphazardly**
       (a) after years of training   (b) since childhood   (c) by chance

*Mark each sentence to show whether the **boldfaced** word is used correctly.*

a = True   b = False

_T_ 11. Mark inherited such a large sum of money that he doesn't have to worry about **eking** out a living.

_F_ 12. After Jolene flunked out of school, her mother **touted** Jolene's accomplishments.

_T_ 13. It was **ironic** that the politician who wanted to reform campaign spending laws had received huge amounts of questionable money for his own campaign.

_F_ 14. Because he dedicates long hour to **frivolity**, Elliott earns excellent grades.

_F_ 15. The boss was **smitten** with his secretary and wanted to fire her.

(Continued)

Choose the word from the box that fits the context of the following paragraph.
Write the letter of each choice on the blank lines to the left of the paragraph.

(a) **bulk**	(b) **calamity**	(c) **initial**	(d) **scrutiny**	(e) **spunky**

16. A parent's (16) thought might be that it's a lot easier to spend

17. the (17) of one's day at home taking care of small children than

18. spend ten hours or more each day working outside the home and

19. commuting. But anyone who has taken care of toddlers knows how

20. (18) they can be, male or female. Great (19) of just about every

move of young children is necessary if the parent is to avoid a (20)

such as a child's head getting stuck in the toilet or a child trying to

"fly" off the roof.

% Correct _____

Comprehension Review, Chapter 3

1. Define *framework*, as it relates to reading: _____
   <u>The major details form a pattern of a reading passage</u>

Match the four logic patterns *with their definitions on the right:*

<u>b</u> 2. *time sequence*   (a) a list of similar points

<u>d</u> 3. *process*   (b) telling a story

<u>a</u> 4. *addition*   (c) groups or categories

<u>c</u> 5. *classification* (d) explaining how to do something

6. How are *time sequence* and *process* similar? <u>they both use chronology</u>

provide the framework for main ideas

7. How are *addition* and *classification* similar? <u>they both involve lists, and they share the same transitions, usually number</u>

Read the following four paragraphs and answer the questions about them.

A. First, take the clean clothes from the dryer while they are still warm. If you wait till they are cold, the wrinkles are harder to shake out. Next, fold each garment into a neat pile of similar garments. For example, put socks in one stack and shirts in another. Finally, put away your clean laundry immediately so it does not get lost or mixed with your dirty clothes.

8. Besides *addition*, what is the *logic pattern* in Paragraph A? <u>process</u>
   If the paragraph had a topic sentence, which of the following would be more effective as the key words?
   (a) three groups of clean clothes
   (b) four groups of clean clothes
   (c) three steps in putting away clean clothes
   (d) four steps in putting away clean clothes

9. What is the *implied main idea*? (Write a complete sentence.)
   <u>There are 3 steps to help have clean</u>

B. The five bandits ran out of the bank with guns blazing and rode their horses out of town. Just riding into town from the opposite direction, the Lone Ranger heard the commotion and urged his horse Silver to run faster. The masked hero turned in his saddle and shouted to his companion, "This way, Tonto!" The two men thundered through town, caught up with the bandits, and captured them without firing a single shot.

Quickly take move the clean clothes, put them in a right direction so you'll not mix dirty clothes with clean clothes

(Continued)

10. What is the *logic pattern* in Paragraph B? _____ time sequence _____

C. One solution to the college's parking problems is to ban student cars on campus. Another solution, equally unpopular with students, is to pave over the football field and use that area as a parking lot. A third solution, more popular with students, is to open "Staff Parking" to students' cars. "Let teachers ride the bus!" yelled the students.

11. What is the *logic pattern* in Paragraph C? _____ addition _____

12. What is the *implied main idea*? (Write a complete sentence.)

There are 3 solutions to reduce the problems of college ~~parking~~

D. ¹It's no secret that Americans have poor eating habits. ²We need to be reminded of a simple dietary principle we were taught in junior high school: regularly eat a sensible amount chosen from the five basic food groups. ³One group, most often neglected, is *leafy green vegetables*, like lettuce and spinach. ⁴Another group is *fruit*, such as oranges, apples, and grapes. ⁵A third is *grains*, like bread, cereal, and brown rice. ⁶A fourth is *dairy products*, supplied by milk, butter, and cheese. ⁷The last group is one that Americans need no encouragement to eat—that is, *protein*, found in meat, poultry, and fish.

13. Besides *addition*, what is the other major *logic pattern* in Paragraph D?

_____ classification _____

What are the four key words (or phrases) in the paragraph that set up the framework?

remind   simple dietary principle   chu a sensible amount ~~chosen~~ ...   five basic

14. Is the main idea stated in a *topic sentence*? (a) yes, sentence # 2   (b) no

15. Using your own words, write a complete sentence (not a fragment) that expresses the main idea of the paragraph.

Americans ~~need~~ should care about what & how much

~~calories and fuel~~ the foods they eat can provide

[who?   needs to do what?]   enough calories

base one   and go are good

a simple

dietary principle   foods that -their meals, so

% **Correct** _____   for their health

~~They have to base on a simple dietary~~

VOCABULARY PREVIEW for Chapter 4

Context Clue #3: Look for Examples

Sometimes you will be able to decide the meaning of a new word by the *examples* an author gives. You will learn in Chapter 4 that example is a common logic pattern that makes the general more specific. An example can also make a difficult word more understandable, more memorable.

Notice how each sentence below contains examples, or specific cases, that give you a clue to the meaning of the word in *italics*. Also, look for helpful clue words that point to an example: *for example, for instance, such as, i.e., e.g.* (from the *Latin exempli gratia,* meaning "for example" or "such as").

■ The speech instructor encouraged his students to avoid using language that has become *trite* from overuse; for example, he said to avoid phrases like "an outpouring of grief" and "a mountain of evidence" and "teeth sparkling like diamonds."

■ The young boy angered the older people in the community with his *profane* acts—such as, riding his motorcycle into the church yard and spitting on his mother's grave.

Practice   Use the examples in the following sentences as clues to the meaning of the word in *italics*. On the blank lines, write what you think the word means.

1. The homeless family sought *sanctuary* from the bitter winter storm: for instance, a freeway overpass or an unlocked church. _____

2. Claudia suspected her new boss was a *misogynist* (e.g., his never promoting women, his telling vulgar jokes about women, and his keeping office supplies stacked in the ladies' lounge). _____

3. The already wealthy nieces and nephews hoped their uncle would leave his millions to them when he died, but his will proved him to be a *philanthropist*; he left all his money to worthy causes like shelters for abused women, college scholarships for poor students, and medical research.

   _____

[*Answers:* 1. safe place   2. women hater   3. one who loves people]

WORDS IN CONTEXT for Chapter 4

Directions: *Examine the **boldfaced** word as it is used in the sentence and write your best guess of the word's meaning. Then look up the word in your dictionary* and write the best definition for its context in the sentence. Begin to look for the roots you are learning in the Homework Lessons as additional clues to the meaning of words.

from Paragraph 4A (p. 133)

1. **ethnic**   (eth′ nik)   *adjective*

   Malcolm X may have given Americans a solution to the problems of **ethnic** diversity.

   Your best guess: _____

   Best dictionary definition: _____

from Paragraph 4B (p. 133)

2. **elective**   (i lek′ tiv)   *adjective*

   I rebel at the notion that I can't be part of other groups, that I can't construct identities through **elective *affinity***, that race must be the most important thing about me.

   Your best guess: _____

   Best dictionary definition: _____

3. **affinity**   (ə fin′ ə tē)   *noun*

   Your best guess: _____

   Best dictionary definition: _____

   [Note: See sentence #2 for context clues to **affinity**.]

4. **luxuriate**   (lug zho͝or′ ē āt′)   *verbal*

   I want to be black, to know black, to **luxuriate** in whatever I might be calling blackness at any particular time.

   Your best guess: _____

   Best dictionary definition: _____

5. **transcended**   (tran send′ id)   *verb*

   Part of me admires those people who can say with a straight face that they have **transcended** any attachment to a particular community or group.

   Your best guess: _____

   Best dictionary definition: _____

from Paragraph 4C (p. 134)

6. **ill**   (il)   *adverb (usually an adjective)*

Sometimes, our parents or grandparents were so harmed by a society that treated them **ill** for speaking their native language [Spanish] that they thought they could save us from that hate by teaching us to speak only English.

Your best guess: _____

Best dictionary definition: _____

[Clue: Do not choose the most common definition; the context is not about health.]

from Timed Reading 4F (p. 139)

7. **facetious**   (fə sē′ shəs)   *adjective*

That's why I was surprised when my father accepted my somewhat **facetious** invitation to go horseback riding.

Your best guess: _____

Best dictionary definition: _____

8. **demeanor**   (di mē′ nər)   *noun*

I saw him only as a distant, hard-working father, whose explosive temper seemed at odds with his normally calm **demeanor**.

Your best guess: _____

Best dictionary definition: _____

9. **incarnate**   (in kär′ nit)   *adjective*

The horse looked like Satan **incarnate**.

Your best guess: _____

Best dictionary definition: _____

10. **spliced**   (splīst)   *verb*

I felt as if a new life had been **spliced** into mine.

Your best guess: _____

Best dictionary definition: _____

11. **prankster**   (prank′ stər)   *noun*

I soon found out that he had been a motorcycle rider, a **prankster**, the leader of his gang.

Your best guess: _____

Best dictionary definition: _____

12. **degradation**   (deg′ ra dā′ shən)   *noun*

The **degradation** these people suffered is beyond belief.

Your best guess: _____

Best dictionary definition: _____

13. **consolation**   (kän' sə lā' shən)   *noun*

These workers shared their "fringe benefits" with the others, but it was small **consolation** compared to the ***trauma*** of watching others starve or be murdered before their eyes.

Your best guess: _____

Best dictionary definition: _____

14. **trauma**   (trô' mə)   *noun*

Your best guess: _____

Best dictionary definition: _____

15. **tenuous**   (ten' yo͞o əs)   *adjective*

Their existence was **tenuous**, just like that of all the others.

Your best guess: _____

Best dictionary definition: _____

16. **perusal**   (pə ro͞o' zəl)   *noun*

I knew that Sam's **perusal** of the table at Passover was more than just happiness with his family.

Your best guess: _____

Best dictionary definition: _____

from Timed Reading 4G (p. 142)

17. **filial** (fil' ē əl)   *adjective*

I tell them, Confucius say a **filial** son knows what color his mother's hair is.

Your best guess: _____

Best dictionary definition: _____

18. **heathen**   (hē' thən)   *noun (or adjective)*

You know, the British call the Irish **heathen**, just like they call the Chinese, she say.

Your best guess: _____

Best dictionary definition: _____

19. **pediatrician**   (pē' dē ə trish' ən)   *noun*

When Sophie take off her shoes, [the baby-sitter] say bare feet is best, even the **pediatrician** say so.

Your best guess: _____

Best dictionary definition: _____

20. **permissive**   (pər mis' iv)   *adjective*

It has nothing to do with John's family, my daughter say. Amy was too **permissive**, that's all.

Your best guess: _____

Best dictionary definition: _____

Exercise, Vocabulary Preview, Chapter 4

Directions: *Choose the best definition for each **boldfaced** word as it is used in its context. Remember: A word may have more than one meaning.*

b   1. Pamela loved to travel to Los Angeles for the great variety and quality of **ethnic** foods and restaurants available at all hours of the day and night; she could have tacos for breakfast, Peruvian chicken for lunch, and sweet-and-sour shrimp for dinner.

   (a) of religious laws   (b) of different cultures   (c) vegetarian

c   2. In addition to the four required classes, Josh was able to choose three **elective** courses from the college catalog.

   (a) basic   (b) computer   (c) optional

c   3. Feeling no **affinity** with any ethnic, religious, or social group, she isolated herself from everybody she met.

   (a) basic difference   (b) automatic hatred   (c) basic similarity

a   4. Joyce liked to **luxuriate** in the rich lushness of her mink coat; yesterday she was stroking its soft collar when the animal rights activists threw their first tomato.

   (a) take delight   (b) brag about   (c) pretend shame

b   5. With the help of self-hypnosis, Sean **transcended** the petty bickering and back-biting in his office; he was pleasant and polite to everyone, moving through his day with complete calm.

   (a) participated in   (b) rose above   (c) resented

a   6. When Maria began attending the American high school, at first the other students made fun of her and treated her **ill** because she didn't speak English as well as they could.

   (a) badly   (b) well   (c) sickly

b   7. Jack was being **facetious** when he told his sister, Jean, that she looked great in her new jacket, since he knew she had stolen it from his closet.

   (a) angry   (b) humorous   (c) complimentary

b   8. Emily's **demeanor** suggested anxiety; i.e. she seemed nervous, breathing rapidly and trembling.

   (a) mother-in-law   (b) manner   (c) video

b   9. Billy looked so pure and innocent in his white choir robe that his parents thought he was an angel **incarnate**.

   (a) from above   (b) in bodily form   (c) in the church

a   10. The film editing crew **spliced** the last segment of tape into the existing movie.

   (a) joined   (b) criticized   (c) copied

_C_ 11. The mysterious **prankster** filled all of the soap dispensers with mayonnaise and replaced the paper towels with plastic wrap.

(a) youngster   (b) burglar   (c) jokester

_b_ 12. It was clear, when Nora walked out of the house with her suitcase, that she was determined to escape the unspeakable **degradation** she had suffered there.

(a) unhappiness   (b) humiliation   (c) insanity

_C_ 13. After losing the contest and the chance at winning the brand-new Lexus, the **consolation** prize of a free car wash left Sam feeling depressed.

(a) silly   (b) painful   (c) comfort

_a_ 14. Malik suffered physical and emotional **trauma** resulting from the car accident that killed his parents and left him disfigured.

(a) shock   (b) discomfort   (c) excitement

_b_ 15. After Marsha insulted the company's top client and spilled wine in his lap, her position with the company became **tenuous**.

(a) secure   (b) weak   (c) terminated

_C_ 16. The women's open **perusal** of the men at the bar made them uneasy; apparently the men didn't like being stared at.

(a) disdain   (b) invitation   (c) examination

_a_ 17. His parents told him that it was his **filial** duty to take care of them when they got old.

(a) due from a child   (b) fitting a Christian   (c) humane

_b_ 18. When white people first settled the American West, they called the native Indians "**heathens**."

(a) white-haters   (b) no culture or religion   (c) cruel to animals

_C_ 19. When two-year-old Sally developed a skin rash, her parents were quick to take her to a **pediatrician**.

(a) skin doctor   (b) druggist   (c) baby doctor

_b_ 20. Joseph's strict grandmother thought his parents had been too **permissive** in the way they disciplined Joseph.

(a) severe   (b) allowing too much   (c) inconsistent

Number of Errors _____

Chapter 4
Connecting Logic Patterns

I. How to Understand More

Note: *Use the preview method before you study-read this article. First, survey. Then, digest the survey by jotting down a few notes at the end of the study unit.*

STUDY UNIT

Connecting Logic Patterns

Chapter 3 introduced you to four major logic patterns and key words. This chapter explains six more logic patterns and focuses on transitions. This additional information will increase your ability to process what you read. Plus, it will help you think more logically.

Look for Transitions

Spotting transitions, and connecting them with their logic patterns, can be as helpful in reading as road signs are in driving. If you've ever had the experience of driving an unknown road, you know how helpful those signposts can be. They alert you to dangers just ahead like hairpin turns and sudden sharp curves. This knowledge of the road helps you to be a better driver.

Good writers offer a similar aid to help you navigate your way through their thoughts. These *transitions* (whether in reading, writing, speaking, or listening) tell you when the "road" of an author's thoughts is about to pass from one idea to another, or to change direction. In your life, a transition may mean a time between two major events, like the time between high school and college. (The root "trans" means "cross.")

In reading, *transitions are single words or brief phrases that reinforce logic patterns.* Some common transitions you use all the time are *and, but, so, because, first, as a result, for example.* Do not confuse transitions that connect and introduce "ideas" with *conjunctions* that connect words or phrases (examples: tall *and* handsome, rich *but* evil).

In the last chapter, you learned some transitions used with the logic patterns of *time sequence, process, addition,* and *classification.* You may have noticed that transitions, especially number transitions, are often used with key words: for example, "*three* easy steps." In this chapter, you will learn transitions for six more logic patterns. Once you train yourself to be aware of transitions, you will find it easier to follow the author's logic when you read.

You already know many transitions and are sensitive to how they signal a change in a speaker's direction. For instance, consider this familiar situation. Someone you know says to you, "You are a fantastic friend. *For example*, you are dependable, trustworthy, and loyal. *Also*, you have a great sense of humor. *In addition*, you are intelligent and considerate of my feelings. *But . . .* "

A phrase such as "for example" after a positive word like "fantastic" is a signpost that catches your interest. Then words like "also" and "in addition" probably keep you nodding your head in pleasure as you lap up your friend's perceptive comments. However, what happens when you hear the word "but"? You know, of course, a change is coming, a change in the opposite direction; so you may start to steel yourself for a list of your faults. "But sometimes you embarrass me when you . . . ."

Practice 1 From the last paragraph on the preceding page, make a list of all the transitions (omitting the transitions in quotation marks).

You should be aware that a longer phrase or a clause, or even a short paragraph, can be a transition. They are easy to recognize because they perform the same function as transition words and short phrases. They connect ideas. They too indicate a change of direction and reinforce the logic pattern.

Throughout the remainder of this article, or study unit, and especially in the model paragraphs below, notice how transitions are used to reinforce logic patterns. (Note: This paragraph is a transition to the rest of this article.)

Six More Logic Patterns

Comparison and *contrast* are words that are often used interchangeably. They can be confused in reading because they both are sometimes used in the same passage. However, *comparison* points out "similarities" and *contrast* points out "differences." The details in these patterns point out what two subjects do or do not have in common.

1. Model paragraph for mostly *comparison* (with transitions in *italics*):

   The twin girls were separated at birth and raised in completely different environments, Laura Lou in a rural Louisiana shack and Elizabeth in a Manhattan penthouse. In spite of their dramatically different backgrounds, when they were reunited as middle-aged women, they had taken many *similar* paths in their lives. Both women had married and divorced at an early age to pursue careers in the *same* field, music. Both were at the top of their singing professions. Laura Lou was a headliner on "The Grand Ol' Opry." *Similarly*, Elizabeth was a soloist for the Metropolitan Opera. An even stranger *similarity* was that both women had, as single mothers, adopted children born to mothers who had died of AIDS.

Practice 2

(a) List two *contrasting* details in the above paragraph.

_____   _____

(b) What are the three key words that set up the framework for the list of comparisons?

   __many__   __similar__   __both__

[Note: A related logic pattern is *analogy*, which explains a difficult concept, an abstraction, by comparing it to something more familiar, or concrete. For instance, in this article, the term "transition," which is abstract, is explained by comparing transitions to road signs (which are concrete).]

Practice 3 Explain how "transitions" and "road signs" are alike.

_____

_____

2. Model paragraph for mostly **contrast** (with transitions in *italics*):

Many high school graduates go straight to college. Others, *in contrast*, go to work full time, then decide later to start college. Graduates who take jobs always run the risk of being unable to let go of that paycheck. They may find it too hard to live the lean life of a student again. *However*, once these people do return to college, they usually bring a maturity that's a big asset in the classroom. These students will be older than the others when they finally get their college degree, *but* these older students are more likely to know from experience what job suits them.

Practice 4   What is mostly being contrasted in Model Paragraph 2?

_____   _____

Cause and **effect** are also frequently confused because they are too frequently used in the same reading passage. *Cause* means simply the "reason why," and *effect* gives the "results."

Examine the *cause-effect* ideas connected in the same sentence below. Insert the transition "so" or the more formal "therefore" between the two ideas and notice how much clearer the logic is.

I have no money, ____So____ I cannot go to the movies with you.

Reverse the order of the two ideas, and insert the transition "for" or "because" for the reverse logic, *effect-cause*.

I can't go to the movies with you, ____for____ I have no money.

[Note: Two related logic patterns to *cause* and *effect* are "problem-solution" and "question-answer."]

3. Model paragraph for **cause** (with transitions in *italics*):

It wasn't Gilbert's fault he couldn't get to class on time. For one thing, he couldn't get up on time, often *because* he didn't hear his alarm. He didn't hear his alarm *because* he had watched television too late the night before. Then, he arrived on campus too late to get a parking space. This problem was *caused* by more students with cars than empty parking spaces. The buses didn't help. When he overslept, he couldn't get to the bus stop on time. He got really angry the few times he did get to the bus stop on time but the bus was late. Sometimes he just gave up in disgust and went home to bed.

Sometimes a supporting detail will have its own supporting detail, or its own cause.

Example: *couldn't get up on time* [caused by] *didn't hear alarm*

Practice 5   List another *cause* of a *cause*.

more students in parking   he went home because the bus was late

4. Model paragraph for **effect** (with transitions in *italics*):

Gilbert's not getting to class on time had several unpleasant *results*. The immediate *effect* was that he was dropped from all of his classes. Another

consequence was that his parents refused to support him any longer. The most serious *result* was a complete change in the direction of his life. Instead of being a lawyer, he was forced to take a job at a fast-food place.

Practice 6

(a) What other major logic pattern, from Chapter 3, overlaps *effect*? Addition

(b) What are three key words that set up the framework?

_____ _____ _____

The last two logic patterns you already know and simply need a reminder: ***example*** and ***description***. They too are used with the other patterns. They are most likely used as minor supporting details that expand and develop the other patterns. They give clarity and life to any reading. Look for these two supporting patterns in all the model paragraphs.

Example, or illustration, uses specific cases to move from the general to the specific. Like *description*, *example* makes an abstraction more concrete.

5. Model paragraph for ***example*** (with transitions in *italics*):

Eloise and Abe liked to challenge themselves on their vacations. *For example*, instead of taking the comfortable steamship *Delta Queen* down the Mississippi River, they took a flatboat. Plus, they navigated it themselves during a thunderstorm. Another *instance* was when they went to Africa. Instead of traveling with a large safari, they backpacked their way through the jungle with only one guide. The most frightening *illustration* of their foolhardiness was their attempt to climb Mount Everest—during a fierce snowstorm. They never returned from that trip.

Practice 7

(a) List the three examples that support the *topic sentence* (the first sentence).

_____

_____

_____

(b) The easier alternative to their trips (beginning with the transition "instead of") represent which of the other logic patterns?

_____

Description improves almost any kind of writing, because it helps the reader see, feel, taste, smell, or hear the person, or the place, or the event. Descriptive details make a person or experience real to the reader. Description often gives the most specific information about the main idea, or even about less important ideas. Like example, description can be used with any of the other logic patterns. To some degree, description is used in any kind of writing.

6. Model paragraph for **description** (with transitions in *italics*):

Hester cautiously entered the dark room, dimly lit by moonlight through its one narrow window on the wall to her *left*. She was overwhelmed by the odor of mildew and cold pizza and by something metallic, like blood. To her *right* was a rusty iron military cot topped by a bare mattress with a dark stain. *On the opposite* wall, she was greeted by her own startled eyes in a broken mirror. As she made her way *across* the damp floor, she heard hungry rats grappling *underneath* her feet in the basement. So intent was she on avoiding a rat, she was unprepared when her face hit the icy feet of a sodden lump hanging from the one light fixture *above* her.

Practice 8 In the blanks to the left, list the senses (besides the obvious sense of sight) that are stimulated in the paragraph. In the blanks to the right, list the descriptive details that stimulate those senses.

senses	descriptive details
_____	_____
_____	_____
_____	_____

Most experienced readers do not consciously search for these logic patterns as they read. However, good readers are familiar enough with the patterns, and their transitions, that they absorb them subconsciously when reading. As a result, they not only understand more of what they have just read, but they also predict what comes next.

Good readers are like experienced cooks, able to prepare several courses of a meal at once, without looking at a recipe. For a while, they may need to look more consciously for the patterns and their transitions. Similarly, you may need to refer to the recipe (or the chart below) frequently. You can improve the other three areas of communication, especially your writing, if you transfer and use this knowledge.

Practice 9 Explain the analogy in the above paragraph.

_____

_____

Study Notes

Review the chart below. Then, on a large index card, reproduce as much of the chart as you can remember. Next, look back at this chart and fill in the missing pieces on your chart. On the back of the card, add definitions for each logic pattern.

Keep your chart for reference—especially for when you write. Experiment with different transitions for variety. Looking frequently at the chart will help you absorb the information without memorizing it. (Note: Some logic patterns use the same transitions. Number transitions, in particular, are common for most patterns.)

Definition

LOGIC PATTERNS	TRANSITIONS
time sequence and process	at first, later, after that, finally, once, earlier, next, then, eventually, when, now [also dates and times]
addition and classification	first, second, third [etc.], and, moreover, more important, least important
comparison	similarly, in comparison, like, likewise, as, same
contrast	but, however, yet, on the other hand, though, although, nevertheless, even though, difference
cause	because, for, the reason, the cause
effect	therefore, as a result, hence, so, thus, consequently, subsequently, in effect
example	for example, to illustrate, for instance, that is, in other words, in illustration, e.g., i.e.
description	right, left, up, down, below, over, under [also any words indicating place or appearance]

Tracing Our Roots

As you read the three paragraphs, look for the logic patterns you have learned. Be open to seeing patterns overlap. Use the transitions as clues. Notice how the patterns of details support the main idea. After answering the questions for each paragraph, check the key.

Exercise 4A: Paragraph

When Malcolm X said, "You have to understand the roots of the tree before you can understand its branches," he may have given Americans a solution to the problems of ethnic diversity. The dark underbelly of "America, the great melting pot!" is crawling with people who hate and fear anyone who is different. Some white Americans say, "Send the black people back to Africa where they belong," forgetting that white people brought them here in chains to be slaves. Some African-Americans say, "Send the Mexicans back to Mexico; they don't even speak English." A century ago, Irish immigrants were considered so low, they were greeted with signs in store windows saying, "No Irish allowed." Yet, in the twentieth century, we elected an Irishman, John F. Kennedy, as President of the United States and honored him and his family as American royalty. We forget that all of us, even the Native American Indians, originally came from somewhere else. We, or our ancestors, were all different once.

1. Choose the sentence that best states the main idea of the paragraph.
   (a) America must put a limit on immigrants or we will never have peace.
   (b) America must use the rise of the Irish as a lesson in tolerance.
   (c) Americans will never get along because we are all so different.
   (d) Americans need to understand their own roots in order to understand others who are different.

2. How many *examples* of prejudice are given in the paragraph? ___3___

3. Explain the analogies, or *comparisons*, in the first two sentences.
   understanding roots of trees [compared to] __understand their own roots__
   _____

   dark things crawling under a pot [compared to] _____
   _____

4. What is the transition that reinforces *contrast*? __yet.__
   Briefly list the two details being contrasted.
   _____ vs. _____

Exercise 4B: Paragraph

Even so, I rebel at the notion that I can't be part of other groups, that I can't construct identities through elective affinity, that race must be the most important thing about me. Is that what I want on my gravestone: Here lies an African-American? So I'm divided. I want to be black, to know black, to luxuriate in whatever I might be calling blackness at any particular time—but to do so in order to come out the other side, to experience a humanity that is neither colorless nor reducible to color. Bach *and* James Brown. Sushi *and* fried catfish. Part of me admires those people who can say with a straight face that they have transcended any attachment to a particular community or group . . . but I always want to run around behind them to see what holds them up.

—HENRY LOUIS GATES, JR., FROM COLORED PEOPLE

1. Using your own words, write a complete sentence that states the main idea of the paragraph.

_____

_____

[who?   wants both what?   and what else?]

2. List the four transitions in the paragraph.

_____   _____   _____   _____

3. What is the logic pattern that provides the framework of the paragraph?
   (a) time sequence   (b) contrast   (c) comparison   (d) classification

4. List the two pairs of details that provide *examples* for the major logic pattern.

_____ vs. _____   _____ vs. _____

Exercise 4C: Paragraph

[1]The language of our *antepasados,* those who came before us, connects us to our center, to who we are and directs us to our life work. [2]Some of us have been lost, cut off from the essential wisdom and power. [3]Sometimes, our parents and grandparents were so harmed by a society that treated them ill for speaking their native language [Spanish] that they thought they could save us from that hate by teaching us to speak only English. [4]Those of us, then, live like captives, lost from our culture, ungrounded, forever wandering like ghosts with a thorn in the heart.

—SANDRA CISNEROS

1. Is the main idea stated in a topic sentence?
   (a) yes, sentence #_____   (b) no

2. In your own words, write a complete sentence that states the implied main idea of the paragraph.

_____

_____

[what?   does what?   for whom?]

3. List the two transitions used in the paragraph.

_____   _____

4. Which logic pattern is *not* used in the paragraph?
   (a) effect   (b) cause   (c) contrast   (d) classification

II. How to Read Faster

As you near the midway point of this book, this is a good time to check your reading speed again. Have you broken the word-by-word habit and started reading for ideas, or in phrases? Are you reading faster than 250 WPM? Have you doubled your reading speed on easy material? If not, more practice in phrase-reading and in breaking bad habits may be useful. If you are phrase-reading already, you probably do not have these bad habits.

Take Another Look at Phrase-Reading

The two untimed exercises that follow give you a different kind of practice with reading in phrases.

1. In the following paragraph, note how the words are arranged into natural phrase clusters. Try to fix your eyes only once per phrase (on the dot in the middle) and still follow the meaning of the paragraph. Repeat several times.

Reading is   a recent development   in the history of language.

The total reading   process is   very complex.   It involves

the whole self   of the reader—   memory, experience, brain,

knowledge, language ability,   psychological and emotional states,

and, of course,   the input   through the eyes.

2. In the next paragraph, many of the functional and repetitive words like articles and prepositions are missing. Focus on the key words that remain. Try to follow the meaning of the paragraph by reading these key words.

physical process   reading   interesting because most
have false ideas about   eyes   doing   when
read.   We know   general   what   doing.
example, we know   decoding-translating   code made
twenty-six   squiggles   English sounds   we heard
babyhood.   We know   reading   unravel   code
left   right across   page,   move down   next line,
decode   again.

The point of these exercises is that you don't have to fixate on every word to get the idea of what you read. As you do the Timed Readings in this chapter, continue to focus mostly on the key words: the *nouns, verbs, transitions.* These words carry most of the meaning.

Break Bad habits

Don't let bad habits slow you down. Look at the following list to identify some bad physical habits that may be symptoms of word-by-word reading. Learn what you can do to break them.

■ *Regressing*, or rereading, means you are not concentrating the first time you read a passage. To avoid regressions, cut out an index card to show only one line or cover up the page above the line being read. Practice on easy reading material. Preview so you will be tuned in. Don't allow yourself to regress for any reason. If you don't allow yourself the luxury of a second reading, your motivation will be higher on the first reading.

- *Lip moving* means you are reading one word per focus. You are thinking one word per focus. This means you are stuck at a speaking rate of 250 WPM or lower. To break the habit, put a pencil between your lips while reading. If it falls out, you know you are moving your lips. If you feel hopelessly stuck on word-by-word reading, try this experiment. Preview an easy, interesting magazine article on a topic familiar to you. Then, as you read the article, count (one, two, three . . .) with your lips, while trying to keep your mind on the ideas in the article.

- *Finger pointing* at each word to avoid losing your place limits your peripheral vision. It limits your thinking power. Your brain can move faster than your finger can. Instead of pointing your finger at each word to keep your place, run your finger down the margin while you read. Point at the *line* you are reading, not at each word. If you wish to break the habit of using your finger completely, hold the book firmly in both hands.

- *Squinting* means you may have a vision problem. Adjust your light source. A 100-watt bulb should illuminate your reading area. If the problem continues, consider having your eyes checked.

Exercise 4D: Phrases

Make a slash through the phrase identical to the key phrase. **Note:** *All phrases follow a verb-adverb pattern.*

Key Phrase

1.	was walking home	was walking along	was walking home	is walking alone
2.	is working hard	is working hard	is waiting long	is looking hard
3.	had knocked twice	had knocked twice	had rung twice	had known once
4.	drove slowly	dried up slowly	drove slowly	read slowly
5.	kissed softly	kidded sweetly	kissed softly	softly kissed
6.	were singing well	was singing wildly	were singing well	were sighing
7.	rode wildly	wrote vividly	rode wildly	rode well
8.	danced fast	dated foolishly	fenced daringly	danced fast
9.	argued lengthily	argued lengthily	answered at length	added slowly
10.	was picked fresh	was picked fresh	pricked his finger	is pickled fast
11.	planted quickly	placed quietly	pleated quilts	planted quickly
12.	is moving always	is ever moaning	is moving always	is melting away
13.	nodded wisely	bobbing wildly	wishing wisely	nodded wisely
14.	handled skillfully	skilled hands	handled skillfully	handled well
15.	stayed awhile	played awhile	stayed awhile	stayed calm
16.	built quite high	built quite high	felt quite huge	built quietly
17.	rang loudly	sang lewdly	ran lightly	rang loudly
18.	is mending now	is bending over	was telling how	is mending now
19.	lied cruelly	lied cruelly	crudely lifted	lies on couch
20.	hurts so much	hugged a lot	hurts to laugh	hurts so much

Time _40_

Number of Errors _0_

Reading Faster and Understanding More, Book Two   **137**

Exercise 4E: Phrases

Make a slash through the phrase identical to the key phrase. **Note:** *All phrases follow a verb-infinitive pattern (which means most are really short imperative sentences).*

Key Phrase

1. plays to win	plan to sin	place to wish	plays to win
2. start to walk	start to walk	start to stop	start to talk
3. learn to drive	learn to rivet	drive to learn	learn to drive
4. forget to write	get his rights	forget to write	forge the writing
5. send to fight	send to fight	mend a fight	fight to send
6. want to provide	provide for wants	wait to prove	want to provide
7. need to think	need to sink	need a drink	need to think
8. had to give	hope to gain	had to give	had to get
9. offer to type	typed offer	offered to tape	offer to type
10. pay to get	get to pay	pay to get	pay two-grand
11. begin to grow	begins to groan	begs to grow	begin to grow
12. love to nurse	love to doctor	love to nurse	listen to music
13. hate to work	hate to work	have to worry	hurry to work
14. agree to form	agree to form	argued to win	aged to form
15. smile to charm	chart the miles	start to harm	smile to charm
16. eat to live	love to eat	eat to live	eat to fly
17. cut to fit	fit to keep	cut to fit	carve to feed
18. meet to decide	meet to desire	meet to decide	decide to meet
19. like to hum	lead to harm	like to hope	like to hum
20. have to stop	stop to hold	had to stoop	have to stop

Time _4 35_

Number of Errors _____

The two longer readings were written in different styles by people with entirely different backgrounds, but they share an interest in their roots. Even though the readings are more personal than those in earlier chapters, notice that the same logic patterns are used to develop a central idea, or the thesis.

Exercise 4F: Timed Reading   *1093 words*

This reading was written by a second-generation Polish-American, the son of survivors of a Nazi concentration camp. The author received a Ph.D. in computer science from the University of Southern California, where he then taught and did research, specializing in artificial intelligence. His success adds relevance to his discovery of his father's role in the Holocaust.

Preview: *Quickly survey the title, the first and last paragraphs, and a few first sentences of paragraphs in between. Write here what you think the author discovered about his father.*

_____

Wait for a signal from your instructor before you begin reading. Try to finish in less than two minutes, if you can. Circle your reading time, and find WPM *when finished.*

Discovering a Father

David Wilczynski

At our most recent Passover dinner I noticed my father inspecting the family as they were gathered around the table. He looked at each of us for a few seconds, saying nothing, moving systematically from one person to another. His eyes did not have their familiar twinkle. Instead, these were probing eyes, especially so when he got to one of his grandchildren. I know that look and I know what was in his heart. Like other survivors of the Nazi Holocaust, he never believed he would live to witness such an occasion. He was trying to reconcile his existence in the Auschwitz death camp with this joyous family get-together. He wondered how it was that he survived and so many others did not. He wondered, but really he knew. I had not always known.

When I was a young teenager living in California, I knew little about my parents. I knew they survived the concentration camps, that we came to this country as Ellis Island immigrants from Germany, and that we were poor. Our move from Brooklyn to Los Angeles coincided with the Dodgers' move. My life was good, as my mother was always quick to point out. My father said little.

Our family often took trips to the country to relax. For me that meant swimming, baseball, and horseback riding. For my parents it meant . . . well, I'm not sure what it meant because we never did anything together except eat. That's why I was surprised when my father accepted my somewhat facetious invitation to go horseback riding with my friend Phil and me. Phil and I had ridden the day before for the first time ever. I reckoned that made us experts compared with my father, Sam, who as far as I had seen, could do nothing more athletic than dog-paddle in a pool.

Sam was about 40 years old at the time. A small man, five and a half feet tall, and 130 pounds, he was quiet, liked to laugh, and had a presence that others in his Jewish community acknowledged. I saw him only as a distant, hard-working father, whose explosive temper seemed at odds with his normally calm demeanor.

At the stables that day, he wandered off as the owner retrieved for Phil and me the same two old, gentle horses we had ridden yesterday. When Sam reappeared after wandering around the stable, the owner asked him if he saw a horse he wanted. Sam pointed to a large, full-blooded, black horse.

"Are you sure?" the owner asked.

"Yes," Sam replied seriously. I was embarrassed, convinced that I had made a mistake in bringing my dad along, and afraid. The horse looked like Satan incarnate. As the owner saddled up the horses, I felt a need to stop him. But before I could, my dad effortlessly leaped on his horse and galloped off down the road. He left a cloud of dust and the three of us speechless.

Nothing in my life had prepared me for this moment. We tried to follow, but my dad was long gone. After some time, we saw him approaching from a distance. He stopped at the side of a steep hill, and rode straight up it and then came straight down like they do in the movies. We were openmouthed when he passed us.

"Watch this," he said.

His horse began to trot slowly. Then my father nudged the horse with his legs and it started to trot in a way that reminded me of a military march. Only later did I learn that this sophisticated technique was called *dressage*. A few moments later, he kicked the horse and galloped back to the stables.

I ran all the way back to the lodge, shook my mother by the shoulders, and told her what had just happened. "Oh, yes, your father," she said smiling casually, "he was a champion horseback rider in the Polish Army."

I felt as if a new life had been spliced into mine. My whole conception of my father was wrong. I soon found out that he had been a motorcycle rider, a prankster, the leader of his gang (such as gangs were in Ishzbitz, Poland), and, of course, this horseback champion. How is it that I was never told? How is it that he never took me riding?

Now that I know more about people like my parents, I know that survivors of disasters suffer guilt for living when others have died. It matters little whether they could have done anything to prevent the disaster or not. Holocaust survivors are especially prone to this problem. The degradation these people suffered is frankly beyond belief. To suffer guilt as well seems inhumanely unfair.

Sam, my father, was one of the strong young men who actually constructed Auschwitz. As a worker, he received special benefits, extra food, better lodging. These workers shared their "fringe benefits" with the others, but it was small consolation compared to the trauma of watching others starve or be murdered before their eyes. Workers were kept alive only so long as they were useful. Their existence was tenuous, just like that of all the others.

My father's fortunes turned when a new commandant came to the camp. Turns out he was a horse fancier. One of his horses was wild, untamable by the Nazi trainer. My father had the audacity to volunteer his help. First, he was beaten for proposing the unthinkable—a Jew, riding a Nazi horse. But the horse remained unridable and my father persisted. Strangely, the commandant let Sam try, expecting him to fail. When he not only succeeded in riding the horse but training him as well, the commandant put him in charge of all the horses. Now, Sam had real privileges and his survival was assured while this commandant was in charge.

Yet, the cost was high. Sam repressed this whole part of his life, ashamed at what he had done, losing one of the few things he could share with his sons. But he did what he had to do in order to survive. Some say the survivors were lucky, but I know better. I grew up among these people. Each of them came to this country with nothing and each now is successful. They are old now, dying one by one. But they have a legacy that testifies to their fierceness. They are not alive now only to celebrate. I knew that Sam's perusal of the table at Passover was more than just happiness with his family; it was also his revenge.

Answer the following recall questions without referring to the article.

1. How did the author view his father before the horseback riding incident?
   (a) good and hard-working, but uninteresting
   (b) strong and athletic
   (c) pretending to be religious, but actually mean

2. What happens during the horseback riding incident that surprises the author?
   _____

3. List one thing his mother tells him about his father that he did not know before the horseback riding incident. _____

You may refer to the article to answer the following questions.

4. The major logic pattern is ___time process___, the one minor supporting logic pattern is _____ .

5. In your own words, write a complete sentence that expresses the thesis.
   _____
   _____
   [who?   discovers what?   about whom?]

Check your answers with the key, and record your scores below and on the Progress Chart.

Words per Minute _____

Percent Comprehension _____

TIMING CHART	
min:sec	wpm
5:28	200
4:58	220
4:33	240
4:12	260
3:54	280
3:39	300
3:25	320
3:13	340
3:02	360
2:51	380
2:44	400
2:36	420
2:29	440
2:23	460
2:17	480
2:11	500
2:06	520
2:01	540
1:57	560
1:53	580
1:49	600
1:46	620
1:42	640
1:39	660
1:36	680
1:34	700
1:31	720
1:29	740
1:26	760
1:24	780
1:22	800

This story is an excerpt from a book of short stories by acclaimed author, Gish Jen, who explores the sometimes funny, sometimes tragic, experiences of Chinese-Americans.

Preview: *Quickly survey the title, author's name, and first and last paragraphs. Write any impressions you get about the narrator, or the person telling the story.*

_____

_____

Wait for a signal from your instructor before you begin reading. Circle your reading time, when finished, and find your WPM.

from *Who's Irish?*

Gish Jen

In China, people say mixed children are supposed to be smart, and definitely my granddaughter Sophie is smart. But Sophie is wild, Sophie is not like my daughter Natalie, or like me. I am work hard my whole life, and fierce besides. My husband always used to say he is afraid of me, and in our restaurant, busboys and cooks all afraid of me too. Even the gang members come for protection money, they try to talk to my husband. When I am there, they stay away. If they come by mistake, they pretend they are come to eat. They hide behind the menu, they order a lot of food. They talk about their mothers. Oh, my mother have some arthritis, need to take herbal medicine, they say. Oh, my mother getting old, her hair all white now.

I say, Your mother's hair used to be white, but since she dye it, it become black again. Why don't you go home once in a while and take a look? I tell them, Confucius say a filial son knows what color his mother's hair is.

My daughter is fierce too, she is vice president in the bank now. Her new house is big enough for everybody to have their own room, including me. But Sophie take after Natalie's husband's family, their name is Shea. Irish. I always thought Irish people are like Chinese people, work so hard on the railroad, but now I know why the Chinese beat the Irish. Of course, not all Irish are like the Shea family, of course not. My daughter tell me I should not say Irish this, Irish that.

How do you like it when people say the Chinese this, the Chinese that, she say.

You know, the British call the Irish heathen, just like they call the Chinese, she say . . .

Sophie is three years old American age, but already I see her nice Chinese side swallowed up by her wild Shea side. She looks like mostly Chinese. Beautiful black hair, beautiful black eyes. Nose perfect size, not so flat looks like something fell down, not so large looks like some big deal got stuck in wrong face. Everything just right, only her skin is a brown surprise to John's family. So brown, they say. Even John say it. She never goes in the sun, still she is that color, he say. Brown. They say, Nothing the matter with brown. They are just surprised. So brown. Nattie is not that brown, they say. They say, It seems like Sophie should be a color in between Nattie and John. Seems funny, a girl named Sophie Shea be brown. But she is brown, maybe her name should be Sophie Brown. She never go in the sun, still she is that color, they say. Nothing the matter with brown. They are just surprised.

The Shea family talk is like this sometimes, going around and around like a Christmas-tree train.

Maybe John is not her father, I say one day, to stop the train. And sure enough, train wreck. None of the brothers ever say the word *brown* to me again. . . .

Nothing the matter with Sophie's outside, that's the truth. It is inside that she is like not any Chinese girl I ever see. We go to the park, and this is what she does. She stand up in the stroller. She take off all her clothes and throw them in the fountain.

Sophie! I say. Stop!

But she just laugh like a crazy person. Before I take over as baby-sitter, Sophie has that crazy-person sitter, Amy the guitar player. My daughter thought this Amy very creative—another word we do not talk about in China. In China, we talk about whether we have difficulty or no difficulty. We talk about whether life is bitter or not bitter. In America, all day long, people talk about creative. Never mind that I cannot even look at this Amy, with her shirt so short that her belly button showing. This Amy think Sophie should love her body. So when Sophie take off her diaper, Amy laugh. When Sophie run around naked, Amy say she wouldn't want to wear a diaper either. When Sophie go *shu-shu* in her lap, Amy laugh and say there are no germs in pee. When Sophie take off her shoes, Amy say bare feet is best, even the pediatrician say so. That is why Sophie now walk around with no shoes like a beggar child. Also why Sophie love to take off her clothes.

Turn around! Say the boys in the park. Let's see that ass!

Of course, Sophie does not understand. Sophie clap her hands, I am the only one to say, No! This is not a game.

It has nothing to do with John's family, my daughter say. Amy was too permissive, that's all.

But I think if Sophie was not wild inside, she would not take off her shoes and clothes to begin with.

You never take off your clothes when you were little, I say. All my Chinese friends had babies, I never saw one of them act wild like that.

Look, my daughter say. I have a big presentation tomorrow.

John and my daughter agree Sophie is a problem, but they don't know what to do.

You spank her, she'll stop, I say another day.

But they say, Oh no.

In America, parents not supposed to spank the child.

It gives them low self-esteem, my daughter say. And that leads to problems later, as I happen to know.

My daughter never have big presentation the next day when the subject of spanking come up.

I don't want you to touch Sophie, she say. No spanking, period.

Don't tell me what to do, I say.

I'm not telling you what to do, say my daughter. I'm telling you how I feel.

I am not your servant, I say. Don't you dare talk to me like that.

My daughter have another funny habit when she lose an argument. She spread out all her fingers and look at them, as if she like to make sure they are still there.

My daughter is fierce like me, but she and John think it is better to explain to Sophie that clothes are a good idea. This is not so hard in the cold weather. In the warm weather, it is very hard.

Use your words, my daughter say. That's what we tell Sophie. How about if you set a good example.

As if good example mean anything to Sophie. I am so fierce, the gang members who used to come to the restaurant all afraid of me, but Sophie is not afraid.

I say, Sophie, if you take off your clothes, no snack.

I say, Sophie, if you take off your clothes, no lunch.

I say, Sophie, if you take off your clothes, no park.

Pretty soon we are stay home all day, and by the end of six hours she still did not have one thing to eat. You never saw a child stubborn like that.

I'm hungry! she cry when my daughter come home.

What's the matter, doesn't your grandmother feed you? My daughter laugh.

No! Sophie say. She doesn't feed me anything!

My daughter laugh again. Here you go, she say.

She say to John, Sophie must be growing.

Growing like a weed, I say.

Still Sophie take off her clothes, until one day I spank her. Not too hard, but she cry and cry, and when I tell her if she doesn't put her clothes back on I'll spank her again, she put her clothes back on. Then I tell her she is good girl, and give her some food to eat. The next day we go to the park and, like a nice Chinese girl, she does not take off her clothes.

She stop taking off her clothes, I report. Finally!

How did you do it? my daughter ask.

After twenty-eight years experience with you, I guess I learn something, I say.

Answer the recall questions without referring to the article.

1. What is the background of Sophie's father?

   (a) Chinese   (b) Irish   (c) Italian

2. The narrator thinks that Sophie's appearance is mostly

   (a) Chinese   (b) Irish   (c) Italian

3. The narrator thinks that Sophie's behavior is mostly

   (a) Chinese   (b) Irish   (c) Italian

4. What does the narrator say to her son-in-law's family to stop them from talking about the color of Sophie's skin? _____

5. What does the narrator do that stops Sophie from taking off her clothes?

   (a) She tells Sophie she can't have anything to eat.

   (b) She tells Sophie she won't take her to the park.

   (c) She spanks Sophie.

   (d) She threatens to tell Sophie's parents.

TIMING CHART	
min:sec	wpm
06:42	200
06:05	220
05:35	240
05:09	260
04:47	280
04:28	300
04:11	320
03:56	340
03:43	360
03:32	380
03:21	400
03:11	420
03:03	440
02:55	460
02:48	480
02:41	500
02:35	520
02:29	540
02:24	560
02:19	580
02:14	600
02:10	620
02:06	640
02:02	660
01:58	680
01:55	700
01:52	720
01:49	740
01:46	760
01:43	780
01:41	800

You may refer to the article for the following questions.

6. What is the purpose of Natalie's analogy [*comparison*] between how people treat the Chinese and how the British treat the Irish?
   (a) to get her mother's sympathy for how she [Natalie] is treated at work
   (b) to stop her mother from insulting the Irish
   (c) to show how the British are more prejudiced than the Irish and the Chinese

7. What does Sophie's brown skin represent to the narrator? _____
   To the Shea family? _____

8. Explain what the narrator means by causing a "train wreck" in the Shea family. _____

9. What is the major *contrast* in the story?
   _____ vs. _____

10. In your own words, write a complete sentence that expresses the thesis.
    _____
    _____
    [who?   clashes over what?]

Check your answers with the key, and record your scores below and on the Progress Chart.

Words per Minute _____

Percent Comprehension _____

Writing and Discussion Activities

1. Write about some experience you have had as a newcomer to a group. For example, you might write about being a newcomer to a particular school, club, neighborhood, or country. (You are not limited to these examples, however.) Be sure to provide supporting details for your ideas about the experience.

2. What place do you consider your real home? Is it where you are living now or some other town or country? Write a paragraph describing the place that your heart calls home. Start with a topic sentence that tells where that place is and why, in general, it is important to you. The details in the rest of the paragraph will expand on the general statement you make in your topic sentence. Choose at least one detail in your paragraph to expand with a third-level detail (detail for the detail).

Vocabulary Review, Chapter 4

Match the vocabulary word on the left with its definition on the right. Write the letter of the answer in the short blank to the left.

_b_   1. **facetious**   (a) optional

_d_   2. **pediatrician**   (b) humorous

_a_   3. **elective**   (c) in bodily form

_e_   4. **tenuous**   (d) baby doctor

_c_   5. **incarnate**   (e) weak

*Choose the best definition for each **boldfaced** word was it is used in its context.*

_c_   6. modern, **permissive** parents
     (a) generous   (b) sacrificing   (c) allowing

_a_   7. received **consolation** after losing the game
     (a) comfort   (b) a deep massage   (c) an analysis of the errors

_c_   8. concerned about saving the **heathens** in underdeveloped countries
     (a) natural resources   (b) starving children
     (c) people with no culture or religion

_b_   9. **spliced** the cables
     (a) tripped over   (b) joined   (c) electrified

_c_   10. interested in **ethnic** clothes
     (a) loose and bright   (b) domestic grown   (c) different cultures

*Mark each sentence to show whether the **boldfaced** word is used correctly.*

a = True   b = False

_F_   11. Because she considered it her **filial** responsibility, she put her aged parents in a state-run nursing home and never saw them again.

_T_   12. So far, mankind has not found a way to **transcend** its mortality.

_T_   13. His **perusal** of his sister's face told him she was lying.

_F_   14. Because Marilyn has an **affinity** for cats, she will not allow them in the house.

_F_   15. Everyone gave the Nobel Prize winner congratulations and **degradation**.

(Continued)

Choose the word from the box that fits the context of the following paragraph. Write the letter of each choice on the blank lines to the left of the paragraph.

<table>
<tr><td>(a) trauma</td><td>(b) cynic</td><td>(c) prankster</td><td>(d) ill</td><td>(e) demeanor</td></tr>
</table>

_d_ 16.   I tell you this story, although I try not to speak __(16)__ of the dead.

_c_ 17. Carlos was such a __(17)__ that his best friend had a hard time telling

_a_ 18. when he was serious and when he was joking. One day Carlos

_e_ 19. bought a coffin, climbed in, and pretended to be dead, frightening

_b_ 20. his friend with his stonelike __(18)__ . It took his poor friend at least a

week to get over the __(19)__ of seeing Carlos suddenly sit up, very

much alive, and laugh. When Carlos was found truly dead in his

bed a short time thereafter, his friend had become such a __(20)__ that

he refused to believe Carlos was really gone until his coffin was

dropped into the grave.

% Correct _____

Comprehension Review, Chapter 4

1. Define *transition* (as it relates to reading and writing) in a clear, complete sentence.

   A *transition* is a ___single word___ or ___brief phrase___ that
   ___reinforce logic patterns___.

   [does what?   between what?   in what?]

Match the logic pattern *on the left with its explanation on the right, by writing the letter of the answer in the short line to the left.*

___d___ 2. contrast   (a) gives reasons

___c___ 3. comparison   (b) gives specific details (often appealing to the senses) to make an abstraction more concrete or to make an experience more real

___a___ 4. cause   (c) points out similarities

___e___ 5. effect   (d) points out differences

___f___ 6. example   (e) gives results

___b___ 7. description   (f) gives specific cases (or illustrations) to make a general idea more understandable or believable

8. *Description* and *example* are more likely to be *minor* supporting details.

   (a) true   (b) false

9. Give a transition for *comparison.* ___Similarly___

10. Give a transition for *effect.* ___result Therefore___

11. The transitions *but* and *however* are used in what *logic pattern*? ___contrast___

Read the following three paragraphs and answer the questions about them.

A. [1]Reading for ideas instead of separate words can result in several benefits. [2]The most obvious is increased speed. [3]A happy side effect of faster speed is more time for non-reading activities. [4]A less obvious result is greater comprehension, caused by reading more actively.

12. Is the main idea stated in a topic sentence?

   (a) yes, sentence #_____   (b) no

13. The logic pattern for this paragraph is *mostly*

   (a) cause   (b) effect   (c) comparison.

14. A *minor* logic pattern is   (a) cause   (b) effect   (c) comparison.

(Continued)

B. ¹The horse was beautifully groomed from head to toe. ²His mane shone like gold in the sunlight. ³His silver saddle was so brightly polished it blinded the eye. ⁴His spotless, ebony hooves clattered noisily on the cobblestone street.

15. The logic pattern for this paragraph is *mostly* ___description___

16. Does this paragraph have a topic sentence?
    (a) yes, sentence #__1__   (b) no

C. For the last half century, audiences have been entertained by movies featuring insects. An early _____ is the 1958 classic, *The Fly*, in which a scientist, played by Vincent Price, merged bodies with a fly. The strange result was a man's body with a fly's head or a fly's body with a man's head. The helpless creature's pitiful cry—"Help me! Help me!"—at the end of the movie haunted moviegoers forever. In the 1986 remake of the same movie, Jeff Goldblum played the unlucky scientist, who was transformed into a more disgusting version of a housefly. Another _____ in 1990 of this type of movie is *Arachnaphobia*, which gave mostly teenage audiences nightmares about spiders. Two more current _____ are the less frightening, animated movies *Antz* and *A Bug's Life*, which appeal to younger audiences.

17. Using your own words, write a complete sentence that states the main idea.
    ___Scary movies all have attracted the audiences since the last half century; for example, The Fly, Arachnaphobia, and Antz___

18. What logic pattern from Chapter 3 provides the *framework* for this paragraph?
    (a) time sequence   (b) process   (c) classification

19. What logic pattern from Chapter 4 provides *most* of the supporting details?
    (a) comparison   (b) example   (c) cause

20. What *transition* for this supporting logic pattern (in question #19) would fit in all three of the blank lines in the paragraph? ___the cause___
    [Clue: The answer is *not* "movie" or "film."]

% Correct _____

Because several famous scary movies as The Fly, Arachnaphobia, and Antz and A Bug's Life, were made for the last half century, they have attracted the audiences

VOCABULARY PREVIEW for Chapter 5

As you work your way through the remaining Vocabulary Previews, continue to look for clues like *synonyms*, *antonyms*, and *examples*—especially in the Exercises. Also look for roots to give you additional clues to meaning.

WORDS IN CONTEXT for Chapter 5

Directions: *Examine the **boldfaced** word as it is used in the sentence and write your best guess of the word's meaning. Then look up the word in your dictionary and write the best definition for its context in the sentence.*

PRONUNCIATION KEY

a	cat	ā	made	ä	bar	k	cot, quit	(	adore
e	pet	ē	these	â	care	s	cent		travel
i	sit	ī	ride	è	term	z	beds	ə {	horrify
o	rot	ō	note	ô	order	j	giant		pardon
u	nut	o͞o	rude	o͝o	foot	th	thank	(	circus
u̇	put	yo͞o	use	o͞o	food	ŦH	this		

from Paragraph 5A (p. 165)

1. **immediate**   (i mē′ dē it)   *adjective*

   Some of these are important and long-term, whereas other benefits are less dramatic, but more **immediate**.

   Your best guess: _____

   Best dictionary definition: _____

2. **carbon monoxide**   (kär′ bən mo nok′ sīd)   *adjective-noun*

   Benefits include ridding the blood of **carbon monoxide**, which robs it of oxygen.

   Your best guess: _____

   Best dictionary definition: _____

from Timed Reading 5F (p. 171)

3. **freaked**   (frēkt)   *verb (slang)*

   Janie took one look at L.A.'s blonde beauties and **freaked**.

   Your best guess: _____

   Best dictionary definition: _____

4. **quest** (kwest)   *noun*

> She began what she called her **quest** for total beauty.

Your best guess: _____

Best dictionary definition: _____

5. **frugal** (frōo′ gəl)   *adjective*

> She was **frugal** all year so she could afford ***rhinoplastic*** surgery.

Your best guess: _____

Best dictionary definition: _____

6. **rhinoplastic** (rī′ nō plas′ tik)   *adjective*

Your best guess: _____

Best dictionary definition: _____

7. **transcendental** (tran′ sen den′ təl)   *adjective*

> She immersed herself in **transcendental** meditation, yoga, t'ai chi ch'uan, and biofeedback.

Your best guess: _____

Best dictionary definition: _____

8. **suspending** (sə spend′ ing)   *verbal*

> She lost her high-pressure sales job—thereby **suspending** funds for other important beauty projects.

Your best guess: _____

Best dictionary definition: _____

9. **chill** (chil)   *verbal (slang)*

> I told her to **chill**.

Your best guess: _____

Best dictionary definition: _____

10. **tranquil** (trang′ kwəl)   *adjective*

> If the fashion this summer calls for a **tranquil**, snub-nosed chick with green hair, she is definitely *in*.

Your best guess: _____

Best dictionary definition: _____

from Timed Reading 5G (p. 174)

11. **fawn** (fôn)   *verbal*

> There's no need for you to **fawn** and ***grovel***; but, to make a good impression, merely be polite and friendly.

Your best guess: _____

Best dictionary definition: _____

12. **grovel**   (grov' əl)   *verbal*

Your best guess: _____

Best dictionary definition: _____

13. **desultory**   (des' əl tôr' ē)   *adjective*

Occasionally a class drags, discussion is **desultory**, students' eyes glaze over with boredom.

Your best guess: _____

Best dictionary definition: _____

14. **catalyst**   (kat' l ist)   *noun*

If you can be the **catalyst** that wakes up a *slumbering* class, everyone will be grateful, including your teacher.

Your best guess: _____

Best dictionary definition: _____

15. **slumbering**   (slum' bər ing)   *verbal (used as adjective)*

Your best guess: _____

Best dictionary definition: _____

16. **obnoxious**   (əb nok' shəs)   *adjective*

If you have visited the birdhouse at a zoo, you may remember the magpie, that one **obnoxious** bird that could remain neither still nor quiet.

Your best guess: _____

Best dictionary definition: _____

17. **futile**   (fyoot' l)   *adjective*

It is **futile** to present work that identifies you as sloppy and indifferent.

Your best guess: _____

Best dictionary definition: _____

18. **mediocrity**   (mē' dē ok' ri tē)   *noun*

If your paper lacks form, neatness, and completeness, and you are content to turn it in, you are putting yourself on record as a person lacking in self-respect, willing to deal in **mediocrity**, whose sole aim is to get by.

Your best guess: _____

Best dictionary definition: _____

19. **flagrantly**   (flā' grənt lē)   *adverb*

If you do not bring the text[book], you are revealing your lack of interest as **flagrantly** as if you wore a *placard inscribed*, "I HAVE NO INTEREST IN THIS CLASS."

Your best guess: _____

Best dictionary definition: _____

20. **placard** (plak′ ärd)   *noun*

   Your best guess: _____

   Best dictionary definition: _____

21. **inscribed** (in skrīb′ d)   *verbal*

   Your best guess: _____

   Best dictionary definition: _____

22. **protractors** (prō trak′ tərz)   *noun*

   Take . . . special necessary tools such as compasses, **protractors**, calculators, and lab notebooks.

   Your best guess: _____

   Best dictionary definition: _____

Exercise, Vocabulary Preview, Chapter 5

Directions: *Choose the best definition for each **boldfaced** word or phrase as it is used in its context. Look for all three types of context clues.*

_a_ 1. Tim's **immediate** response was to run for cover, even though, in his rational mind, he knew it was unlikely that he was hearing gunfire from a helicopter in downtown Palm Springs.
(a) instant   (b) delayed   (c) last

_b_ 2. The latest fear for the average American family is the danger of **carbon monoxide** poisoning; as a result, detectors are sold out at hardware stores.
(a) infected blood   (b) poisonous gas   (c) home invasion

_b_ 3. Janine **freaked** when she realized how much studying she was really required to do in college.
(a) focused   (b) became very upset   (c) dropped out

_a_ 4. Some people seem to be on a never-ending **quest** for the perfect mate; they keep looking and looking, but no one ever lives up to their expectations.
(a) search   (b) wait   (c) date

_c_ 5. Lou Ann was a **frugal** shopper; she always brought her coupons and searched out the bargains.
(a) fast   (b) wasteful   (c) thrifty

_b_ 6. Beverly Hills was to be the world capital for **rhinoplastic** surgery; in high school I knew five girls with perfectly good noses who had the surgery done before graduation.
(a) tummy tuck   (b) nose job   (c) face lift

_b_ 7. John tried **transcendental** meditation as a way to relieve stress and give focus to his life.
(a) drug-induced   (b) rising above   (c) reality-based

_a_ 8. Charlene decided that **suspending** judgment about her daughter's new boyfriend was the best way to keep peace in the family.
(a) delaying   (b) renewing   (c) making

_b_ 9. Mary became visibly upset at the idea of robbing the convenience store, but Robert told her to **chill**.
(a) get ready   (b) calm down   (c) get tough

_c_ 10. As Elizabeth gazed out over her quiet, **tranquil** neighborhood, the tension caused by her noisy, busy office melted away.
(a) middle-class   (b) suburban   (c) peaceful

_a_ 11. Gordon wanted to please his wife so badly that he would **fawn** over her the minute he walked in the door, asking her how her day was and how she wanted her dinner prepared.

(a) flatter too much   (b) scratch her back   (c) lie too much

_c_ 12. Her faithful dog never cared how he was treated; he liked to **grovel** at her feet whenever she spoke.

(a) scratch   (b) bark   (c) cringe

_c_ 13. Since they were not getting paid enough for the project, their work was **desultory**.

(a) resentful   (b) thorough   (c) half-hearted

_b_ 14. Maybe, through your example, you can be the **catalyst** that persuades your losing team to try harder.

(a) winner   (b) inspiration   (c) player

_a_ 15. The handsome prince kissed Snow White as she lay **slumbering** in her bed of flowers.

(a) sleeping   (b) dying   (c) pretending

_a_ 16. The quiet atmosphere of the library was disturbed by an **obnoxious** drunk who kept singing loudly and bumping into tables.

(a) detestable   (b) half-conscious   (c) unfamiliar

_c_ 17. Their efforts to turn in their essays before the deadline were **futile**, for they had started working on their essays too late.

(a) hurried   (b) successful   (c) useless

_b_ 18. She never tried for standards of excellence; she was content with **mediocrity**.

(a) failure   (b) ordinariness   (c) high standards

_b_ 19. After he won the lottery, Al displayed his new wealth **flagrantly**, making his old friends envious.

(a) modestly   (b) obviously   (c) dangerously

_b_ 20. The protestors carried large **placards** that read, "Don't buy here. Unfair hiring practices."

(a) labels   (b) signs   (c) pamphlets

_c_ 21. She had her gravestone **inscribed**, "All things considered, I would rather be in Beverly Hills."

(a) destroyed   (b) painted   (c) engraved

_a_ 22. The architect used a **protractor** to help him calculate the angles in the building.

(a) measuring tool   (b) blueprint   (c) computer program

Number of Errors _____

Chapter 5
Organizing Details

I. How to Understand More

II. How to Read Faster

Key words:
    "s" words

    groups   patterns
    steps   problems
    points   solutions
    ways
    differences
    Issues

I. How to Understand More

Note: *Remember to preview and take preliminary notes before you begin study-reading.*

Organizing Details

When we think about organizing details, we need to answer two questions: *why* and *how?* Why do we need to organize details when we read—or when we write, for that matter? Why organize anything? Why not put our shoes in our underwear drawer? Then, if we *do* see a value to order, as opposed to just being "spontaneous and creative," how do we organize our ideas when we read—and especially when we write? We need a system, just as we do when we organize our closet.

Why Organize Details?

Organizing details is often another exercise in telling the difference between general and specific, or whole and part. In looking at the ten logic patterns, we learned that some are more important than others. Some patterns like "addition" can provide the framework for a paragraph or article; thus, the points in the list are the most important ones. Other patterns, like "description," usually expand those points, or simply make them more vivid. Spotting the *level of importance* for the details is another way to process what you read. It is every bit as important as understanding the logic that connects the details.

In study-reading, you will overload your circuits if you try to remember all the details you read. A good study tip is *to try to retain only the most important details*. Many readers seem to retain facts and figures, or unimportant details, and nothing else. Think about how you might study for a history test on the Civil War. Why memorize the fact that Major Robert Anderson was the commander of Fort Sumter and ignore the more significant fact that firing on Fort Sumter officially started the war? Again, see the big picture first. Learn the causes for the war, when it began and ended, and turning points before you try to remember minor battles or minor dates. This obvious, timesaving study tip is the basis for organizing details. Make distinctions. Then make connections.

How to Organize Details

One way to learn how to mentally organize a passage as you read or as you write is *to practice outlining on material you read*. You may feel some natural resistance to this skill that has been around a long time and requires concentration and lots of practice. The good news is that you have already been writing rough outlines in your Study Notes at the end of these Study Units. When you grouped important ideas together and definitions of terms together, you were getting ready to outline. If you reflected the difference between major and minor details by the way you arranged them on the page (like indenting), you were outlining. Your beginning outline might look like this:

A transition is a word or phrase that reinforces logic patterns.
Examples: but, and, as a result

Now it is time to practice another step. For the sake of simplicity, we can *reflect the importance level of supporting details by assigning them numerical value.* For example, the most important points that explain the main idea may be called *first-level* details. A *second-level* detail would be less important; it would expand or explain a first-level detail. These minor, second-level details might be used to entertain or add color. You may have noticed in your own writing that there are many places where you could give first-level, second-level, even *third-level* details. How far you go depends on how specific you need to get. (Usually, the more specific the details are, the better the writing is.)

Looking at level of importance is another way of looking at levels of specificity—general to specific.

Practice 1   Assign numerical levels of importance to the details under the topic "sports." Note reinforcement of indenting.

                          sports
        tennis   _____ level
          racquet   _____ level
            handle   _____ level

Consider the level of details in the following paragraph. Notice how your awareness of logic patterns and transitions gives you clues. Notice that the paragraph has three major divisions, or three types of headaches. (What is the logic pattern for the three types?) The supporting details for each type give the same kind of information and follow the same order. This consistency in order helps you anticipate what is next.

It would be difficult to find anyone who has not suffered from a severe headache. However, not many people know there are three different types of headaches. Of these three types, the *tension* headache is the most common and least painful. This muscular headache is usually described as a dull ache in the scalp, jaw, neck, or shoulders. The second, more severe type, the *migraine* headache, affects twice as many women as it does men. The migraine, a combination of muscular and vascular contractions, is described as a throbbing pressure. Some sufferers see flashing lights or dots or lines just before their migraine strikes. Others have nausea and vomiting. The most severe and least common, the *cluster* headache, affects only 1.5 percent of the population, but it makes a person unable to function. The cluster headache focuses on eyes, neck, and temples. It is described as a hot branding poker rammed into the head. Its name comes from its tendency to hit quickly, one after the other.

—NANCY GOTTESMAN

(a) Underline all the transitions in the preceding paragraph about headaches.

(b) What are the major patterns that provide the framework for the paragraph?
    classficaiton   addition

(c) What are the three key words that set up the framework for the paragraph?
    _____3_____   types   _____

d) What are two of the minor patterns that expand the major pattern?
    description   contrast

Practice 3   Examine the "scrambled list" below (based on the headache paragraph), and draw a square or a rectangle around the three most general items.

[Note: This scrambled list will be used as reference for the next three Practice exercises.]

scrambled list:

More severe and affects twice as many women as men
Muscular—dull ache in scalp, jaw, neck, and shoulders
Tendency to hit quickly, one after another
Nausea and vomiting experienced by others
Tension headache
Focus on eyes, neck, and temples
Only 1.5 percent of population affected
Muscular and vascular contractions—throbbing pressure
Cluster headache
Migraine headache
Like a hot branding poker rammed into head
Victim unable to function
Most common and least painful
Flashing lights, dots, or lines seen before headache hits
Most severe and least common

Three Types of Outlines: Mapping, Topic, Sentence

The next step in learning to outline is to organize the details from the headache paragraph into three types of outlines. Just as you adjust your reading rate to fit the material and purpose, you can adjust the type of outline to fit the material and purpose. An outline is simply a chart or map of the ideas in a passage. Many people find it easier to understand and remember the important points in a reading selection if they put them in some kind of outline. Outlining is especially helpful if the reading material is difficult. It is the most advanced form of study notes you can write—and the most useful for review.

*The most informal and visual type of outline is the **mapping outline***. You have seen these diagrams before in some of the Study Units. This system of rectangles, ovals, triangles, and arrows shows the level of importance of major details to minor. It shows how these details relate to each other. Mapping can be a fast, easy way to chart the points in a lecture or a short reading passage. It can help you really "see" a difficult concept in biology—like how the digestive system works. Or, in a health class, mapping can help you understand the characteristics of three types of headaches.

Practice 4 Finish the *mapping outline* on the next page using all the items in the scrambled list (Practice 3) of details in the headache paragraph. Fit these items from the list on the preceding page into the diagram. To practice parallel wording (to represent parallel ideas), use the exact wording in the scrambled list. Make sure you follow the logic and order of the details in the headache paragraph. Fill in the rectangles with *first-level* details, the ovals with *second-level* details, and the triangles with *third-level* details.

Mapping Outline:

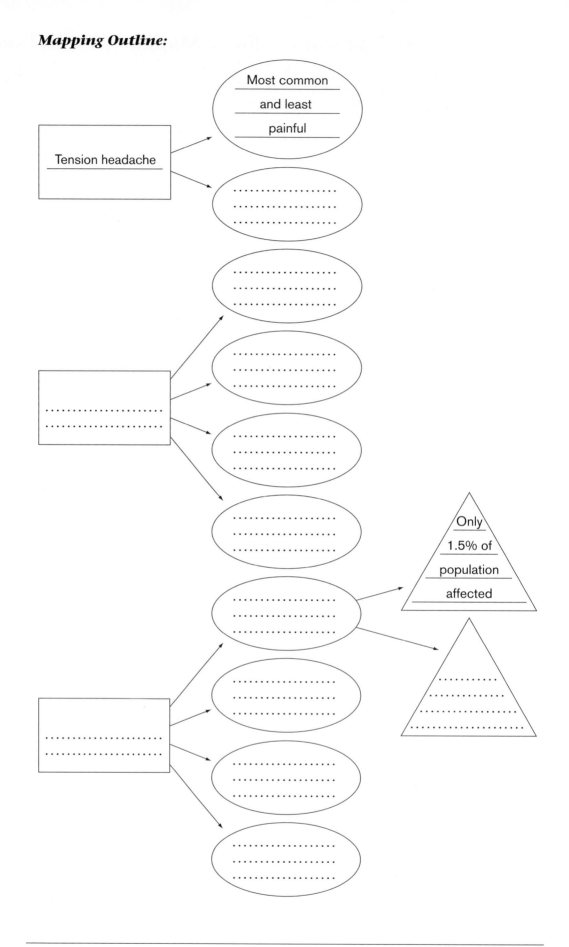

A more traditional outline—made up of fragments, indenting, and labels (both letters and numbers)—is the **topic outline**. The topic outline is a slight refinement on the lists you have been making for your Study Notes. Now, you can expand those lists of important points by indenting underneath them any minor, supporting details. Then label the items with a system of numbers and letters (instead of rectangles and ovals). In a *topic outline*, Roman numerals (I, II, III, IV, V) are comparable to the rectangles in the *mapping outline*. Capital letters are comparable to the ovals, and Arabic numbers (1, 2, 3) to triangles.* Or just remember that you alternate numbers and letters. And remember to indent less important details to the right.

The *topic outline* is useful for study notes, lecture notes, or as a rough plan for informal writing. Except for the main idea, all the items in a topic outline are *fragments*, or incomplete sentences. The key to an effective outline is brevity. No extra details, no extra words.

> **Practice 5** Arrange the same information from the scrambled list (Practice 3) into a *topic outline*. Place each item to the right of its appropriate label. Make sure the items in your outline are worded exactly like those in the scrambled list. Again, follow the order of the details in the paragraph. The topic outline should have the same basic organization and content that you used in the mapping outline. However, you will need to add a title and a main idea.

topic outline:

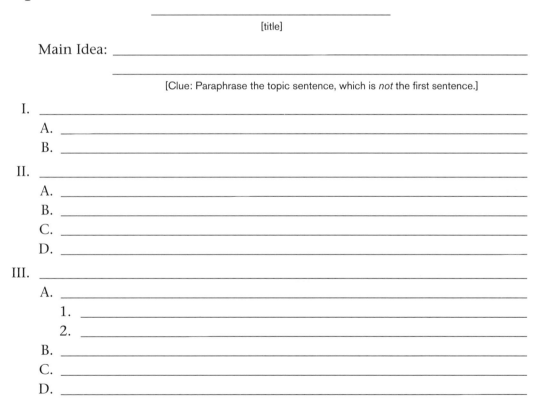

_____
[title]

Main Idea: _____

_____

[Clue: Paraphrase the topic sentence, which is *not* the first sentence.]

I. _____
   A. _____
   B. _____

II. _____
   A. _____
   B. _____
   C. _____
   D. _____

III. _____
   A. _____
      1. _____
      2. _____
   B. _____
   C. _____
   D. _____

_____

*For a long essay or chapter, you might find yourself going into *fourth-level details* with lowercase letters, *fifth-level details* with Arabic numbers in parentheses, or *sixth-level details* with lowercase letters in parentheses.

*The more formal **sentence outline** can be identical to the topic outline, except it uses complete sentences instead of fragments.* You use the same indenting and the same labels to represent the same organization—most important to least important. Details that are parallel in importance have parallel indentation, parallel labels, parallel wording. Some instructors, or employers asking for a business report, may require the more formal, sometimes more detailed *sentence outline*. Obviously, a sentence outline requires writers to think even more clearly and express themselves in complete thoughts. Your instructor may ask you to write sentence outlines in addition to, or instead of, topic outlines.

> **Practice 6**   On your own paper, practice writing a *sentence outline* on the same headache paragraph. Remember, this outline is identical to the topic outline; even the title and the main idea can be the same. Your task is to convert the fragments (below the main idea) into complete sentences.
>
> *Example:* I. <u>Tension headache</u> [from topic outline . . . becomes]
>
> I. <u>One type is the tension headache.</u> [in the sentence outline]

The writer usually chooses which outline type (*mapping, topic,* or *sentence*) to use. You can even mix the three, especially helpful in study notes. What is important is that you use some method of organizing your thoughts, whether in reading, writing, listening, or speaking.

This organization, or outlining, is much easier and more effective if you use what you have learned in earlier chapters. What is the topic? What is the main idea? What logic patterns are used? Which details are major and which minor? What clues are given through transitions and key words?

When you get in the habit of outlining, it becomes an automatic part of your thinking. In reading, this ability to organize your thoughts quickly is guaranteed to help you read faster and understand more.

Note: Your instructor may give you additional practice in outlining from the Instructor's Manual.

Study Notes

On separate paper, write a study outline of this study unit, "Organizing Details." Use any of the three outline types, or use a mixture of all three. Try to be brief and paraphrase the authors' words. Be selective: don't attempt to copy half the information in the article. Use headings and subheadings, boldface and italics, as clues to what is important enough to include in your outline. Make sure you include a clear explanation of the three outline types—both how they are similar and how they are different. Note: Your instructor may give you a partial outline from the Instructor's Manual to get you started.

Outlining a Paragraph

As you read the paragraph, continue to look for logic patterns and connecting words. Be prepared to write all three types of outlines for the one paragraph. Check with the instructor for the model outlines, which are in the Instructor's Manual.

Exercise 5A: Paragraph

[1]Even longtime smokers who finally manage to quit gain a number of benefits. [2]Some of these are important and long-term, whereas other benefits are less dramatic but more immediate. [3]The most important results are the lower risks of having a heart attack or of getting lung cancer. [4]Plus, life expectancy increases in general. [5]The other, more immediate, benefits include ridding the blood of carbon monoxide, which robs it of oxygen. [6]The ex-smoker will also get better sleep and have more energy. [7]The senses, especially taste and smell, will sharpen. [8]And smoker's cough will begin to disappear.

—BASED ON DATA FROM JANE BRODY, THE NEW YORK TIMES GUIDE TO PERSONAL HEALTH.

1. Which sentence (also the most general sentence) is the topic sentence? _1_

2. Write the key words (from the topic sentence) that set up the framework.
   a number _of_ _benefit_.

3. Based on the *mapping* outline below, what are the logic patterns that connect the following:
   (a) between the title and the rectangles? _cause and effect_
   (b) between the two rectangles? _contrast_.
   (c) between the ovals and their rectangles? _example_
   (d) among the ovals? _addition_.
   (e) between the triangles and their oval? _example_

4. Complete the following *mapping* outline of the paragraph's supporting details.

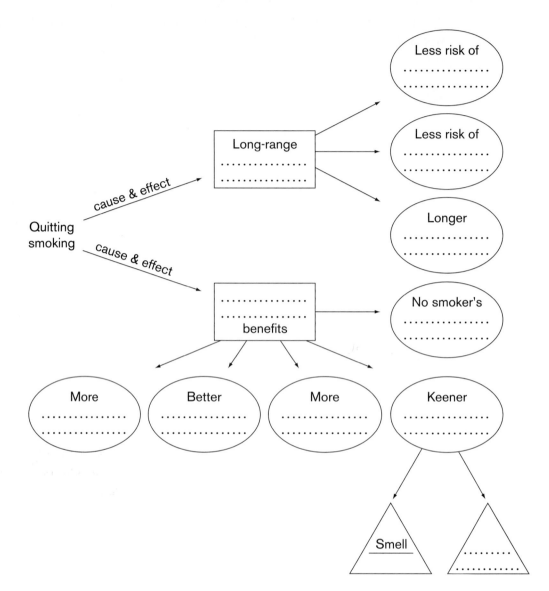

Exercise 5B: Paragraph

Fill in the blanks below to complete the topic *outline on the same paragraph in Exercise 5A. Refer to the* mapping *outline for clues. Remember, the main idea is a complete sentence but, all other items are fragments.*

_____
[title]

Main Idea: _____

_____

   I. Long-range benefits
     A. Less risk of heart attack
     B. _____
     C. _____

  II. _____
     A. _____
     B. _____
     C. _____
     D. _____
        1. Smell
        2. _____
     E. _____

Exercise 5C: Paragraph

On your own paper, write a sentence *outline. Remember, the title, main idea, and the format will be the same as for the* topic *outline, but you will have to convert the fragments in the body of the outline to complete sentences.*

II. How to Read Faster

Assess Your Progress

You are ready now to assess your "Words per Minute" on the Timed Readings. First, turn to the Progress Chart at the end of the Appendix. Do you see a pattern yet to your scores in comprehension and WPM? Notice what has increased and what has decreased over the course of the last three chapters. Is your WPM faster than 250 WPM yet?

First, transfer your Pretest scores for WPM and comprehension to the appropriate lines below. Then transfer your highest scores for Timed Readings in Chapter 3 or 4.

Pretest: WPM _____   Percent Comprehension _____

Chapter 3 or 4: WPM _____   Percent Comprehension _____

Change: WPM _____   Percent Comprehension _____

Now compare your Pretest scores and chapter scores, looking for change. Indicate the amount of change, with a plus (+) sign in front of the change if it is higher, with a minus (-) sign if it is lower.

Set a Goal

Choose which situation best describes your scores.

- Your rate is up by at least 50 WPM, and your comprehension has not fallen below 70 percent. **What to do?** *Congratulate yourself. Set a new goal for WPM. Add another 50–100 words to your WPM. Try to keep the comprehension at the present level, but don't be surprised if it drops at first.*

- Your rate is up by at least 50 WPM, but your comprehension has fallen below 60 percent. **What to do?** *Keep practicing on easy material and see if your comprehension improves. Be sure to study the vocabulary words in the Vocabulary Preview before you start the chapter. Also, make sure you preview with a questioning mind that looks for the big picture. Note: If the material is too difficult, slow down a little.*

- Your rate is the same as on the Pretest, but your comprehension has improved and is 70 percent or above. **What to do?** *You are ready to push much faster. Set a new goal of adding another 50–100 words to your WPM.*

- Your rate and your comprehension have not changed since the Pretest. You're feeling discouraged. **What to do?** *Check your attitude. You may not feel comfortable going faster or changing your habits, and you may be resisting change. Or possibly you have an eye problem or some other condition that is holding you back. In any case, you should speak with your instructor.*

Now fill in the lines below with your new goal for the readings in this chapter. Be realistic. Don't expect that your WPM will double in one week or that your comprehension will shoot up to 100 percent if it has been 50 percent so far. Do expect that, with your best effort, you will make steady improvement.

Goal for WPM: _____   **Goal for Percent Comprehension:** _____

Exercise 5D: Phrases

Make a slash through the phrase identical to the key phrase. **Note:** *All the key phrases follow a modifier-subject-verb pattern (meaning they could be short sentences).*

Key Phrase

1.	his mother waits	her brother walks	his mother waits	the matter waits
2.	the birds sing	the birds sing	the boys sing	the bells ring
3.	the waves crash	the crashing waves	wash the caves	the waves crash
4.	their house burns	the mouse turns	the burning louse	their house burns
5.	a star fell	a star is born	a falling star	a star fell
6.	her plant grew	her new planter	her plant grew	in plain view
7.	his brother cooks	his father's books	his brother cooks	cooking's a bother
8.	all roses die	roses all die	doll in rose	all roses die
9.	the cat purrs	the cat purrs	a purring cat	the fat cat
10.	our father knows	my father knew	a knowing father	our father knows
11.	a girl laughed	a girl laughed	a laughing churl	a girlish figure
12.	the moon rose	the moon race	the moon rose	their mom knows
13.	that door shut	the door slammed	that door shut	that poor hut
14.	my tooth hurts	my horn toots	my toe hurts	my tooth hurts
15.	their ice melted	their ice melted	her eyes squinted	their nice pelt
16.	that dog bites	that dog fights	that dog bites	that bitter dog
17.	the days pass	the passing days	the daisy's petals	the days pass
18.	a spider toils	the soup boils	a sprained toe	a spider toils
19.	my goat left	my good leg	my little goat	my goat left
20.	the story ended	the storybook ending	the story ended	the ending stinks

Time _35"_

Number of Errors _2_

Reading Faster and Understanding More, Book Two   **169**

Exercise 5E: Phrases

Make a slash through the phrase identical to the key phrase. **Note:** *All the key phrases follow an adjective-adjective-noun pattern.*

Key Phrase

1. big red barn	big old bear	big red barn	red barn door
2. quiet rainy day	quiet rainy day	quite a day	quite high pay
3. soft little hand	sold the band	soft little hand	soft little man
4. crisp white dress	crisp salad dressing	cruel wild deed	crisp white dress
5. smooth clean skin	smooth clean skin	most clean skin	some skin cleanser
6. cloudy gray sky	clear gay eyes	cloudy gray sky	clouds in the sky
7. fresh young thing	fears your ring	things from youth	fresh young thing
8. bright new lamp	big new lamp	light new blimp	bright new lamp
9. rich old lady	itchy old lady	rich old lady	tickle the lady
10. ancient torn book	ancient tame bear	ancient torn book	any torn book
11. smart eager girl	small eager gulls	good smooth eggs	smart eager girl
12. calm cool nurse	calm cool nun	calm cool nurse	calm down, nurse
13. strong hot sun	strong hot sun	hot sunny strand	strong hot tea
14. nimble quick fingers	fine green thimble	nimble quick fingers	nice quick fingers
15. full soft lips	full soft lips	full red tulips	fail to tip
16. blue china bowl	blue china chest	blue china bowl	big china bull
17. tiny sharp teeth	tiny sharp teeth	tiny shark jaws	two sharp teams
18. small beady eyes	big eager smiles	small beady eyes	eye some beads
19. fast funny jokes	four fast jokes	jokes for fun	fast funny jokes
20. good ole boy	buy good oil	good ole boy	dead ole boy

Time _____ 30″

Number of Errors _____

Outlining Essays

The first selection is the traditional five-paragraph essay, the type that might be written by a freshman composition student. The second was written *for* students. As you read, try to pick out the framework to make outlining easier. Also, notice how outlining a paragraph (in the Paragraph Practice) is similar to outlining an essay.

IN A PARAGRAPH		IN AN ESSAY
topic sentence	→	introduction with thesis
supporting details	→	supporting paragraphs (each often with its own topic sentence and supporting details)
concluding sentence (maybe)	→	concluding paragraph (usually)

Exercise 5F: Timed Reading

308 words

Preview: *Quickly survey the title, the first paragraph, the first sentence of the next three paragraphs, and the last paragraph. Write here what you think the thesis is and at least one supporting point. Indent the point.*

_____

_____

Wait for a signal from your instructor before you begin reading. Try to finish in less than one minute, if you can. Circle your reading time and find your WPM *when finished.*

Quest for Total Beauty

Two years ago, my cousin Janie moved to Los Angeles from a small town in Iowa. Proud of her fresh, natural looks, I showed her off to my friends at the beach and some of my favorite clubs. Janie took one look at L.A.'s blond beauties and freaked. To my dismay, she began three unfortunate projects in what she called her quest for total beauty.

Janie's first project was her search for perfect hair. I envied the way her hair swung softly whenever she moved her head, but she tortured her lovely, shiny, straight brown hair through two permanents—the first wasn't curly enough. Before her hair had time to recover, she bleached it. Then she streaked it to give it that L.A. sun-damaged look. Her fine hair overreacted and turned an immobile frizzy green.

Last year's project was her nose. She was frugal all year (good for her diet, she said) so she could afford rhinoplastic surgery. She had a distinctive Roman nose that perfectly suited her rather long, thin face. Now she has a cute little nose that seems to belong to someone else's cute little pixie face.

Finally, this year, Janie decided she must have inner peace to achieve outer beauty. I don't think she realized that it was her high-energy drive that made her successful in her sales job. She, in turn, immersed herself in transcendental meditation, yoga, t'ai chi ch'uan, and biofeedback. When she wasn't *ohming*, she was contorting her body into a pretzel. She was so peaceful, as a result,

min:sec	wpm
01:32	200
01:24	220
01:17	240
01:11	260
01:06	280
01:02	300
00:58	320
00:54	340
00:51	360
00:49	380
00:46	400
00:44	420
00:42	440
00:40	460
00:39	480
00:37	500
00:36	520
00:34	540
00:33	560
00:32	580
00:31	600
00:30	620
00:29	640
00:28	660
00:27	680
00:26	700

that she lost her high-pressure sales job—thereby suspending funds for other important beauty projects like facials and manicures.

Janie doesn't go out a lot these days. I told her to chill. If the fashion this summer calls for a tranquil, snub-nosed chick with green hair, she is definitely *in*.

You may refer to the article to answer all of the following questions.

1. Write a complete sentence that states the thesis.

   _____

   _____

   [who?   does what?   why?]   [Clue: Stay objective—no moralizing like "Beauty is as beauty does."]

2. The major patterns are time sequence and (a) _____.

   The minor patterns are description, cause-effect, (b) _____

   [before-after], and (c) _____ [second paragraph].

3–10. Use your organizing skills to complete the *mapping outline* on the next page. Be as brief as possible.

Check your answers and mapping outline with the key, and record your scores below and on the Progress Chart. (Give yourself 10 percent for each correct answer, including the eight answers for the outline.)

Words per Minute _____

Percent Comprehension _____

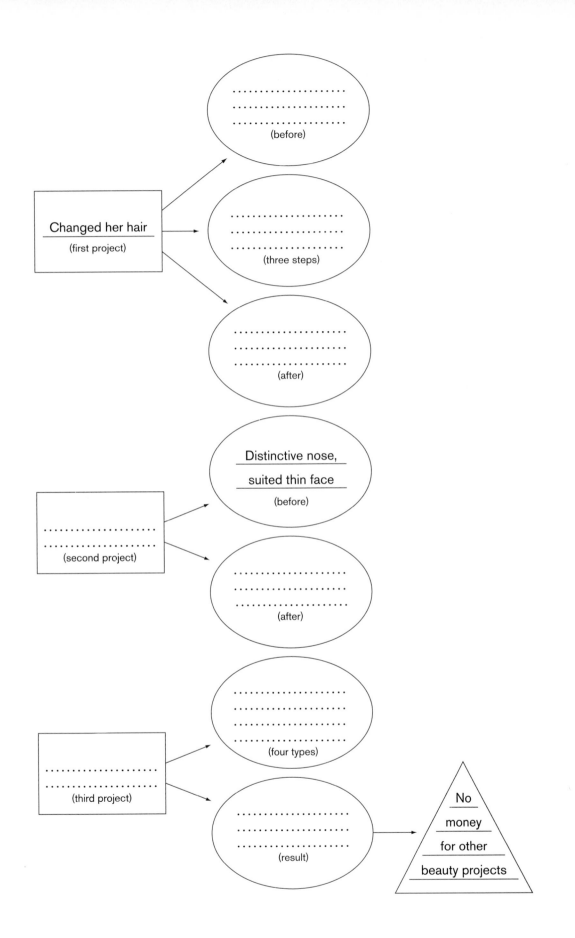

This last selection gives practical advice on how to succeed as a student, while providing practice in a combination of summarizing and outlining. Use the headings and subheadings to help you organize your outline.

Preview: *Quickly survey the title, author's name, first paragraph, and all headings and subheadings.*

(a) *List any advice you remember from your preview:* _____

_____

(b) *How many major headings does this article have?* _____
   How many minor headings? _____

Wait for a signal from your instructor before you begin reading. Circle your reading time when finished, and find your WPM.

Student and Teacher as Partners

W. H. Armstrong, M. W. Lampe, and G. Ehrenhaft

Just as you do, teachers like being treated with respect. There's no need for you to fawn and grovel, but to make a good impression, merely be polite and friendly, and most teachers will respond in kind. When you come to class late, be courteous enough at the end of the period to explain why. When you have returned from an absence, show enough concern to ask the teacher what you have missed and to pick up the homework or other assignments. Like other people, teachers have bad days. Occasionally a class drags, discussion is desultory, students' eye glaze over with boredom. Most teachers know very well when a lesson seems to be stuck. Make it your challenge to come to the rescue. Ask a thoughtful question or make a provocative, but relevant, comment. If you can be the catalyst that wakes up a slumbering class, everyone will be grateful, including your teacher, who won't forget your effort. . . .

What Kind of Student Are You?

How would you classify yourself as a participant in class? In light of the above hints, how would you rate your behavior as a student? Which of the following kinds of students are you?

■ *Would you be an unprepared bluffer?* This is the person who attempts to cover up his ignorance by asking unrelated questions or volunteering unreliable information gathered from television and movies.

■ *Would you be the fluttering magpie?* If you have visited the birdhouse at a zoo, you may remember the magpie, that one obnoxious bird that could remain neither still nor quiet. A student who is like the magpie interrupts constantly, always before he gives any thought to what he is going to say. More often than not, he repeats something that has been stated clearly and thoroughly already, and he repeats it inadequately.

■ *Would you be the sensitive hopeful?* This is the person who has prepared sufficiently to contribute, but is afraid of what the teacher and other students will think of the comment or question.

- **Would you be the accomplished leader?** This is the person who has prepared the assignment, reviewed the essentials, and then established a point of view for possible discussion and a frame upon which to hang the answers to questions asked.

Developing Confidence in Your Abilities

There are many ways to become an accomplished leader. First try to make your attitude the best possible for the class. Then develop confidence in your abilities as a student. Here are some practical hints that will help you become well prepared and secure in your knowledge.

- **Go to class with your assignments prepared.** While this instruction may appear self-evident, it is all too common for students not to follow it, to prepare little or to prepare sloppily. One way to check up on yourself is to ask yourself questions that will help to reveal the quality of your work.

  To judge the quality of your written work, ask yourself these three questions. *First, am I pleased with what I have done?* It is futile to present work that identifies you as sloppy and indifferent. If your paper lacks form, neatness, and completeness, and you are content to turn it in, you are putting yourself on record as a person lacking in self-respect, willing to deal in mediocrity, whose sole aim is to get by. *Second, will my work satisfy the teacher?* Make sure that, even if you cannot complete the assignment, your work reflects sufficient responsibility and effort to portray your desire to do the very best of which you are capable. Follow carefully all the "mechanical" instructions: use appropriate paper, put the heading in the proper place, follow the specific instructions your teacher has given for the assignment. *Third, will my work be judged the best paper in the class?* Others may have more mastery of the subject, but no one can prevent you from making your best effort. Your teacher very quickly learns your capabilities and assesses the kind of effort you put forth. A good effort, even if you miss many answers, is a great booster of marks. . . .

- **Go to class with the proper tools.** Take your textbook. If you do not bring the text, you are revealing your lack of interest as flagrantly as if you wore a placard inscribed, "I HAVE NO INTEREST IN THIS CLASS." Take notebook, pen or pencil (well sharpened), pad for recording assignments, and special necessary tools such as compasses, protractors, calculators, and lab notebooks. If you were playing center field, and inning after inning went out without your glove, do you think your coach would keep you on the team for very long? Imagine going to a music lesson and forgetting to take your instrument or music. Arriving at a class without the tools will very quickly put you off the team or out of the lesson.

- **Follow instructions.** Write down, *clearly,* your assignments in a division of your notebook set aside for assignments or in a special assignment pad. Make sure you write down and follow the general instructions your teacher gives about the format for work done in the course. If your teacher asks, for example, for your name to be in the upper right-hand corner of the paper, put it there, every time.

TIMING CHART

min:sec	wpm
04:03	200
03:59	220
03:39	240
03:22	260
03:08	280
02:57	300
02:44	320
02:35	340
02:26	360
02:18	380
02:11	400
02:05	420
01:59	440
01:54	460
01:50	480
01:45	500
01:41	520
01:37	540
01:34	560
01:31	580
01:28	600
01:25	620
01:22	640
01:20	660
01:17	680
01:15	700
01:13	720
01:11	740
01:09	760
01:07	780
01:06	800

You may refer to the article to answer all of the following questions.

1. Choose the sentence that best expresses the thesis of this article.
   (a) If you sign a contract with your teacher promising to follow instructions, you will succeed in class.
   (b) To succeed as a student, cooperate with your teacher by being a prepared, confident participant in class.
   (c) A confident, polite student will win over the teacher every time.
   (d) Always go to class with homework done neatly and with appropriate tools, and you will succeed as a student.

2. Two major logic patterns are *cause* and *effect*. What is the logic pattern represented by the subheadings in italics and boldface, underneath the heading "Developing Confidence in Your Abilities"? _____

3–20. Use your organizing skills to complete this combination outline (part topic, part sentence, part summary). Include all headings and subheadings, and write a short summary under each one. As much as possible, paraphrase the author's words.

Introduction:
   A. _____
   B. _____

I. What kind of student are you?
   A. Would you be an unprepared bluffer?

   _____

   _____
   [Write a brief summary of information found under the first subheading.]

   B. _____
   [Use second subheading in italics and boldface.]

   _____

   _____
   [Summarize information under the second subheading.]

   C. _____

   _____

   _____

   D. _____

   _____

   _____

II. _____
   [Use second major heading.]

   A. _____
   Ask yourself three questions:

   _____

   _____

   _____

   B. _____

   _____

   _____

C. _____
_____
_____
_____

Check your answers for question 1 and 2 and for the 18 items in your outline with the key. (The questions and the items in the outline are worth 5 percent each.) Record your scores below and on the Progress Chart.

Words per Minute _____

Percent Comprehension _____

Writing and Discussion Activities

Another key skill in organizing and remembering details is the ability to summarize accurately. A summary is a brief restatement of the main points in something you read or hear. In certain ways, a summary is like an outline. It contains the author's most important points about a topic. It also has supporting details where necessary to clarify a point. But a summary sometimes appears in the form of a paragraph or essay, not in the numbered form of an outline. Additional discussion of summary, with practice, is in the Instructor's Manual.

1. Working as a team with the person sitting next to you, first list the important points in Timed Reading 5F. Then, working by yourself, use this list to write a one-paragraph summary in your own words. Start your summary by stating the thesis of the selection. Then present the first level details. Use additional supporting details if a point is not clear without them. **Writing tip:** to keep your sentences from sounding choppy, use transitions as you move from one point to the next.

2. Reread any of the Timed Readings in Chapters 1 through 4, and write a one-half to one-page summary.

Vocabulary Review, Chapter 5

Match the vocabulary word on the left with its definition on the right. Write the letter of the answer in the short blank to the left.

___d___ 1. **fawn** (a) half-hearted

___a___ 2. **desultory** (b) obviously

___e___ 3. **transcendental** (c) engraved

___c___ 4. **inscribed** (d) flatter too much

___b___ 5. **flagrantly** (e) rising above

*Choose the definition for each **boldfaced** word as it is used in its context.*

___b___ 6. The cowboy's efforts to lasso the cow were **futile**; the rope slipped off its neck every time.
(a) skilled   (b) useless   (c) clumsy

___c___ 7. The surgeon moved her instruments with **precision**.
(a) quickness   (b) assistance   (c) exactness

___b___ 8. **Invariably**, Bob got a raise from his boss when he requested one.
(a) sometimes   (b) always   (c) surprisingly

___c___ 9. The teenage girl became so hysterical over her favorite movie star's marriage that her brother had to tell her to **chill**.
(a) get mad   (b) get even   (c) calm down

___a___ 10. The driver's behavior was **obnoxious**; he kept honking his horn and trying to pass us.
(a) detestable   (b) dangerous   (c) aggressive

*Mark each sentence to show whether the **boldfaced** word is used correctly.*

a = True   b = False

___F___ 11. Plants produce **carbon monoxide**, which helps purify the air we breathe.

___T___ 12. Trying to be **frugal**, Bob emptied his bank account and bought a second convertible.

___F___ 13. Lisa decided her belly was so large that she should have **rhinoplastic** surgery.

___T___ 14. She tearfully apologized again and again for wrecking her brother's car, but he forced her to **grovel** for weeks before he forgave her.

___T___ 15. Joan created a quiet, **tranquil** atmosphere in her home at night so she could go to sleep easily.

(Continued)

Choose the word from the box that fits the context of the following paragraph. Write the letter of each choice on the blank lines to the left of the paragraph.

(a) **immediate**	(b) **catalyst**	(c) **climate**
(d) **mediocrity**		(e) **slumbering**

___C___ 16.   The _(16)_ on campus has changed in numerous ways in the last

___d___ 17. two decades. The _(17)_ concern of many students is to earn a degree,

___b___ 18. seen as a ticket to a good job. This greed for money, not for knowl-

___a___ 19. edge, is the _(18)_ for too many students. Instead of striving for

___e___ 20. excellence, they are willing to settle for _(19)_ . Instead of attending

class, these students often can be found _(20)_ in their beds.

% Correct _____

Comprehension Review, Chapter 5

Match the outline type with its description on the right.

C   1. mapping outline

(a) made up of fragments, except for the main idea (or thesis)

a   2. topic outline

(b) made up of complete sentences, except for the title

b   3. sentence outline

(c) made up of figures, like rectangles and ovals, and of arrows

Read the paragraph below (from Chapter 3), answer the two questions, and complete the outline on the next page.

[1]What's your girlfriend doing right now? [2]Or your sister? [3]Or your mother, for that matter? [4]Chances are good that she's got her nose deep in a type of book that tops the list of best-sellers week after week. [5]These women are reading the historical romance, a kind of novel that's really more romance than it is history. [6]What's the big attraction? [7]For one thing, it has characters larger than life. [8]These handsome, brave, tight-lipped heroes make Clint Eastwood look like a wimp. [9]And their full-bosomed, flashing-eyed heroines are every bit their match—though these spunky woman would make a modern feminist cringe at their tendency to turn to mush in their hero's manly arms. [10]Another appeal is the novels' dramatic action. [11]Pirates! [12]Kidnapping! [13]Close calls! [14]Of course, these novels' special appeal is their exotic settings. [15]They take place in exotic locations such as southern plantations, sultans' harems, kings' courts—during earlier, exciting times we've read about in history books. [16]Could it be that these books—so popular with women—tell us something important about what we've lost? [17]Are we tired of being tame city dwellers, mired in routine? [18]Do we long for the brave deeds and bold kisses of a more romantic time gone by?

4. What logic pattern connects the major details in the rectangles?
        example

5. List the three transitions from the paragraph that connect those same three major details.
   For 1 thing   Another   of course
                    appeal

(Continued)

6–10. Finish the *mapping outline.*

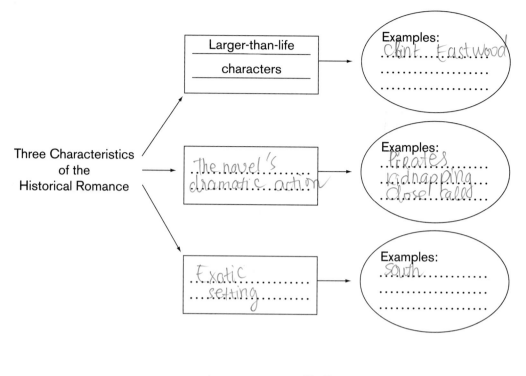

	Larger-than-life characters	Examples: Clint Eastwood
Three Characteristics of the Historical Romance	The navel's dramatic action	Examples: Pirates kidnapping close calls
	Exotic setting	Examples: South

% Correct _____

VOCABULARY PREVIEW for Chapter 6

Directions: *Examine the **boldfaced** word as it is used in the sentence and write your best guess of the word's meaning. Then look up the word in your dictionary and write the best definition for its context in the sentence.*

a	cat	ā	made	ä	bar	k	cot, **q**uit			adore
e	pet	ē	these	â	care	s	cent			travel
i	sit	ī	ride	è	term	z	beds	ə	{	horrify
o	rot	ō	note	ô	order	j	giant			pardon
u	nut	ōō	rude	ŏŏ	foot	th	thank			circus
u̇	put	yōō	use	ōō	food	ŦH	this			

from Paragraph 6A (p. 197)

1. **dogma** (dôg′ mə)   *noun*

   Although few questioned the Church's **dogma** on creation, one small departure from this idea was suggested in 1753 by Linnaeus's French **contemporary**, Georges-Louis Leclerc de Buffon (1707–1788).

   Your best guess: _____

   Best dictionary definition: _____

2. **contemporary** (kən tem′ pə rer′ ē)   *noun*

   Your best guess: _____

   Best dictionary definition: _____

   [Note: See sentence #1 for context clues to **contemporary**.]

   [Clue: The word is used as a noun, a "person," not an adjective.]

from Paragraph 6B (p. 198)

3. **fixity** (fik′ sə tē)   *noun*

   A decade later, someone else joined the doubters of the **fixity** of species.

   Your best guess: _____

   Best dictionary definition: _____

4. **heralded** (her′ əld id)   *verb*

   In his ramblings, he referred almost incidentally to certain relationships among animals that, strangely, **heralded** a number of important ideas that would later be embraced by Charles [Darwin].

   Your best guess: _____

   Best dictionary definition: _____

5. **heritability**   (her′ ə tə bil′ ə tē)   *noun*

   Among these [ideas] were the importance of competition in the forma-tion of species, the effect of environment on changes in species, and the **her-itability** of these changes.

   Your best guess: _____

   Best dictionary definition: _____

6. **musings**   (myoo′ zingz)   *noun*

   The influence [of Darwin's grandfather] may not have been very great because Charles apparently never had much use for the **musings** of his grandfather.

   Your best guess: _____

   Best dictionary definition: _____

from Paragraph 6C (p. 199)

7. **era**   (ir′ ə)   *noun*

   Other people of that **era** were also beginning to toy with the notion of the changeability of species.

   Your best guess: _____

   Best dictionary definition: _____

8. **protégé**   (prō′ tə zhā)   *noun*

   Jean Baptiste de Lamarck [a **protégé** of Buffon's] boldly suggested that not only had one species given rise to another, but that humans themselves had arisen from other species.

   Your best guess: _____

   Best dictionary definition: _____

9. **fossil**   (fos′ əl)   *adjective*

   Lamarck also observed that the **fossil** animals found in older layers of rocks seemed to be somewhat simpler than those in more recently deposit-ed rock.

   Your best guess: _____

   Best dictionary definition: _____

10. **surmised**   (sər mīzd′)   *verb*

    He couldn't immediately account for how such changes might have arisen, but he finally **surmised** that there was some "force of life" that caused an organism to generate new structures or organs to meet its biolog-ical needs.

    Your best guess: _____

    Best dictionary definition: _____

from Timed Reading 6F (p. 206)

11. **writhing**   (rī TH′ ing)   *verbal*

    Struggling and **writhing**, the young man lay on his back, his arms and legs *flailing* in the cool Argentine air.

    Your best guess: _____

    Best dictionary definition: _____

12. **flailing**   (flāl′ ing)   *verbal*

    Your best guess: _____

    Best dictionary definition: _____

13. **exuberant**   (eg zōō′ bər ənt)   *adjective*

    He was happy and **exuberant** these days.

    Your best guess: _____

    Best dictionary definition: _____

14. **beatitudes**   (bē at′ ə tōōdz′)   *noun*

    He seemed to be more concerned with beetles than **beatitudes**.

    Your best guess: _____

    Best dictionary definition: _____

15. **prowess**   (prou′ is)   *noun*

    Darwin's academic **prowess** had been so thoroughly unremarkable that at one point, his father had told his *trifling* son, "you care for nothing but shooting, dogs, and rat catching."

    Your best guess: _____

    Best dictionary definition: _____

16. **trifling**   (trī′ fling)   *verbal (used as adjective)*

    Your best guess: _____

    Best dictionary definition: _____

17. **desolate**   (des′ ə lit)   *adjective*

    The *Beagle* [a ship] reached South America and headed down the coast . . . finally turning northward along the **desolate** coasts of Chile and Peru.

    Your best guess: _____

    Best dictionary definition: _____

18. **gauchos**   (gou′ chōz)   *noun*

    Darwin, an excellent rider himself, soon developed the greatest respect for the riding skills of the rugged **gauchos** who often accompanied him.

    Your best guess: _____

    Best dictionary definition: _____

19. **tenets**   (ten' its)   *noun*

   The physical sciences were less hampered by religious **tenets**.

   Your best guess: _____

   Best dictionary definition: _____

20. **motley**   (mot' lē)   *adjective*

   Among these were a **motley** group that were not unlike the finches he had collected on the South American mainland.

   Your best guess: _____

   Best dictionary definition: _____

21. **withering**   (hwiŦH' ər ing)   *verbal (adjective)*

   It is important to realize that Darwin developed his idea not only in the face of **withering** opposition, but also without hard proof.

   Your best guess: _____

   Best dictionary definition: _____

22. **paltry**   (pôl' trē)   *adjective*

   Although Darwin feared he might be "scooped," he asked that Wallace be permitted to present his paper first and receive credit for the idea, rather than have anyone think he had behaved in a "**paltry** spirit."

   Your best guess: _____

   Best dictionary definition: _____

23. **psychosomatic**   (sī' kō sə mat' ik)   *adjective*

   His infirmities have been diagnosed time and again by medical historians who first suggested that they were **psychosomatic**.

   Your best guess: _____

   Best dictionary definition: _____

24. **facetiously**   (fə sē' shəs lē)   *adverb*

   Lord Wilburforce, a clergyman, **facetiously** asked Huxley in a debate if he was related to the apes on his father's or his mother's side.

   Your best guess: _____

   Best dictionary definition: _____

25. **fray**   (frā)   *noun*

   Of course, Darwin's defenders did not join the **fray** empty-handed.

   Your best guess: _____

   Best dictionary definition: _____

Exercise, Vocabulary Preview, Chapter 6

Directions: *Choose the best definition for each **boldfaced** word as it is used in its context.*

a 1. George's biggest problem was the church **dogma**, which he found too rigid to fit into his life of pleasure.

   (a) body of beliefs (b) dress code (c) elaborate ceremonies

c 2. My daughter and her **contemporaries** have no idea who Captain Kangaroo and Mr. Green Jeans are, since they grew up in the time of Big Bird and Elmo.

   (a) friends (b) enemies (c) peers

b 3. Before Darwin's theories on how people evolve and change, most people instead believed in the **fixity** of human beings.

   (a) changeability (b) stability (c) ability

b 4. Many newspapers have the word "**herald**" in their titles to suggest that they are the official presenters of the news.

   (a) listen (b) announce (c) praise

b 5. Cynical people have argued against the **heritability** of complex human traits such as kindness, gentleness, and evil.

   (a) validity (b) existence (c) passing on

c 6. The **musings** of Henry David Thoreau about nature and a solitary life in *Walden Pond* affected a generation of Americans.

   (a) musical style (b) comedy (c) deep thoughts

a 7. The **era** of Ronald Reagan signifies big business and big money to many people.

   (a) time period (b) politics (c) presidency

b 8. Dr. Masten's **protégé**, Kurt, never let his public opinions contradict those of his protector.

   (a) son (b) special student (c) employee

c 9. **Fossils** found in the layers of the Grand Canyon gave scientists evidence of prehistoric life.

   (a) insect larvae (b) history books (c) imprints of organisms

a 10. Alfred **surmised** that his neighbor, Ella, had left him the birthday cake in his absence, for he recognized her china pattern on the empty cake plate.

   (a) guessed (b) knew (c) hoped

c 11. The badly injured man lay, **writhing** in pain, beside his wrecked car.

   (a) screaming (b) howling (c) twisting

_a_ 12. Susan's father threw her in the pond to teach her to swim, but her **flailing** about in the water scared the fish.

(a) thrashing   (b) crying   (c) yelling

_b_ 13. Tracy felt **exuberant** after winning the swimming trophy she had worked toward for so long.

(a) disappointed   (b) high-spirited   (c) exhausted

_b_ 14. It comforted Christy to recite the **beatitudes** whenever she felt blessed after suffering a long depression.

(a) song lyrics   (b) Bible verses   (c) Girl Scout oath

_c_ 15. The Amazing Amazon's **prowess** as a wrestler was legendary; she was rarely challenged.

(a) record   (b) weakness   (c) ability

_a_ 16. Thinking that he was being romantic, Joey gave Vanessa lots of **trifling** gifts, which she often threw in the trash unopened, confident that they were as worthless as he was proving to be.

(a) insignificant   (b) wonderful   (c) poisonous

_a_ 17. The drive through **desolate** farmland in late November made Sam feel sad and lonely.

(a) deserted   (b) damaged   (c) fruitful

_c_ 18. The tanned, dashing Señor Orozco was modest about his days as a **gaucho** on his father's ranch in South America.

(a) chef   (b) carpenter   (c) cowboy

_a_ 19. George lived by one simple **tenet**: fair play.

(a) rule   (b) game   (c) command

_c_ 20. Charlie Brown has a **motley** collection of players on his team, including his dog, Snoopy.

(a) talented   (b) special   (c) varied

_b_ 21. His fifth-grade teacher gave him a **withering** look when he handed her his report, since it was dirty, stained, and looked as if the dog had been chewing on its corners.

(a) warm   (b) tired   (c) angry

_b_ 22. The cost of the zirconium diamond engagement ring was **paltry** when compared with what he might have paid for a real diamond.

(a) costly   (b) insignificant   (c) ridiculous

_a_ 23. Her family convinced her that the pain in her left leg must be **psychosomatic** since the doctors couldn't find any medical explanation.

(a) in her head   (b) physical   (c) severe

_c_ 24. After watching her teenage son devour half the pie she had planned to serve for dinner, she asked him **facetiously** if he would like a little dinner with his dessert.

(a) quietly   (b) angrily   (c) jokingly

b 25. The girls could not bear to stand by and watch their dates being beaten by the muggers; so, with umbrellas poised, they fearlessly entered the **fray**.

(a) store (b) battle (c) storm

Number of Errors _____

Chapter 6
PRO and Study-Outlining

I. How to Understand More

Note: *Perphaps, more than in any other chapter, you need to preview and check important points before you begin study-reading.*

PRO and Study-Outlining

This chapter provides you with the opportunity to put it all together. You are now ready to tackle the most difficult reading material in the book, using what you have already learned (about previewing, reading actively, and taking study notes). You will apply the expanded PRO study method (introduced briefly in Chapter 1) to a college textbook chapter. This reading material is to be "studied," not read to build speed. Your study notes on this reading will be more detailed and will reflect what you have learned about outlining.

Why PRO?

Before answering "Why *use* PRO?"—we might consider the answer to "why the *name* PRO?" It is to help you remember it. *PRO* is an *acronym*, or a word formed from the first letters of several words.

P = **P**repare
R = **R**ead
O = **O**rganize

Another example of an acronym is MADD (Mothers Against Drunk Driving). Like MADD, which implies that these mothers are angry, the name PRO has an underlying purpose. PRO is also an abbreviation of a word meant to remind you of study-reading. PRO is the abbreviation of "professional." The authors intend for you to associate PRO with people you admire, like pro-basketball players or professional musicians. In this context, of course, the pro is a professional _____. This memory association is called a *mnemonic* device. What other memory tricks are being used in this passage? _____. (*Clue:* How many times have you read the term PRO now?)

The point then is that *experienced scholars use a study technique like PRO.* It provides that extra push that takes them from average to excellent, from a C to an A. It forces them to read *actively* instead of *passively*.

Most untrained students begin a reading assignment in a textbook "cold." Instead of using the *preview* method, they begin reading the first word of the material and continue passively until they reach the last word. They pass their eyes over page after page, recognizing words but not processing them into ideas. They read without system, without questioning, without much interest. Result: They finish reading with little idea of what they have read.

So these inexperienced students reread, again passively. They find it necessary to *regress* more than usual. Or they may become active enough to mark with a felt-tip pen everything they "guess" is important. We all have seen these "yellow pages"; almost every line has been highlighted, with false hopes that the information will magically move from felt-tip pen, up the arm, and into the brain. These students make no distinction between major and minor points, or *first-level* and *second-level* details. They cannot recite the content in any organized way because they have not seen any logical connection between ideas or details. Some have difficulty reciting any point because it has no meaning for them.

Usually they complain, "I just can't get into this subject" or "I study and study, but I can't remember anything."

If this sounds like you, try the PRO method. It forces you to wake up. It forces you to challenge yourself. It forces you to organize your thoughts before, during, and after you read—and to organize in your own words. Try to take study notes that are so concise and so well-organized that you can use your notes—instead of the textbook chapter itself—for review.

How to PRO

Before you begin study-reading, *set your goals*. Select a short unit within a chapter that you know you can "read and absorb" in the time available for you to study. A unit should be any clearly marked section of your book, such as one chapter or the pages between two large or prominent subheadings. You must allow yourself time for all three steps in this study period.

Step 1. P = Prepare

This step will bring to light the topic and main ideas. Some experts call this first step *prereading, preview, survey,* or *overview.* You have been practicing this on every Study Unit and Timed Reading in this book. Whatever you call it, it means to read selectively and aggressively—and to skip selectively. Preparing gives you some background on your reading material so you don't have to read it "cold." It makes you think. It arouses your interest and makes your mind receptive. The idea is to "start with the large" before you "fill in the small." See the skeleton, the major patterns. What logic pattern holds the ideas together? Is it addition? Is it *cause* or *effect*? See the whole so the parts will have meaning for you.

First, **look over the unit to be studied**. Consider carefully the title or chapter heading, the author, and subheadings (or subtitles—used to indicate divisions within the unit). Become familiar with any system of print or numbering used to show the importance and relationships of the subheadings. Note size, color, and position of subheadings. Are they in boldface print or italics? (Examine the system used in this article.) Next, read the introduction or first paragraph. Then read the first one or two sentences underneath each subheading (or in each paragraph if you have time). Remember that these first sentences usually contain the topic sentences. Finally, read the summary or last paragraph. If time permits, look over illustrations, charts, graphs, and questions at the end of the unit.

Second, **stop to digest the information you know at this point**. Think over what you have surveyed. In 70 to 90 percent of most informative prose, you will have a good idea of the general content. You will know the author's topic, main idea, and important supporting ideas (or *first-level details*). You should also have picked up some idea of the author's organization. Do you remember many details? If you do, you were not selective enough in your skipping. Don't read the details until Step 2 (R = Read).

Third, to prepare even more aggressively, **ask yourself questions about your preview or start your outline**. What does the title or topic mean? How many subdivisions are there? How do these develop the author's main idea? How much of this do you know already? How does the knowledge fit into the course? Into your life? At the very least, mentally turn the title and subheadings themselves into questions. Or you might jot down a list of the questions—perhaps some questions that might appear on a test. For really effective studying, you can write the questions down as the first stage of a rough outline. But leave room between each question for important notes you will fill in after you actually read the unit.

An alternative to starting an outline is to begin a system of study notes on index cards. For example, on the front of small index cards, you might write the italicized terms, *acronym* and *mnemonic,* that you saw in your preview. As a part of the last step of PRO, you will be able to write definitions and examples on the backs of the cards. Another example is to use larger index cards, or cards in a different color, for important or difficult ideas. Or formulate questions from your preview that you expected to be answered when you finish reading this article.

sample:

(front, unlined side of index card)

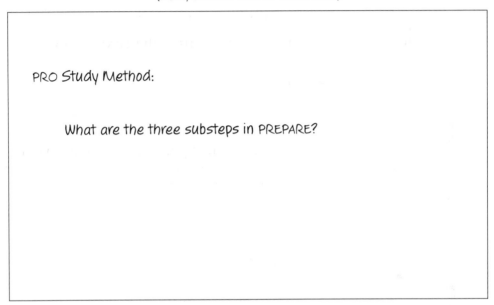

PRO Study Method:

What are the three substeps in PREPARE?

Step 1—Prepare—enables you to approach the actual reading with an inquiring mind. It forces you to become involved with the subject, even though you may think you have no interest in it.

Step 2. R = Read

Read through the entire study unit without stopping, from the title or section heading to the end. As you read, relate the main ideas to the supporting details. Allow what you know about the author's organization or framework to aid you. Keep a pencil in your hand to make a quick checkmark next to important ideas as you read. But do not stop to underline or take notes. This will interrupt your train of thought. Save your underlining and note-taking for Step 3.

Step 3. O = Organize

Finally, to make the most of the first two steps, you must organize the information you have previewed and read.

First, ***digest what you have read*** to implant firmly in your memory the most important ideas. "How" you digest depends on the subject matter and your needs. It also depends on your ability to organize your thoughts mentally, orally, or on paper. At the very least, go over in your thoughts what you have read; that is, repeat the main points to yourself. A more effective way is to tell someone else, perhaps another student with whom you are studying. This forces you to clarify your thoughts even more.

Second, the most effective way to organize your thoughts is to **finish your outline, or at least take notes**. If you started the framework of an outline in Step 1, you now fill in the supporting details. How many of your questions from Step 1 were answered? Show by labeling and indenting the difference between first-, second-, third- (and fourth-, if necessary) level details. (Use the size and type of print of the subheadings as clues for what you should label and indent.) Do not use the author's exact words; use your own. You have not learned anything unless you can tell it in your own words. The key to a good study outline is to be brief but specific. (*Hint:* in your notebook, save a blank page opposite your outline for the teacher's lecture notes on that unit.)

As an alternative to outlining, or as a part of it, finish the note cards you began in the Prepare step.

sample:

(back, lined side of index card)

Substeps for PREPARE:

1. Stop to think about what you read or tell a study buddy.

2. Finish your outline or take notes or finish your note cards.

3. Review what you have organized right away and make improvements.

Third, **immediately review the material you have organized**. This can make the difference between a B or an A on a test. Skim (but do not reread) quickly through the study unit again. Look for any important material you may have remembered wrong or forgotten entirely. Change or add to your outline. Stress what the author seems to stress. Add the notes from the teacher's lecture to your outline. (If you want to be a model student, retype your outline and incorporate the teacher's lecture notes.) Since by now you know what is important and what is not, this is the time to underline or mark in your text or notes. Mark sparingly, no more than once per paragraph (and often less). Make more note cards, or formulate new questions and practice answering them.

Some Short Cuts on PRO

1. **Break your way gently into the PRO method**. Are you in the habit of waiting until the last minute to study? Until the night before the test? Does the PRO technique seem like too radical a shock to your system? Try this. Take five or ten minutes before class to Preview the assigned chapter

"before" the instructor's lecture. Does your attention in class wander as much as it did when you had not prepared at all? (You might think of this skill as pre-PRO.) Does your note-taking seem easier?

2. ***Try a Preview-plus technique on newspaper or magazine articles***. If you get most of your news from television, switch to reading for a few months. Choose an article that interests you, and Preview-plus it. Read the title, author, subheadings, *plus* the first sentence of a few paragraphs. Or, if you frequently read newspapers and magazines, try Preview-plus on articles you might skip because you think you don't have time to read them. This semi-reading will give you at least the main points of the articles. That's more than you got before when you didn't read them. Preview-plus also prepares you for *skimming*, covered in more detail in Chapter 7.

3. ***Preview a book before you buy it or check it out from the library***. Why waste time or money on a book that does not interest you—especially when you have so many choices? Apply the Preview method. For fiction, you might want to preview "more" of the first few pages to see if you like the setting, main characters, and author's style. Of course, you might not want to preview the conclusion, especially of a mystery novel.

When you apply PRO to the following textbook chapter, follow the directions exactly, even if they seem slow and awkward at first. Remember that you will be a PRO—a professional student—only if you learn to use the method with your other course work. PRO provides more flexibility than most study formulas because you can modify it to fit your textbook type, your purpose, and your time limits. Use PRO and you will become more aggressive and directed in this hardest reading task of all—study-reading.

Study Notes

For more practice in outlining and to reinforce PRO, complete the outline below. To reinforce the correct format, write your outline on separate paper. Use the subheadings in the article as clues. Also use clues provided in the study-outline itself. How many levels of details are used in the study-outline? _____

Or, as an alternative, make note cards for difficult terms and for summarizing important ideas.

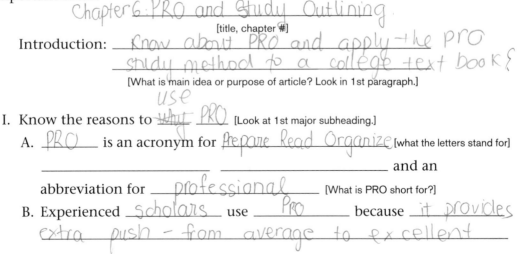

Chapter 6: PRO and Study Outlining.
[title, chapter #]

Introduction: _Know about PRO and apply the pro study method to a college text book?_
[What is main idea or purpose of article? Look in 1st paragraph.]

I. Know the reasons to ~~what~~ *use* PRO [Look at 1st major subheading.]
   A. _PRO_ is an acronym for _Prepare Read Organize_ [what the letters stand for]
   _____ _____ and an
   abbreviation for _professional_ [What is PRO short for?]
   B. Experienced _scholars_ use _PRO_ because _it provides extra push – from average to excellent_

PRO ~~prevent~~ for students in passively

C. ~~Inexperienced study student~~ _____

  1. ~~Regress~~ Don't begin reading cold to ~~warm up~~

  2. Don't know about between major and minor points

          [1 and 2 are how _not_ to study.]

II. Know how to ~~Set PRO~~ goals [2nd major subheading]

  A. Set your goals by ~~3 steps~~ Selecting _____

  B. Learn the steps for PRO:

    1. Step 1 is ___Prepare___, also called _preReading, preview, sur_
          [_not_ Preview]   overv

      a. First, _look over the unit to be studied_ by reading the following:

        (1). _read the introduction_ (3). _topic sentence → find_

        (2). _read sentences under_ (4). _read the summary or las_

      b. _stop to digest the information you know at this_

      c. Third, ask yourself _questions_ or _start your outline_

        (1). _Connect the information to what you know._ [how?]

        (2). _list the questions may on the test_ [how?]

        (3). ~~Study on~~ _Take notes on index cards_ [how?]

           [a,b,c are substeps for Step 1. See boldfaced italics.]

    2. Step 2 is _____ [do what? how?]

      a. Do not _____

      b. Do not _____

    3. Step 3 is _____

      a. _Digest_ _____

        (1). _Repeat the main points in your mind._ [how?]

        (2). _____ [how?]

      b. _Finish_ _____ or _____

        (1). _____ [how?]

        (2). _____ [how?]

      c. _Review_ _____

        (1). _Skim, but do not reread, the section you studied._ [how?]

        (2). _____ [how?]

        (3). _____ [how?]

        (4). _____ [how?]

          [a,b,c are substeps for Step 3. See boldfaced italics.]

III. Try some _____ to using _____. [3rd major heading]

  A. _____

  B. _____

  C. _____

  Conclusion: Use PRO on _____, and become

  _____. [Look at last paragraph.]

(left margin notes:)
(1) how using tittle and subtittle
(2) read introduction

inclue questions in your outline

Studying a Science Textbook

*The three paragraphs, taken from a science chapter about evolution, provide more practice in **study-outlining**, before you apply the PRO method to the whole chapter in Timed Reading 6F. Paragraphs 6A, 6B, and 6C discuss the ideas of three eighteenth century scientists who preceded Charles Darwin. Their ideas departed slightly from the church's widely accepted view of creation. These paragraphs are meant to ease you into the challenge of study-reading a college-level textbook. You will find the paragraphs and the chapter easier to understand if you review the Words in Context for Chapter 6.*

After answering the questions for each paragraph, check the key.

Exercise 6A: Paragraph

Although few questioned the Church's dogma on creation, one small departure from this idea was suggested in 1753 by [Swedish botanist] Linnaeu's French contemporary, Georges-Louis Leclerc de Buffon (1707–1788). In 1753, Buffon proposed that, in addition to those animals that had originated in the creation, there were also lesser families "conceived by Nature and produced by Time." He explained that changes of this kind were the result of imperfections in the Creator's expression of the ideal.

—ROBERT A. WALLACE

1. Paraphrase the first sentence, which is the topic sentence.

   _____

   _____

2. What is being *contrasted* in the paragraph?

   _____ vs. _____

3. Fill in the box below, as if it were the front of an index card you were going to use as a flash card for study.

(front of card)

(name? dates born and died?)

4. Fill in the box below, as if it were the back of the same index card.

(back of card)

His theory: ....
....
....
....
....
....
....
....
....
....
....

(Paraphrase: do *not* use author's exact words)

Exercise 6B: Paragraph

[1][A decade after Buffon's proposal in 1753] someone else joined the doubters of the fixity of species. [2]This was Erasmus Darwin (1731–1802), the grandfather of Charles. [3]Erasmus was a peculiar fellow, not only a physician but an amateur naturalist who wrote about botany and zoology, often in rhyme. [4]In his ramblings, he referred almost incidentally to certain relationships among animals that, strangely, heralded a number of important ideas that would later be embraced by Charles. [5]Among these were the importance of competition in the formation of species, the effect of environment on changes in species, and the heritability of these changes. [6]As you might expect, there has been a great deal of speculation on the extent to which Charles may have been influenced by Erasmus. [7]However, the influence may not have been very great because Charles apparently never had much use for the musings of his grandfather.

—ROBERT A. WALLACE

1. In as few words as possible, paraphrase the second, third, and fourth sentences to express the main idea of this paragraph. (Include only the most important details.)

   _____

   _____

   _____

   _____

2. Briefly summarize three of Erasmus Darwin's ideas.

(a) _____

_____

(b) _____

_____

(c) _____

_____

Exercise 6C: Paragraph

[1]Other people of that era [mid and late eighteenth century] were also beginning to toy with the notion of the changeability of species and the heritability of those changes. [2]In France, Jean Baptiste de Lamarck (1744-1829) . . . boldly suggested that not only had one species given rise to another, but that humans themselves had arisen from other species. [3]A passionate classifier, Lamarck held to the old notion that every organism has its position on the "scale of nature"—with humans, of course, firmly at the top, thereby revealed as the highest form of life. [4]Lamarck also observed that the fossil animals found in older layers of rock seemed to be somewhat simpler than those in more recently deposited rock. [5]This difference suggested to him that the older ones had gradually given rise to the more recent ones (or become "higher"). [6]He couldn't immediately account for how such changes might have arisen, but he finally surmised that there was some "force of life" that caused an organism to generate new structures or organs to meet its biological needs. [7]Once formed, such structures continued to develop through use, and their development in the parents was inherited by the offspring. [8]In this way, he said, the structure became perfected in succeeding generations. [9]Lamarck's most famous example of such change was his explanation of how the giraffe developed a long neck. [10]He maintained that the long neck evolved as giraffes of each generation stretched their necks in an effort to reach the topmost branches of trees. [11]He argued that this effort altered the animals' hereditary materials so that a longer neck was passed along to the offspring. [12]This example did not bring him great respect. [13]In fact, it brought guffaws of derision and even today it is cited as a classic case of scientific error.

—ROBERT A. WALLACE

1. Which sentence in the paragraph is the topic sentence? _____

2. Write a complete sentence that states the main idea of this paragraph.

_____

_____

[who?   where?   what time period?   had what theory?]

3. Beginning with sentence #6, which logic pattern is *not* used in Lamarck's "force of life" theory?

(a) example   (b) cause   (c) effect   (d) classification   (e) process

4. Explain Lamarck's theory by finishing the mapping outline.

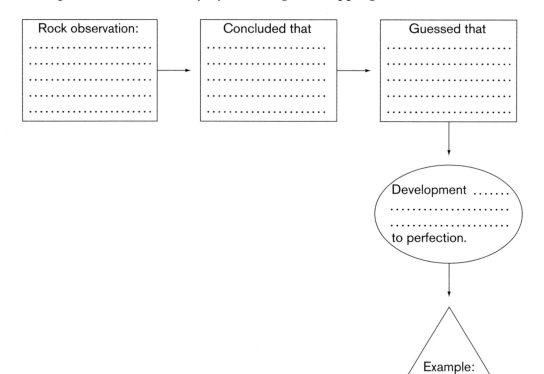

Chapter 6

II. How to Read Faster

In the first half of this book, you have practiced *reading faster* and *understanding more* on mostly easy reading selections. But, in this chapter, you will go further with PRO, the method for study-reading you first began in Chapter 1. You will read and study a unit excerpted from a college textbook. Because your purpose is no longer to read easy material for entertainment, you will need to read at a more careful rate.

Still, you may be pleased to find that the more active approach you have developed in the last five chapters has side benefits. You may find your rate in general has improved, even on difficult material. Also, your vocabulary and comprehension techniques may have improved to the point that you do not have to pause and ponder or reread as much as you once did on harder material.

Adjust Your Speed to Fit Purpose

Speed can vary according to your purpose. Are you studying for a test? Are you reading for pleasure? Notice how difficult material calls for a different approach—or reading process—which necessarily results in a lower rate:

Reading Process	Type of Material	Possible Rates
Study-reading	Textbooks, technical manuals, "how-to" instructions	200–300 WPM
General reading, entertainment	Most magazines, newspapers, easy novels	300–600 WPM
Previewing, skimming for overview	Easy material, review of more difficult material already read	500–800 WPM

Consider Your Attitude

This halfway point in the book is a good place to commit yourself again to this course of study, just as you did in the first chapter. Many people find they can help bring about changes in their lives by making positive statements to themselves on a daily basis. Some people call these statements "affirmations"; some call them "goals." An analysis of the word "affirm" shows us its positive, active direction. The prefix "a" means "toward", and the root "firm" means "strong." Affirmations can be powerful tools to confirm in our own minds the image of how we want to be. For example, as a student you might say:

- I make a conscious effort each day to improve my vocabulary.
- I preview all reading material before I begin reading.
- I always look for the author's logic patterns.
- I am becoming better at reading phrases of meaning, instead of word-by-word.
- I choose to spend more leisure time reading for entertainment.

On the lines below, write two affirmations about your reading and study skills. You will repeat these to yourself each day. You may use some of the affirmations you just read or make up your own.

1. _____

2. _____

Exercise 6D: Phrases

Make a slash through the phrase identical to the key phrase. **Note:** *All phrases follow a verb-modifier-object pattern.*

Key Phrase

1. lights the fire	lights the fire	fired the lady	lights the lamp
2. holds the net	hauls the net	holds the net	held the nut
3. eats a meal	earns a medal	meets an eel	eats a meal
4. plays a game	plays a game	play a gag	gives a play
5. flies a kite	finds a kitten	flies a kite	feeds a bite
6. saves a place	shaves a face	saves a place	saves old lace
7. bakes a cake	bakes a cake	breaks a cup	takes a case
8. waves a flag	waves a flag	flies a flag	waves a wand
9. reads the book	needs the hook	reads the story	reads the book
10. buys a flute	floats a buoy	buys a flute	buys a fluke
11. picks a peach	peels a peach	packs a pickle	picks a peach
12. writes a song	writes a song	writes a poem	rights a wrong
13. pays the bills	bills the pills	pays the bills	pays the piper
14. makes a wish	bakes a fish	makes a wish	wakes a miss
15. jumps a wall	jumps a wall	judges a ball	jabs a wall
16. watches the rain	catches the rein	waters the roses	watches the rain
17. takes a bath	makes a path	takes a bat	takes a bath
18. climbs a tree	climbs a tree	cuts a tree	calls a truce
19. hugs the boy	has a boy	lugs the body	hugs the boy
20. washes her car	waxes his car	washes her car	wipes her cap

Time _____

Number of Errors _____

Exercise 6E: Phrases

Make a slash through the phrase identical to the key phrase. **Note:** *All phrases follow a verb-modifier-object pattern.*

Key Phrase

1.	hits the ball	hates the doll	hits the ball	holds a pail
2.	hides a yawn	hides a yawn	yields the hide	has a yen
3.	crosses the wire	carries the wine	crosses the wire	wires the crosses
4.	toes the line	toes the mark	trails the vine	toes the line
5.	kisses the hand	kisses the hand	heard the wind	kicked the man
6.	sips the drink	skips the drink	spills the ink	sips the drink
7.	shuts the window	shifts the weight	sands the window	shuts the window
8.	rings a bell	rings a bell	sings a ballad	brings a roll
9.	fields the catch	files the latch	fields the catch	fuels the batch
10.	combs his hair	combs his horse	combs his hair	cooks the hare
11.	runs a mile	runs a yard	runs a mile	runs a minute
12.	hears the phone	holds the phone	has the flu	hears the phone
13.	meets a friend	finds a mate	meets a friend	marries a fiend
14.	beats the drum	bears the drill	drums the beat	beats the drum
15.	sails the boat	seal the letter	sails the boat	sells the bat
16.	sees a ghost	sees a ghost	seats a guest	spies a frog
17.	waters the fern	wastes the fuel	waters the fern	watches the fire
18.	leads the way	leads the way	loses the wax	wades the bay
19.	walks the plank	planes the wall	wrote the plan	walks the plank
20.	finds a job	pens a joke	finds a job	finds a judge

Time _____

Number of Errors _____

Apply the PRO Method

Exercise 6F: Timed Reading

The root of the word "science" means "to know." The word still carries that original idea of seeking knowledge. It implies a curiosity in the world around us and a desire to understand. Try to develop that intellectual curiosity as you read about Charles Darwin and his theory that still stirs controversy. This is the longest and most difficult reading in this book; but, if you *apply the PRO method* carefully, you will meet the challenge.

Note: Because of the difficulty of the chapter, it is imperative that you work through the vocabulary words in the Vocabulary Preview, Chapter 6.

Step 1. P = Prepare

Preview or survey the title and introduction, up to the first subheading, or first major division. Note the size and position of that first subheading. Flip through the reading and find the other subheadings that are the same size. How many major divisions does this reading have? _____ Notice size and position of the smaller subheadings, like "Puzzling Change and Variation" and "The Galapagos Islands." Which is more important? _____ Keep this level of importance in mind as you survey the other subheadings. Notice how they connect. Read the first sentences following the headings. Examine the map of Darwin's journey and the chart that puts him into historical perspective. Read the questions in the last paragraph of each major division; they prepare the reader for the next division. Finally, read the summary, all six items; they will tell you what to focus on when you read the chapter.

To digest what you have surveyed, picture Darwin in his setting (place and time). What did you learn about eighteenth-century scientific thinking, about the church's role, and about Darwin the person? Did you notice three major logic patterns—*time sequence* for the narrative and *cause-effect* for influences on Darwin?

Finally, before you go to Step 2, get something down on paper. A minimum effort is to *form some questions based on the survey*. You might convert the major headings to questions. The maximum effort is to *begin your outline* or note cards at the end of the chapter. (See the partial outline on page 218.) Write in at least the subheadings—BUT NO DETAILS UNTIL YOU READ THE WHOLE UNIT. Leave plenty of space between headings for those details to be filled in later. A conservative estimate is one line per paragraph.

Now you are ready to read the chapter. Your investment of time and work will help you concentrate as you read.

Note: Because of time limitations, you may choose to divide the chapter into smaller sections or units, but be sure to divide it between one of the four major subheadings. Or, you may choose to read and outline one unit during each study session.

Step 2. R = Read

Study-read the chapter (or unit) carefully. Read straight through. Do not stop to underline or take notes. Quickly put a check in the margin by any details you may want to add to your outline.

Even though you are not practicing your speed-reading on this chapter, circle your reading time, when you finish the Introduction and first unit on page 209 and find your WPM. You should know what your study-reading speed is; the knowledge helps you plan your study time. Now wait for a signal from your instructor before you begin reading.

A Brief History and the Enchanted Isles

Robert A. Wallace, from Biology: The World of Life

Struggling and writhing, the young man lay on his back, his arms and legs flailing at the cool Argentine air. It was a most curious site. Yet, there he was, twisting convulsively on the ground, dust and bits of glass flying around him. Who could have guessed that this lad, only months earlier, had been walking his dog down an English lane on his way to have lunch with his wealthy uncle? Furthermore, who could have known that this same young man would, years later, throw the entire Western world into an anxious turmoil? And why was he now rolling on the ground?

Curious eyes watched from the Argentine pampas. They had never seen anything like this before. Some animals darted for cover, but one large bird, overcome with curiosity, stepped closer for a better look. As the bird drew nearer, young Charles Darwin, aglow with good health and a crack shot to boot, leaped to his feet, snapped his rifle to his shoulder, and dropped the curious bird on the spot. That night the rhea would be served aboard the good ship, *Beagle*.

This was not the most curious thing that Darwin had ever done. His shipmates, in fact, had come to expect strange things from this bright and energetic young man with his notable strength and amazing endurance. He had climbed hill after hill, just to be the first Englishman to view the magnificent beyond. He relentlessly collected all sorts of plants and animals and would go sleepless, working night and day, to retrieve some fossil before the ship again set sail. His shipmates had marveled at this strength, and their admiration increased when he once saved a group that had become stranded without supplies. He was happy and exuberant these days, but, in time, this was all to change.

But what was young Darwin doing in South America? After all, he was of the British upper class, given to riding and hunting, good food, and an occasional rousing game of blackjack. He was apparently not unusual in most respects and was well liked. But he had not always pleased his father.

Darwin's father was a huge, commanding man, a noted physician of great will and principle. He often wondered aloud about his son, though. He had tried to send Charles to medical school when the boy was 16. But Charles couldn't stand the sight of blood and almost fainted while first witnessing surgery. Then young Darwin tried the clergy. He spent three years at Cambridge studying theology, but even then he spent much of this time wandering around the countryside, adding rocks, insects, feathers, or whatever, to his collections. Indeed, he seemed to be more concerned with beetles than beatitudes. He was not alone in his interest, however. At that time, the English countryside was alive with amateur butterfly collectors, rock hounds, and plant fanciers whose position and wealth permitted them to indulge in such hobbies. Even so, Darwin's academic prowess had been so thoroughly unremarkable that at one point, his father had told his trifling son, "you care for nothing but shooting, dogs, and rat catching, and you will be a disgrace to yourself and all your family."

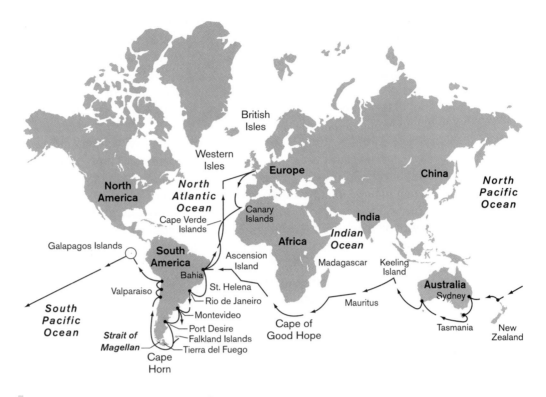

The Voyage of the *Beagle*

It must be admitted that at this point in Charles Darwin's career there was little to suggest that his mind would come to be regarded as one of the most brilliant and inquisitive in history. In a short time, however, this diffident young man was to hear, through his friend the Reverend John Henslow, of an offer of free passage on a survey ship called the *Beagle*. A naturalist companion was needed for a voyage that was to last five years. There would be no pay, and the person chosen would have to sleep in a hammock in the cramped chart room (although he would be permitted to share the captain's table). Armed with Henslow's recommendation, Darwin eagerly applied for the position, but was nearly rejected because of the shape of his nose. Captain Fitzroy, himself only 23, believed that the nose reflected the character of its bearer, and Darwin's nose just didn't show much character.

Darwin's family required some persuasion to accept this "madcap scheme," which they considered scarcely suitable for a prospective clergyman. And evidently, Charles had his own trepidations about such a momentous decision. In a letter to his sister Susan he wrote:

> *Fitzroy says the stormy sea is exaggerated; that if I do not choose to remain with them, I can at any time get home to England; and that if I like, I shall be left in some healthy, safe and nice country; that I shall always have assistance; that he has many books, all instruments, guns, at my service. . . . There is indeed a tide in the affairs of men, and I have experienced it. Dearest Susan, Goodbye.*

Ultimately all the arrangements were made, and in 1831, the H.M.S. *Beagle* set out from Devonport with Charles Darwin gazing, perhaps a bit apprehensively, at the slowly retreating shoreline of his homeland. As the heavy wooden vessel (about the size of a tugboat) creaked and groaned its way across the Atlantic toward South America, Darwin's worst fears were realized. To begin with, shipboard life was tougher than he expected, but worse yet, he tended to

---

get seasick! But he made the best of it, sometimes spending days in his bunk, as the boat continued relentlessly, captained by tough, young Fitzroy, even then, one of the world's best navigators. At long last, the *Beagle* reached South America and headed down the coast on the first leg of its voyage—sailing past the coasts of Brazil and Argentina, weaving through the terrible pounding gales of Cape Horn, and finally turning northward along the desolate coasts of Chile and Peru.

Fortunately, there were periods of respite when the *Beagle* dropped anchor to put foraging parties ashore. Darwin wasted no time getting to land. After resting a bit and regaining his land legs, he was irresistibly drawn deeper into these new places—places that harbored all manner of new and fascinating things. Darwin took copious notes on everything he saw and he brought back to the ship all manner of things, much to the amusement and occasional dismay of the crew. Since the ship sometimes remained anchored for months, he ventured far inland into the wild South American terrain. Darwin, an excellent rider himself, soon developed the greatest respect for the riding skills of the rugged gauchos who often accompanied him.

To understand just what this adventure meant to Charles Darwin (and would later mean to the world), we must stop at this point to consider the state of scientific thinking at that time. What was known of the biological world? What prejudices or beliefs did Darwin have? More important, what seeds of ideas? What hunches? . . .

The Beginnings of Biology

Until the eighteenth century, science was largely limited to topics dealing with the inanimate, such as mathematics, astronomy, and physics. The study of living things was largely exempt from such investigation because of the philosophical and religious influences of that time. After all, it was one thing to search for the physical laws that described salts, stones, or stars, but quite another to probe at the essence of life. Implicit in the reverence for life was the notion that since people are living things, life must surely have some special purpose, some grand design. People simply weren't ready to see themselves as just another physical phenomenon.

In addition, most scientists of that day believed that all species, or kinds, of living things were created in their present form—in other words, that they had not changed during their time on earth. This was certainly the view of the Swedish botanist Carl von Linné (1707–1778), who devised a system of classification for all living organisms, naming them in Latin. In his fondness for Latin, he even called himself Carolus Linnacus.

Although few questioned the Church's dogma on creation, one small departure from this idea was suggested in 1753 by Linnaeus's French contemporary, Georges-Louis Leclerc de Buffon (1707–1788). In 1753, Buffon proposed that, in addition to those animals that had originated in the creation, there were also lesser families "conceived by Nature and produced by Time." He explained that changes of this kind were the result of imperfections in the Creator's expression of the ideal.

Interestingly, a decade later, someone else joined the doubters of the fixity of species. This was Erasmus Darwin (1731–1802), the grandfather of Charles. Erasmus was a peculiar fellow, not only a physician but an amateur naturalist who wrote about botany and zoology, often in rhyme. In his ramblings, he referred almost incidentally to certain relationships among animals that, strangely, heralded a number of important ideas that would later be embraced by Charles. Among these were the importance of competition in the formation of species, the effect of environment on change in species, and the heritability of these changes. As you might expect, there has been a great deal of speculation on the extent to which Charles may have been influenced by Erasmus. However, the influence may not have been very great because Charles apparently never had much use for the musings of his grandfather.

Other people of that era were also beginning to toy with the notion of the changeability of species and the heritability of those changes. In France, Jean Baptiste de Lamarck (1744–1829), a protégé of Buffon's, boldly suggested that not only had one species given rise to another, but that humans themselves had arisen from other species. A passionate classifier, Lamarck held to the old notion that every organism has its position on the "scale of nature"—with humans, of course, firmly at the top, thereby revealed as the highest form of life. Lamarck also observed that the fossil animals found in older layers of rocks seemed to be somewhat simpler than those in more recently deposited rock. This difference suggested to him that the older ones had gradually given rise to the more recent ones (or become "higher"). He couldn't immediately account for how such changes might have arisen, but he finally surmised that there was some "force of life" that caused an organism to generate new structures or organs to meet its biological needs. Once formed, such structures continued to develop through use, and their development in the parents was inherited by the offspring. In this way, he said, the structure became perfected in succeeding generations.

Lamarck's most famous example of such change was his explanation of how the giraffe developed a long neck. He maintained that the long neck evolved as giraffes of each generation stretched their necks in an effort to reach the topmost branches of trees. He argued that this effort altered the animals' hereditary materials so that a longer neck was passed along to the offspring. This example did not bring him great respect. In fact, it brought guffaws of derision and even today it is cited as a classic case of scientific error.

Whereas Lamarck's arguments did little to persuade his lecture audiences, he did create some lively discussions in intellectual circles. (Certain recent findings have revived the discussions in modern scientific circles.) Nineteenth century society at large, however, held to the firm conviction that each form of life had arisen through special creation. The matter seemed settled. The English were more interested in discussing the French Revolution. They were still discussing it when Charles Darwin was born. . . .

Note: Stop here and get your WPM. *Then continue reading.*

Words per Minute _____

The Development of Darwin's Idea of Evolution

When Charles Darwin set out on the voyage of the *Beagle,* he had no quarrel with the prevailing notion that life had originated through special creation and that species were fixed in form. Furthermore, he was aware that many scientists felt that the goal of science should be twofold: first, to discover how nature worked and, second, to use the findings to demonstrate the wisdom of the Creator. Darwin hoped to join in the parade of scientists and clergy as they

TIMING CHART	
min:sec	wpm
10:42	160
09:30	180
08:33	200
07:47	220
07:08	240
06:35	260
06:07	280
05:42	300
05:21	320
05:02	340
04:45	360
04:30	380
04:17	400
04:04	420
03:53	440
03:43	460
03:34	480
03:25	500
03:17	520
03:10	540
03:03	560
02:57	580
02:51	600

marched arm in arm to produce a better world. Instead, he was to reluctantly whistle the parade to a stop.

The Impact of Lyell

Darwin's questions about life did not leave him alone among scientists. The physical sciences were less hampered by religious tenets, and there were signs of rumblings and stirrings in these disciplines, disturbances that would one day make it easier for some to fall into step with Darwin as he slowly marched away from the parade. Among the physical scientists who were also marching to a different drummer and developing bold new ideas about the earth was Charles Lyell (1797–1875) himself only a few years older than Darwin. Lyell had set forth many of his new ideas in his book *Principles of Geology*, the first volume of which was published before the *Beagle* set sail. Darwin had acquired a copy and had asked to have the second volume sent to him en route. Lyell (who was to become a good friend of Darwin) had some rather startling things to say about the physical evolution of the earth. He said that the world was much older than anyone had imagined; that over long periods of time, continents and mountains rose slowly out of the sea; and that they just as slowly subsided again or were washed away. Most importantly, Lyell claimed that the very forces that had so changed the earth in the past were still at work and that the world was still changing.

Darwin's own observation of South American geology seemed to confirm Lyell's position at every hand. In his adventurous climbing of the Andes, he had found fossil clam shells at 10,000 feet. Below them, near an ancient seashore at 8000 feet, he found a petrified pine forest that had clearly once lain beneath the sea because it, too, was interspersed with seashells. In fact, the *Beagle* had arrived in Peru just after a strong local earthquake had destroyed several cities, in some places *raising the ground level by two feet*. The earth had changed and clearly was still changing.

Darwin was excited by his developing idea, but he kept the most revolutionary of his thoughts to himself because he was sometimes uneasy with his ideas and often full of doubts. After all, he had studied for the ministry and had believed in the literal truth of the Bible.

Puzzling Change and Variation

While Darwin continued to divide his time aboard the *Beagle* between reading and hanging over the rail, the heavy, wooden boat had creaked and groaned across the Atlantic and was now making its way up the west coast of South America.

Darwin, of course, darted ashore at every chance, watching, collecting, probing, and taking notes. He was particularly interested in the South American plant and animal life and the fossil beds he found there. Quite early in the voyage he was struck by how living things could vary so markedly from one place to the next. He collected shells from the Atlantic shore and found that they were not like those picked up on the Pacific beaches. He wrote about how birds and mammals differed from one place to the next. He noted that, in some cases, species changed gradually, from one place to another, one type giving way to another almost unnoticeably. But, in other cases, one kind of organism would suddenly disappear, another having appeared in its place. This natural variation that Darwin noticed would play an integral role in the theory that Darwin would develop—after a momentous visit to a small group of islands.

The Galapagos Islands. When the *Beagle* finally left the shores of South America, an impatient Captain Fitzroy, concerned with completing charts, measuring harbors, and preparing the way for British commerce, set the sails of his sturdy craft (a dog to windward) for a straight run to the Galapagos, a chain of islands lying about 580 miles off the coast of Ecuador. It was these remarkable islands that history would most closely associate with an unsuspecting Darwin.

When the anchor clattered into the shallow waters of St. Stephen's harbor of the island the British called Chatham, Darwin scrambled ashore as usual, but as soon as he had looked around, he was almost ready to leave. Chatham was rough, crude, and barren, and he didn't like it. But as he began to explore the place, he encountered a very strange, and even fascinating, assortment of animals. "A little world in itself," he wrote, "with inhabitants such as are found nowhere else." There were lizards three feet long, grazing on seaweed beneath the turbulent sea—in Darwin's words, they were "imps of darkness, black as the porous rocks over which they crawl." And he saw the giant tortoises that had for years been captured by seafarers to be stacked upside down on the decks of their boats where the hardy beasts could somehow survive for months, providing fresh meat on the long voyages.

Darwin was more interested in the plants than the animals and soon spent most of the time "botanizing" over the dry and barren islands. He was struck by the strange animals of the islands, however, and collected not only the marine lizards, but also their land-bound cousins further inland as well. He also collected various kinds of birds, many of which, he was convinced, were undescribed species. Among these were a motley group that were not unlike the finches he had collected on the South American mainland.

Darwin later regretted that he had been storing all the bird species collected from the islands together on the boat. He came to recognize the importance of separating them according to where they were taken one day while he was examining a few of the finches. He noticed that two of them taken from different islands differed in the size and shape of their bills. This struck him as odd and possibly significant. The importance of his observation was driven home as he was walking the four miles to the settlement of political outcasts, banished from Ecuador, who had been sent to Charles Island. His companion that day was the acting British governor of the island who informed Darwin that he was able to tell from which island any of the tortoises came. He explained that they differed, for example, in the size and shape of the carapace (shell) and in the length of their extremities. Darwin wondered if each island was somehow producing its own forms of creatures, and from that day on, he carefully separated his collections from each island. This was to prove a critical decision once he was home in England. Years later, Darwin had his finch collections examined by a British specialist, and it was decided that there were 13 species, differing primarily in size and shape of their beaks. Darwin surmised that these birds must have come originally from the South American mainland, since the volcanic islands of the Galapagos would have been formed later than the continent. But why were these birds so different from those on the mainland, and why did the assortment of each island differ so much from one to the next? Years would pass before Darwin would conclude that the birds were descended from mainland stock that had accidentally been blown out to the islands, and that the various islands themselves had changed the populations over time.

As the voyage continued, Darwin concluded not only his collecting, but also his questioning of how things came to be. His letters and observations were reaching England and had the scientific community anxiously awaiting more of his findings. In fact, he was told that upon his return, he would be invited to take his place among the British scientific establishment. The letters waiting at various ports of call encouraged him and sent him bounding into the hills of each new land, his hammer joyously ringing against the rocks.

When Darwin agreed to go on the expedition, he had expected to be gone about two years, but five years were to pass before his return. When the *Beagle* finally made its way back to England, Darwin was greeted enthusiastically by his family, the scientific community, and his dog. His reception among the scientists of the day was a warm one, and immediately the questions began. What had he seen? What had he brought back? A new phase of work had just begun. (Because of the focus on Darwin and British science, it sometimes seems that the rest of the world was on hold during this time, but the timeline below shows this was not the case.)

The Impact of Malthus

Darwin was grateful to be back among his friends, his new colleagues, and his books. After a flurry of activity, he married his cousin, Emma Wedgewood, and retreated to the country and began to enjoy the quiet mornings when he could find time to work.

Timeline

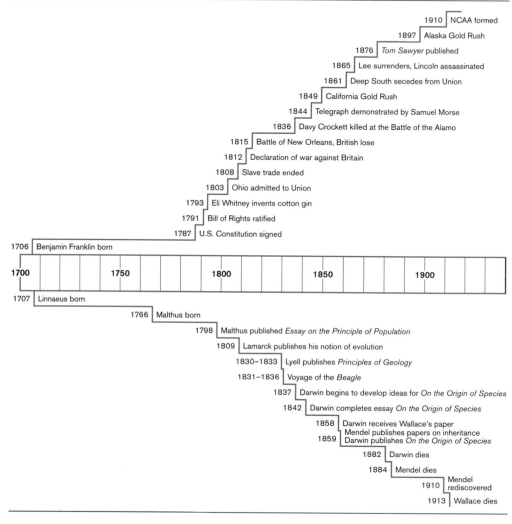

In his reading, he came across an old essay by the Reverend Thomas Malthus (1766–1834) that was probably the first clear warning of the dangers of human overpopulation. In the essay, which appeared in 1798, Malthus pointed out that populations tended to increase in a geometric (exponential) progression, and that if humans continued to reproduce at the same rate, they would inevitably outstrip their food supply and create a teeming world full of "misery and vice." Malthus's message may been theological, but Darwin applied the idea to his own work and concluded that species have a high reproductive potential, but that not all individuals reproduce, because of differences in their survival abilities. The idea was that populations are kept in check partly because not all animals survive long enough to reproduce.

Malthus's paper set Darwin to thinking. He calculated that even a pair of elephants, notoriously slow breeders, could produce 19 million progeny in only 750 years. Yet, it seemed that through the years, the number of elephants on the earth stayed about the same. Something was obviously interfering with their reproductive output. But was that "something" exerting an equal effect on all elephants, or did individuals differ in their ability to reproduce? Were some less successful at leaving offspring? And, if this were the case, Darwin wondered what factors determined which ones were to be successful.

Natural Selection

Darwin's answer came to him in part because of his background as a country gentleman. He was familiar with the principles of **artificial selection**, he knew that through careful selection of animals for mating, breeders were able to accentuate desired characteristics in the offspring. Breeders, then, determine the reproductive success of individuals. For example, by mating only the offspring of the greatest milk producers, breeders could develop high-yield dairy cattle. And by breeding only the offspring of good laying hens, they could eventually produce hens that were veritable egg-laying machines. The results of such artificial selection could be seen in only a few generations.

Darwin envisioned some sort of process of **natural selection** in which nature determines the reproductive success of individuals. It was analogous to the artificial selection imposed by the breeders. He remembered the variation he had observed in populations of plants and animals during his journey aboard the *Beagle*. Some of those variations, he reasoned, would give their bearer a competitive edge and increase that individual's chance of surviving and reproducing. Thus, nature would select the best of the individuals for mating. Natural selection would be far less efficient than artificial selection since individuals with only *somewhat* less-desirable characteristics might be able to produce at least *some* offspring, and thus their traits would take longer to disappear from the population. (Of course, those individuals with traits totally out of keeping with their environment would leave no offspring at all; hence, those traits would more quickly disappear from the population.) On the other side of the coin, the traits of those individuals with some reproductive *advantage* could be expected to *increase* through the generations.

Eventually, Darwin would express his idea of natural selection in his book, the *Origin of Species*:

> *How will the struggle for existence . . . act in regard to variation? Can the principle of selection, which we have seen is so potent in the hands of man, apply in nature? I think we shall see that it can act most effectively. . . . If such [variations] do occur, can we doubt (remembering that many more individuals are born than can possibly survive) that individuals*

having any advantage, however slight, over others, would have the best chance of surviving and of procreating their own kind? On the other hand, we may feel sure that any variation in the least degree injurious would be rigidly destroyed. This preservation of favorable variations and the rejection of injurious variations, I call Natural Selection. . . .

Briefly, natural selection involves (1) overproduction of offspring, (2) natural variation within a population, (3) limited resources, and the struggle for survival, and (4) selection by the environment for those with traits that enable the individual to survive and reproduce.

Natural selection, then, came to be defined as the process through which certain types of organisms are more reproductively successful than other types, thereby disproportionately passing along those traits that led to their success.

Natural selection could account for many of Darwin's observations, such as the variety among the Galapagos finches. Their basic similarity suggested that they had all descended from the same ancestral stock. Yet the species differed from each other in critical ways, such as in color, bill size, foraging behavior, and food choice. By applying the principles of natural selection, Darwin could see how each island would have presented the original colonizers with its own array of opportunities and threats, and from among the variable offspring of any population, those with the traits best suited to a specific environment would best thrive and reproduce. In time, each environment would have molded the birds into populations so distinct that each become a species, distinct from the others.

Since the notion of natural selection depended on inequalities among members of a population, the source of the variation, of the inequalities, had to be accounted for. Why, then, are the individuals different? What brought about their inequalities? Darwin proposed that such variations (inequalities) appear randomly—that no driving force, no direction, and no design are necessary. He decided that if some new variation provided an advantage that increased the reproductive output of its bearer, it would spread through future populations. This meant that if the long neck of the giraffe is inherited and is helpful in acquiring food, then the giraffes with longer necks will be better nourished, and thus will be more likely to have the energy to leave offspring. Among those offspring, he suggested, some will have longer necks than others, and these, in turn, will be more successful than their shorter-necked brothers and sisters.

Since long-necked giraffes would leave more offspring, the result would be a general tendency for any generation to be composed of animals with longer necks than those of any preceding generation.

It is important to realize that Darwin developed his idea not only in the face of withering opposition, but also without hard proof. There was no experimental evidence he could offer, and to make things worse, he knew almost nothing about the field we now call genetics. If he had understood what was going on in genetics across the Channel in the garden of a monastery he would have been able to save himself much grief. Because of such problems, he was reluctant to present his ideas. He felt he should be able to explain the mechanism by which variation appeared.

Then, in 1858, something happened that prompted the thoughtful Darwin into action. He received an unfinished paper from a young biologist working in Indonesia, Alfred Russel Wallace (1823–1913). Wallace wanted Darwin's opinion of the merit of the paper that was, in effect, a sketchy outline of the principles of natural selection. By this time, Darwin had already planned to present his theory of natural selection to the Linnaean Society of London. Startled by the letter, and at the urging of the geologist Lyell, the botanist Joseph Hooker, and the scientific philosopher Thomas Huxley, he began to hasten his work.

Hooker and Lyell agreed to assist Darwin, whose young son had just died, by editing and condensing an earlier paper of his with a letter he had written the American botanist, Asa Gray, describing his developing principle of natural selection. Although Darwin feared he might be "scooped" (in science, being first often means being foremost), he asked that Wallace be permitted to present his paper first and receive credit for the idea, rather than have anyone think he had behaved in a "paltry spirit." The outcome was that the papers were read at the same meeting, with Darwin's presented first, in keeping with his much more substantial evidence. The papers were presented in July and published in August 1858. Darwin then went furiously to work, putting aside his idea of a huge monograph describing his theory. Instead, he completed an "abstract" of the idea: the *Origin of Species*, which was published in 1859. The first edition sold out on the first day.

Darwin's carefully formulated ideas were greeted with enthusiasm in some quarters, but, needless to say, the response was not universal. He was forced to defend his idea of "descent with modification" not only against scientists who demanded hard evidence, but also against the attacks of philosophers, theologians, and a general public who thought the idea was heretical.

One difficulty from the start was the issue of human evolution. Then—as today—when the principles of evolution were applied to other species, humans were bound to find themselves under this great explanatory umbrella as well. A lot of people resented being placed in the shade with the worms and moles and did not believe they shared the expectations of other creatures. Moreover, the acquisition of such noble traits as a bipedal gait, thumb and hand dexterity, and extensive learning capacity was simply not to be attributed to a mere natural process. In the human desire to be set apart from other creatures, great ideological clashes began.

The battle grew and was soon full blown. Darwin himself was poorly equipped for such a fight. He had fallen ill upon returning to England after his journey, and he never recovered his health. He had become a dedicated family man, spending a great deal of time with his wife and children. He continued his experiments and observations, but, because of weakness, he generally could only work from mid-morning until noon. His infirmities have been diagnosed time and again by medical historians who first suggested that they were psychosomatic, but some then suggested that Darwin may have contracted Chagas' disease by once allowing himself, as an experiment, to be bitten by a benchuga bug. This idea has now been largely discounted. So the source of Darwin's infirmity remains a puzzle to this day. (Darwin and Wallace had become good friends by this time and, as Wallace grew increasingly depauperate [poor], Darwin arranged a government stipend for him; Wallace would later serve as Darwin's pallbearer.)

While Darwin was developing his theory, he became plagued by anxiety and self-doubt. He and Emma lived a rather quiet and somewhat reclusive life at Down House in the country, and Darwin became even more withdrawn when the noisy debate over natural selection started. However, he had formidable defenders. Many of the best minds of the time leaped to the defense of the grand idea—brilliant, hard-nosed, and combative souls who savored the taste of intellectual battle. Among his most brilliant defenders was his long-time friend, the great debater Thomas Huxley. (When Lord Wilburforce, a clergyman, facetiously asked Huxley in a debate if he was related to the apes on his father's or his mother's side, Huxley is reported to have muttered, "The Lord hath delivered him into my hands." He then won applause by saying that he would rather be related to an ape than to a man who refused to use his God-given powers of reason.) Of course, Darwin's defenders did not join the fray empty-handed. Here, after all, was a unifying concept, one that made sense of it all. It accounted for the observations. It was not to be rejected on any basis other than a better explanation. And there was none.

Summary

1. Charles Darwin served as a naturalist during a five-year voyage from England to many places around the world, including South America, aboard the H.M.S. *Beagle*. He collected specimens of plants and animals, and wondered about the variability among organisms he observed. . . .

2. At this time, most scientists believed that God created all types of living organisms in their present form. A few scientists, such as Buffon, Erasmus Darwin (Charles's grandfather), and Lamarck suggested that species change through time. Lamarck believed that, when necessary, some "force of life" allowed organisms to generate new structures that could be developed through use and passed to offspring.

3. The ideas of Lyell and of Malthus were important to the development of Darwin's thoughts on how species might change over time. Lyell argued that the earth was much older than was thought. Therefore, there would have been time for the changes in living organisms that Darwin would come to suggest had occurred.

4. Malthus pointed out how quickly populations can grow. Darwin realized that population size remains under control only when some individuals do not survive and reproduce.

5. Darwin put Malthus's ideas together with what he knew about artificial selection and proposed the process of natural selection, a process in which nature selects the individuals who reproduce, leaving offspring possessing their parents' traits. As a result of natural selection, the traits of the successful breeders increase through successive generations, but the traits of less successful breeders become less common. He believed the variation appeared through random processes. Those traits of a species that allow an individual to leave more offspring than others would spread through future generations. Natural selection could account for many of Darwin's observations, including the variety among the Galapagos finches.

6. Darwin didn't publish his ideas until he realized that Alfred Russell Wallace had similar thoughts on natural selection. The papers of Darwin and Wallace were presented at the same scientific meeting in 1858, and Darwin's book, *Origin of Species*, was published in 1859. It met with strong protest as well as grateful acceptance.

Step 3. O = Organize

Get something down on paper. As a minimum, *answer the questions* you formulated after your survey. As a maximum, *finish your outline* and note cards. Fill in the details. But be selective, be brief, and use your own words. Be guided by what you might be asked on a test—or by what you might be expected to know as an educated person. Experiment with different types of outlining; pick the type to fit the content. Or summarize parts of the chapter—similar to the chapter summary above, but in more detail.

Last, *review the chapter and your completed study-outline*, as if you were studying for a test. Now is the time to underline and make additional note cards. Instead of answering the usual comprehension questions, you may be asked to take a sample test provided by your instructor.

Study Outline

_____
[complete chapter title]

Introduction:

A. _____
[Darwin's traits and interests?—only those connected to later theories]

B. _____
[his father's opinion of him?]

C. _____
[his academic history—what did he study that prepared him for later success?]

I. What is important about Darwin's voyage on the Beagle? [question from 1st heading]

A. _____
[his job on ship? when? where?]

B. _____
[his reaction to sailing? how long was voyage?]

C. _____
[his time spent on shore?—connect to later theories]

II. _____
[form a meaningful question from 2nd major heading.]

A. Before the 18th century, science was limited to inanimate subjects.

B. Most scientists then believed _____

1. Example: Carl von Linne (1707–1778) devised a system of classification for all living things.

C. A few departures from the theory, "fixity of species," influenced Darwin:

1. Georges-Louis Leclerc de Buffon (1707–1788) believed _____

_____

2. _____

_____

3. _____

a. He suggested that _____

_____

b. He guessed that _____

_____

(1). Example: _____

D. Nineteenth-century society mostly stuck with the theory of each form arisen from special creation.

Check this part of your outline with the model in the key. For a comprehension score, each item filled in correctly is worth 6.7%. After your review (last part of PRO), your instructor may ask you to finish outlining the chapter or give you a practice test on the chapter (or on a portion of the chapter). Record your scores below and on the Progress Chart.

Words per Minute _____
[See page 209.]

Percent Comprehension _____

Writing and Discussion Activities

1. Look over your outline for Exercise 6F (the science chapter). Pick one major point (represented by a Roman numeral and all the points indented underneath it) from the outline. Write a summary paragraph expanding that portion of the outline.

2. Apply the PRO study-reading method to a textbook chapter you have been assigned in another class.

Name: _____

Date: _____ Class: _____

Vocabulary Review, Chapter 6

Match the vocabulary word on the left with its definition on the right. Write the letter of the answer on the short line to the left.

d 1. **musings** (a) insignificant
a 2. **trifling** (b) high-spirited
e 3. **era** (c) body of beliefs
c 4. **dogma** (d) deep thoughts
b 5. **exuberant** (e) time period

Choose the definition for each **boldfaced** word as it is used in its context.

b 6. A **motley** group of citizens were waiting outside the editor's door after the insulting newspaper article on the city's reputation as having the nation's rudest residents.
(a) angry (b) varied (c) polite

a 7. An important **tenet** to live by is "Do unto others as you would have them do unto you."
(a) rule (b) possibility (c) freedom

b 8. Her **prowess** as a swimmer was well-known even before she successfully swam the English Channel.
(a) goal (b) ability (c) training

a 9. At first the candidate hung back shyly during debates, but after a little more experience with public speaking, he eagerly entered the **fray** and spoke out at the remaining debates.
(a) battle (b) building (c) dressing room

c 10. Tossed into the boxing ring with a larger, more skillful opponent, Arthur's only defense was **flailing** his thin arms.
(a) hiding behind (b) building up (c) thrashing about

Mark each sentence to show whether the **boldfaced** word is used correctly.

a = True   b = False

F 11. On the evening of January 1, 2000, people who had never celebrated New Year's Eve, gathered to **herald** the beginning of a new century and a new millennium.
F 12. The student's notebook was bulging with a **paltry** number of lecture notes.
T 13. Rick likes reading Early American history because he likes learning about his **contemporaries**.

(Continued)

____ 14. The bullfighter spent long hours with his **protégé**, teaching him how to move quickly and gracefully.

____ 15. The friendly, out-going girls liked to give their parties in a **desolate** area so they and their friends would feel safe.

Choose the word from the box that fits the context of the following paragraph. Write the letter of each choice on the blank lines to the left.

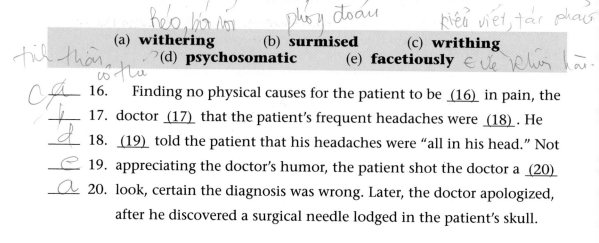

(a) **withering**   (b) **surmised**   (c) **writhing**
(d) **psychosomatic**   (e) **facetiously**

____ 16.   Finding no physical causes for the patient to be __(16)__ in pain, the

____ 17. doctor __(17)__ that the patient's frequent headaches were __(18)__ . He

____ 18. __(19)__ told the patient that his headaches were "all in his head." Not

____ 19. appreciating the doctor's humor, the patient shot the doctor a __(20)__

____ 20. look, certain the diagnosis was wrong. Later, the doctor apologized, after he discovered a surgical needle lodged in the patient's skull.

% Correct _____

Comprehension Review, Chapter 6

1. When studying a textbook chapter, why is using the PRO technique more effective than just reading the chapter and highlighting parts of it?
   Because PRO forces students to read actively instead of passively through previewing,

and push em from average to excellent

2. Give your own example of an *acronym* that is not used in the chapter.
   PRO = *Prepare Read Organize*
   [acronym]   [what it represents]

3. PRO is an *abbreviation* for *professional*, which suggests that a student who uses the PRO technique is a(n) *active* *student*.

4. The first major step in the PRO technique is P = *Prepare*. [Clue: *not* Preview]

5. List any supporting detail (or substep) for the first major step in PRO.
   Look over the unit to be studied

6. During the second major step in PRO (R = Read), which of the following is more effective?
   (a) Read the entire unit you have selected straight through without stopping, making only quick checkmarks next to ideas you want to put in your notes later.
   (b) Read a paragraph or a page; then underline important ideas or take notes on that portion before reading the next paragraph or page.

7–13. *Finish the mapping outline on the next page for the third step in PRO. Copy all the figures, arrows, and words provided onto your own paper; then supply the missing words for the dotted lines.*

reading actively, and taking study notes.

⟨5⟩ - Look over the unit to be studied

- Stop to digest the information you know at this point

- Ask yourself questions or starts your outline

(Continued)

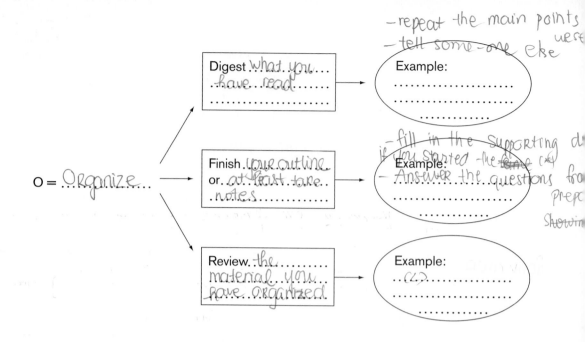

Digest .what. you....have. read......

Example:
—repeat the main points
—tell some-one ese were

Finish .your. outline. or. at. least. take. .notes...........

Example:
—fill in the supporting de if you started the time (*)
—Answer the questions fro Prepo Showin

O = .Organize....

Review. .the........ material. .you.. have. .organized.

Example:
..(2)..............

14. Which combination of major logic patterns is used in the mapping outline above?

(a) comparison and contrast   (b) cause and effect
(c) addition and process

15. When taking notes on a textbook chapter or outlining it, you should always use the author's exact words so you will learn the material accurately.   (a) true   (b) false

(*) framework of an outline in the Prepare

% Correct _____

(1) labeling and identing the difference between 1st, 2nd, 3rd and etc level details.

— finish the note-cards that begin in the Prepare step.

(2) skim quickly through the study unit again

— look for any important material that may have remember wrong or forgotten

— Changed or add of the outline

— Stress what the author seems to stress

— Add the notes from the teacher's lecture to the out

— Underline or mark in the test OR notes
— Make more note-cards, or formulate new questions or pratic

VOCABULARY PREVIEW for Chapter 7

WORDS IN CONTEXT

Directions: *Examine the **boldfaced** word as it is used in the sentence and write your best guess of the word's meaning. Then look up the word in your dictionary and write the best definition for its context in the sentence.*

PRONUNCIATION
KEY

a	cat	ā	made	ä	bar	k	cot, quit		adore
e	pet	ē	these	â	care	s	cent		travel
i	sit	ī	ride	è	term	z	beds	ə	horrify
o	rot	ō	note	ô	order	j	giant		pardon
u	nut	ōō	rude	ŏŏ	foot	th	thank		circus
ù	put	yōō	use	ōō	food	ŦH	this		

from Practice 2 (p. 235)

1. **diversified**   (də vèr′ sə fīd)   *verbal (adjective)*

    This is the typical day of a relatively typical soul in today's **diversified** world.

    Your best guess: _____

    Best dictionary definition: _____

from Timed Reading 7G (p. 248)

2. **elite**   (i lēt′)   *noun*

    Members of Venezuela's ruling **elite** call it "the snake."

    Your best guess: _____

    Best dictionary definition: _____

3. **stems**   (stemz)   *verb*

    The show's popularity **stems** from the fact that it broke with many of the old conventions binding television programs.

    Your best guess: _____

    Best dictionary definition: _____

    [Clue: Use the verb definition, not the more common noun definition.]

answering them

4. **coups** (ko͞oz)   *noun*

"The authors and the producers skillfully took full advantage of the material provided by growing social conflicts, two failed **coups** and innumerable cases of corruption."

Your best guess: _____

Best dictionary definition: _____

5. **authentic** (ô then' tik)   *adjective*

"They connected its plot with **authentic** political, financial and sexual scandals."

Your best guess: _____

Best dictionary definition: _____

6. **gubernatorial** (go͞o' bər nə tôr' ē əl)   *adjective*

They [soap opera characters] include the likes of Don Chepe, a **gubernatorial** candidate, who is *launching* his campaign.

Your best guess: _____

Best dictionary definition: _____

7. **launching** (lônch' ing)   *verb*

Your best guess: _____

Best dictionary definition: _____

[Note: See sentence #6 for context clues for **launching**.)

8. **diabolical** (dī ə bol' ə kəl)   *adjective*

Finally, there is Mauro, a **diabolical** drug trafficker.

Your best guess: _____

Best dictionary definition: _____

9. **melodrama** (mel' ə drä' mə)   *noun*

Of course, [the soap opera] has kept the traditional elements of the **melodrama**. And it has done so without giving up the *banalities* that keep many viewers glued to the screen.

Your best guess: _____

Best dictionary definition: _____

10. **banalities** (bə nal' ə tēz)   *noun*

Your best guess: _____

Best dictionary definition: _____

11. **subversion** (səb vėr' zhən)   *noun*

The USIA expressed its views in a recent memorandum titled, "*Por Estas Calles: Soap Opera or* **Subversion**?"

Your best guess: _____

Best dictionary definition: _____

12. **influx** (in' fluks)   *noun*

These [themes and issues] include the corruption that accompanied the **influx** of oil revenues.

Your best guess: _____

Best dictionary definition: _____

13. **anarchic** (a när' kik)   *adjective*

According to the reviewer, there is no doubt the show "depicts a modern-day Caracas as an **anarchic** den of ***iniquity***."

Your best guess: _____

Best dictionary definition: _____

14. **iniquity** (in ik' wə tē)   *noun*

Your best guess: _____

Best dictionary definition: _____

15. **unrequited** (un ri kwīt' id)   *adjective*

"Individual problems of **unrequited** love, cross-class marriages, surprise pregnancies, secret affairs, and murdered girlfriends are still more vital to the program than any notion of social justice."

Your best guess: _____

Best dictionary definition: _____

from Timed Reading 7H (p. 252)

16. **charismatic** (kar' iz mat' ik)   *adjective*

The speaker is a **charismatic** Asian in his late thirties, a Brahmin by birth, an engineer by training, and a social activist by choice.

Your best guess: _____

Best dictionary definition: _____

[Clue: To understand the adjective meaning for this word, you may need to refer to the noun definition.]

17. **fledgling** (flej' ling)   *adjective*

The September 18 observances were a few recent public signs of a **fledgling** international movement against an ancient evil commonly called child labor.

Your best guess: _____

Best dictionary definition: _____

18. **prohibition** (prō' ə bish' ən)   *noun*

It requires its 600 suppliers in fifty countries to adopt a code of conduct that includes a **prohibition** against the employment of children under 14.

Your best guess: _____

Best dictionary definition: _____

19. **caste** (kast)   *adjective (usually a noun)*

The abuses are even worse in India's carpet factories, which hold many low-**caste** children in bondage.

Your best guess: _____

Best dictionary definition: _____

20. **reprehensible** (rep' ri hen' sə bəl)   *adjective*

Applied to such a wide range of different conditions, the same label implies that the harmful practices it covers are equally **reprehensible**, when they are not.

Your best guess: _____

Best dictionary definition: _____

21. **conscripted** (kən skript' id)   *verbal*

The Anti-Slavery International of London argues that children **conscripted** into the full-time labor force before a certain age (say 14 or 15). . . are suffering from a contemporary form of slavery.

Your best guess: _____

Best dictionary definition: _____

22. **perpetuates** (pər pech' o͞o āts')   *verb*

"No government can scale down unemployment without curbing child labor," which he insists **perpetuates** poverty.

Your best guess: _____

Best dictionary definition: _____

23. **reverberate** (ri vėr' bə rāt')   *verbal*

Gompers' words need to **reverberate** throughout the global economy, wherever choices are made affecting child ***servitude***.

Your best guess: _____

Best dictionary definition: _____

24. **servitude** (sėr' və to͞od)   *noun*

Your best guess: _____

Best dictionary definition: _____

Exercise, Vocabulary Preview, Chapter 7

Directions: *Choose the best definition for each* **boldfaced** *word as it is used in its context. Remember: A word may have more than one meaning.*

_____ 1. To avoid financial disaster if one product failed, Burt invested only in companies that had **diversified** their products.

(a) decreased   (b) varied   (c) improved

_____ 2. In many areas of South Africa, only members of the **elite** were allowed to move freely throughout the cities at night, while the lower classes were often required to remain in restricted areas.

(a) government   (b) upper class   (c) royalty

_____ 3. Donald's mistrust and suspicion toward women probably **stems** from the fact that his mother abandoned him as a small boy.

(a) comes   (b) goes   (c) ends

_____ 4. The general successfully led the **coup**, replacing the king and installing his own puppet government.

(a) army   (b) march   (c) takeover

_____ 5. It is difficult to find **authentic** Mexican food in many parts of the country, even though the Mexican style of cooking has been imitated everywhere.

(a) good-tasting   (b) genuine   (c) gourmet

_____ 6. Kathleen Brown was the third Brown (following in the footsteps of her father Pat and brother Jerry) to enter California's **gubernatorial** race.

(a) mayoral   (b) governor's   (c) presidential

_____ 7. Tanya's grandfather always took her to see every **launching** of the space shuttle until he became too ill to make the trip.

(a) setting into motion   (b) landing   (c) building

_____ 8. Peter's scheme to seize the family business from his father and sisters is **diabolical**, for he plans to squeeze them out entirely and ruin their reputations.

(a) fiendish   (b) illegal   (c) improper

_____ 9. **Melodrama** became a way of life for Lucinda; she kept herself, her friends, and her family in a continuous cycle of drama and tragedy.

(a) dramatic reading   (b) exaggerated drama
(c) stand-up comedy

_____ 10. Bertha never uttered an original word; one **banality** after another came out of her mouth.

(a) poem   (b) speech   (c) cliché

_____ 11. The CIA has been strongly criticized for planning **subversion** against the governments of many third-world nations.

(a) patriotism (b) charity (c) destruction

_____ 12. The Rose Bowl Parade in Pasadena, California, every January is blamed for the **influx** of new residents in California during the following months, for the sunny skies of California appeal to the people snowbound in the north and northeastern states.

(a) inflow (b) outpouring (c) birth rate

_____ 13. After the king and prime minister were shot, and for some time not replaced, the people of the small country suffered **anarchic** conditions.

(a) improved (b) disorderly (c) orderly

_____ 14. When the crime lords took over the elegant hotel and brought in drugs, gambling, and prostitutes, the place became a hopeless pit of **iniquity**.

(a) sin (b) inequality (c) poverty

_____ 15. Female country and western singers these days are more likely to sing upbeat songs about revenge and independence than mournful songs about **unrequited** love.

(a) satisfying (b) lost (c) unreturned

_____ 16. A **charismatic** speaker can often hold an audience's attention much longer than one who is educated or even qualified to speak on a given subject.

(a) knowledgeable (b) magnetic (c) loud

_____ 17. The **fledgling** club struggled and stumbled along for several months with no manager and few members, until it finally folded for lack of interest.

(a) chess (b) inexperienced (c) long-established

_____ 18. During the 1920s in America, because of a **prohibition** on liquor, places called "speakeasies" opened and sold liquor illegally.

(a) tax (b) shortage (c) ban

_____ 19. Hindu society has a rigid **caste** system, with Brahmins at the top and Untouchables at the bottom.

(a) social class (b) school (c) government

_____ 20. Most civilized people would consider the mistreatment of helpless children to be the most **reprehensible** of acts.

(a) shameful (b) careful (c) admirable

_____ 21. The armies in many countries are made up of reluctant soldiers **conscripted** into military service.

(a) force-marched (b) invited (c) enrolled by force

_____ 22. President Clinton believed that welfare, without job training, **perpetuates** more welfare and more poverty.

(a) reduces (b) prolongs (c) creates

_____ 23. Their full voices, one soprano and one bass, **reverberated** off the walls of the deep cliffs around them: "I am calling you-hoo-hoo-hoo!"

(a) slid down   (b) clanged   (c) echoed back

_____ 24. After many years of near **servitude**, Gwen finally gathered the courage to quit her crummy job and return to school.

(a) slavery   (b) low pay   (c) employment

Number of Errors _____

Chapter 7
skimming and Scanning

I. and II. How to Read Much Faster but Understand Less

STUDY UNIT: *skimming and Scanning*

                  Skim for Overview

                  Scan for Answers

SKIMMING AND SCANNING PRACTICE

TIMED READINGS: *The Global Village*

                  Soap Operas and Social Change

                  from ***Outlawing the Crime of Child Slavery: Stolen Childhood***

I. and II. How to Read Much Faster but Understand Less

Note: *Again, preview before you read.*

Skimming and Scanning

In Chapter 6, your purpose was to learn how to apply PRO, the study method of the Pros. You probably saw your WPM slow down as you dedicated yourself to thorough comprehension. In this chapter, your reading purpose is entirely different. Your purpose is to *skim*—read extra fast while picking up just the main ideas—and to *scan*—look for specific details or bits of information. As a result, you will see a big change in both your speed and comprehension.

The terms *skimming* and *scanning* are often used interchangeably. Both involve selective skipping at high speeds. Both are a kind of semi-reading. Both involve focus: skimming has a wide focus and scanning a narrow focus. Each has a different technique and different uses. *Skimming is reading for the general idea or the big picture. Scanning is looking for exact answers to specific questions.*

Skim for Overview

Some reading experts boast of *skimming at 800 WPM or more*. These claims may intimidate you. You may think, "I have just struggled to get my reading speed above 250 WPM. How can I possibly read at 800 WPM with any understanding?"

The answer to that question is that you already have skimmed reading material at 800 WPM. You have been doing a type of skimming when you have previewed articles in this book. You have skimmed articles when you have been in a hurry. Example: You are standing in the checkout line at the grocery store, and a headline from a tabloid newspaper screams out at you: *"EIGHTY-YEAR-OLD WOMAN HAS QUINTUPLETS AND NAMES HIGH-LEVEL POLITICIAN AS FATHER."* You know the article is false and you wouldn't be caught dead buying the tabloid, but you quickly sneak a peak at the juicy highlights. Plus, you do this while your groceries are being checked. This is skimming.

Obviously, skimming is not the same as study-reading. It is not even the same as the kind of fast reading you have been practicing on the easier practice readings in this book. Skimming is purposeful *skipping*. It is "once over lightly" for only the most important points. When you skim nonfiction, you look for major ideas and ignore the minor ones. When you skim fiction, you try to follow only the major characters and main events in a plot line and ignore the minor ones. If you read a lot of fiction, you already skim if you tend to skip over parts that don't interest you. Skimming fiction is like pushing the "Fast Forward" button on your VCR remote. When the advertisement (or episode that bores you) is over, you hit the "Play" button (or the "Read" button).

We have emphasized in this book that *it is natural to switch speeds to fit your reading purpose and time limits.* The speed should be your choice. Unless you have a skimming speed, you have few choices. Your reading is like having only two gears on your motorcycle. (If you are still reading everything word-for-word, you have no choices—and your motorcycle will never use all its power.)

Your long-term *goal with skimming is 700 or 800 WPM.* But that's a goal requiring frequent practice over a period of time. If you have already met your goal of doubling your WPM, set your skimming goal at tripling your earlier reading speed.

Take a moment to look at your Progress Chart, and note your WPM for the last readings in Chapters 4 and 5. To skim, you may need to double or triple your highest speed. With regular practice, you'll soon draw closer to your long-term goal of 800 WPM.

You may get an added bonus from even attempting to skim. Whether or not you succeed in reaching your skimming goal, you may raise your top speed, simply as a result of the attempt. For some people, unless the material is extremely difficult, even their study speed is increased.

When to Skim

You will not always want or need to read everything. Instead, you should skim if your purpose is one of the following.

1. To reread material you have already studied
2. To sort out and discard, as with the junk mail in your home or office
3. To "try before you buy"—or really read—a new book or magazine
4. To pass over minor or uninteresting sections when you are reading for pleasure—for example, to follow the major plot in a light, easy novel
5. To keep informed in a general way about the news
6. To review your lecture notes after class
7. To see which reference materials might be useful to your term paper
8. To be able to discuss the general content of a reading assignment in class when you didn't have time to study-read it

How to Skim

Skimming should give you a general overview, not detailed knowledge. Good skimmers read selectively, skipping over some sentences, paragraphs, and even whole pages. They know they can always come back and read for details, if they wish. When you *skim*, follow these steps:

1. Preview first for the topic, length of the material, and its organization. Look for logic patterns. Note any subdivisions or spaces with headings or subheadings. Also look for any numbered lists, capital letters, italics, or boldfaced print.
2. Read the title and the first paragraph, looking for the thesis. If the thesis is not in the first paragraph, read the second paragraph. Also read the last paragraph. The thesis or main points may be restated there.
3. Now look for main ideas in the first and, if necessary, second sentence of each paragraph. (If the material is too long or you don't have much time, read the first sentence under each heading or division. Usually it's a topic sentence.)
4. Read almost in a zigzag pattern down the page, skipping over more than one line at a time. (You may use your fingertips to guide you if you find it helpful.) A good practice on narrow newspaper columns is to draw a vertical line down the middle of the column and try to read vertically.
5. Look for context clues. Be alert for any sequence of ideas, for logic patterns. Anticipate connections between ideas—and between whole sections.
6. Look for important transitions, e.g., *but, a second reason, the result is.* . . .
7. Above all, resist the temptation to read everything.

Practice 1 Below is a paragraph from one of the Timed Readings in this chapter. It has been altered to show how a good *skimmer* might read it, skipping the words omitted here. Read the paragraph and answer the questions.

Normally, soap opera characters are ordinary people mistreated by life. But in *Por Estas Calles*.............anything but ordinary.....anything but victims. ....include.............Don Chepe, ...candidate,............launching.......campaign. Then ....Lucha,..........ambitious lover. And Dr. Valerio, ... doctor married.........Governor's daughter. ....owns.............clinic. ....made....fortune..........dubious business dealings. Another ....Natalio Vega,.............police....frustrated with.........inefficiency, takes justice.........hands....kills....thugs. Finally,.........Mauro,...diabolical drug trafficker.

(a) State the main idea. _____

_____

(b) Give one supporting detail. _____

(c) Give four transitions. _____   _____   _____   _____

Practice 2 Read the paragraph below, from "The Global Village Finally Arrives" by Pico Iyer, and follow the directions underneath it.

This is the typical day of a relatively typical soul in today's diversified world. I wake up to the sound of my Japanese clock radio, put on a T-shirt sent to me by an uncle in Nigeria and walk out into the street, past the German cars, to my office. Around me are English-language students from Korea, Switzerland and Argentina—all on this Spanish-named road in this Mediterranean-style town. On TV, I find, the news is in Mandarin; today's baseball game is being broadcast in Korean. For lunch I can walk to a sushi bar, a tandoori palace, a Thai café, or the newest burrito joint (run by an old Japanese lady). Who am I, I sometimes wonder, the son of Indian parents and a British citizen who spends much of his time in Japan (and is therefore—what else?— an American permanent resident)? And where am I?

(a) Underline the topic sentence twice.

(b) Underline ten representative examples (brief phrases only). Do not include any extra words.

(c) Reread the paragraph, skipping from one group of underlined words to another. Could you get the gist of the paragraph if, in the beginning, you had read only the underlined portions?

In these two Practice exercises, you just reinforced phrase reading, the basis for skimming, If you were able to read most easy newspaper and magazine articles this way (without trying to skip dots and underlining phrases, of course), think how much time you would save.

If you find yourself resisting skimming, you may be hearing the advice of a parent or former teacher: "If it's worth doing at all, it's worth doing right." Or: "Take your time and you won't make mistakes." Remember, skimming is not meant to take the place of study-reading. No matter how fast you are capable of skimming, your speed won't get stuck at that gear. You will always have the choice to slow down. It is more likely that, at this point, you don't have the choice to speed up.

Scan for Answers

Scanning takes skimming a step further. If skimming is selective skipping, scanning is "super skipping." *When you scan print, you are looking for one thing in particular.* You have a specific question or word or number in mind, and you race through the material at extremely high speeds until you find the answer. Then you stop, fixate, and read only what you need.

The scanning rates many experts suggest may be intimidating. They speak of 2000 WPM and up. Actually, you have practiced scanning many times, at speeds this high and higher. In fact, WPM rate is meaningless in scanning because you are selecting so little and ignoring so much. When scanning, you may seem to skip paragraphs, or pages, or even chapters. If you think this is "not" reading at all, remember that you are making a rapid judgment about what to skip. That means you are processing the information in some fashion, even in the material you choose not to really "read."

Scanning can be the simple task of finding the exact words—as in the Phrase Practice exercises. Or it can be more difficult, as when the wording of your answer is different from the wording of your question, as in the Vocabulary Review exercises. The goal is to recognize what you are looking for, without wasting time reading unrelated material.

Simple Scanning

Sometimes, when you scan, you do it almost without thinking. Your purpose is simple and familiar, as in the following situations.

1. Finding a name in the phone book, a word in the dictionary, "Cleaners" in the yellow pages, or a certain page of this book
2. Locating a certain street or town on a map
3. Looking for news of a specific athlete, meeting, or auto accident in the newspaper
4. Finding the subject, author, or title you want on a shelf in the library
5. Using office skills such as filing, billing, and checking for errors
6. Locating information in a book index or table of contents
7. Looking for a specific item as you do in the phrase exercises in this book

Complex Scanning

Some scanning tasks require you to translate your ideas and be flexible about where to look. Many of the comprehension questions for the reading selections have required you to practice complex scanning. When you looked back for the answers to these questions, you didn't reread the whole article to find the answer; you *scanned* for the answer. You may have to translate the question into related words.

The following scanning tasks require some translation of your ideas, some flexibility of where to look. But they still assume that you have a specific question and will know when you find the answer.

1. Looking in the movie ads or TV guide for "any good show" (you may, in the process, rule out all westerns, porno films, etc.)
2. Looking in the classified newspaper ads for rentals, furniture, etc., that are available in your area or in your price range
3. Finding out when and how many buses or planes travel between two cities
4. Using a reference guide or a book index for information, say, on "Women's Rights"—it may be listed under "Sex Discrimination," "Employment," or "Equal Rights"
5. Looking for answers to multiple-choice questions

How to Scan

When you scan, you zero in on specific answers like a hawk swooping down on a mouse. The image is not extreme if you have ever done a research paper or worked in a busy office. You need good perception, a clear idea of what you're looking for, and the discipline to ignore everything else.

When you scan, follow these steps:

1. Clearly fix in your mind the information for which you are scanning.
2. Use any headings or subheadings to find quickly the part of the page (or chapter or book) that probably contains your information.
3. Look for synonyms, alternate ways your information might be worded. For example, information about "whales" might be listed under "marine life" or "oceanography," or even "mammals."

Practice 3   **Draw a line to match each scanning question on the left with its related title on the right that is most likely to have information on that topic.**

(a) Why can't Johnny read?   No Calculators Allowed in
                                       Math Classes

(b) How expensive is college?   A Return to Phonics in
                                       Schools

(c) Should the Internet be restricted? Street Violence on the Rise

                                       Rising Prices of Textbooks

                                       Child Porn on World
                                          Wide Web

Practice 4　To develop more skill in *complex* scanning, write two related titles for each topic below. (Pretend you are writing a research paper on these topics and you are looking through a list of titles in the library.)

Example: How to Relieve Stress　Tension—its Causes and Cures

　　　　　　　　　　　　　　　Drug-Free Aids for Daily Tension

(a) How to Build Body Strength　_____

　　　　　　　　　　　　　　　_____

(b) Teenage Road Rage　　　　_____

　　　　　　　　　　　　　　　_____

Remember, *skimming* and *scanning* are not meant to take the place of your other reading speeds. They are simply another gear or tool. They have a specific purpose and, of necessity, result in only partial comprehension. But they are worth mastering; like a motorcycle rider, every good reader needs a passing gear.

Study Outline

Use both simple *and* complex scanning *to complete the sentence outline.*

_____
[title, Ch. #]

Introduction:

A. Skimming is _____

B. Scanning is _____

I. Students skim for _____ at _____ WPM.
                                 [See first subheading.]

A. _____
                                 [What is skimming *not* used for?]

B. _____

C. Your long-term goal for skimming is _____ WPM, but you

    should decide *your* personal goal by _____

D. List two examples of when you might want to skim.

    1. _____

    2. _____

E. List two techniques for skimming.

    1. _____

    2. _____

II. Students _____ for _____ at around _____ WPM.

A. List two examples of when you already use _____ scanning.

    1. _____

    2. _____

B. List two examples of when you might use _____ scanning.

    1. _____

    2. _____

C. List two techniques for scanning.

    1. _____

    2. _____

Conclusion: _____

_____
[In one sentence, paraphrase the most important point in the last paragraph.]

The next four exercises provide practice—first in *scanning* and then in both *skimming* and *scanning*.

Exercise 7A: Scanning

Scan the opposite page, taken from a typical college schedule of classes, for answers to questions that students might encounter in choosing an English class.

1. What instructor teaches English 2R, beginning at 10 A.M., in room H4?

   _____

2. What is the prerequisite for taking English 2R? _____

3. In what room does C. Paul teach English 2R, section 6118? _____

4. On what days does W. Miller teach English 2R, section 6113? _____

5. How can you avoid taking the English Placement Test and still get into a class with a prerequisite? _____

   _____

Check your answers with the key, and record your scores below.

Scanning Time _____

Number of Errors _____

English
(Division of Humanities)

NOTE: Students must take the English Placement Test to help with the assessment of appropriate skill levels before enrolling in English R, 2R, B, A, 1A, or 72. A student seeking further review of a placement recommendation may obtain appropriate forms through the Counseling Office. Students who earned a C or better in a prerequisite course at another college are not required to take the English Placement Test. These students must present a grade slip or transcript at registration to verify that the prerequisite has been satisfied at another institution. SAT scores may be substituted for the English Placement Test scores. Students should see their counselors for further information.

English 2R—3 Units *Developmental Reading and Writing*
Prerequisite: Credit in English R or qualification by testing (English Placement Test) and assessment

6090	8:00–9:50 M Lecture	Kistler, R.	H 6
	8:00–8:50 W Lecture		H 6
	9:00–9:50 W Lab		H 6
6092	8:00–9:50 M Lecture	Littles, B.	H 4
	8:00–8:50 W Lecture		H 4
	9:00–9:50 W Lab		H 4
6093	8:00–9:50 M Lecture	Newbury, I.	H 1
	8:00–8:50 W Lecture		H 1
	9:00–9:50 W Lab		H 1
6095	8:00–9:50 T Lecture	Newbury, I.	H 6
	8:00–8:50 Th Lecture		H 6
	9:00–9:50 Th Lab		H 6
6097	8:00–9:50 T Lecture	Sutch, P.	H 4
	8:00–8:50 Th Lecture		H 4
	9:00–9:50 Th Lab		H 4
6099	8:00–9:50 T Lecture	Paul, C.	MCS 219
	8:00–8:50 Th Lecture		MCS 219
	9:00–9:50 Th Lab		MCS 219
6101	8:00–9:50 T Lecture	Tyo, J.	MU 201
	8:00–8:50 Th Lecture		MU 201
	9:00–9:50 Th Lab		MU 201
6103	8:00–9:50 T Lecture	Staff	H 15
	8:00–8:50 Th Lecture		H 22
	9:00–9:50 Th Lab		H 22
6105	10:00–11:50 M Lecture	Sutch, P.	H 4
	10:00–10:50 W Lecture		H 4
	11:00–11:50 W Lab		H 4
6107	10:00–11:50 M Lecture	Kistler, R.	H 1
	10:00–10:50 W Lecture		H 1
	11:00–11:50 W Lab		H 1
6109	10:00–11:50 M Lecture	Littles, B.	H 6
	10:00–10:50 W Lecture		H 6
	11:00–11:50 W Lab		H 6
6111	10:00–11:50 M Lecture	Hoehn, S.	MU 202
	10:00–10:50 W Lecture		MU 202
	11:00–11:50 W Lab		MU 202
6112	10:00–11:50 M Lecture	Kawell, S.	SS 207
	10:00–10:50 W Lecture		SS 207
	11:00–11:50 W Lab		SS 207
6113	10:00–11:50 T Lecture	Miller, W.	H 6
	10:00–10:50 Th Lecture		H 6
	11:00–11:50 Th Lab		H 6
6115	10:00–11:50 T Lecture	Sutch, P.	H 4
	10:00–10:50 Th Lecture		H 4
	11:00–11:50 Th Lab		H 4
6117	10:00–11:50 T Lecture	Tyo, J.	MU 201
	10:00–10:50 Th Lecture		MU 201
	11:00–11:50 Th Lab		MU 201
6118	10:00–11:50 T Lecture	Paul, C.	MCS 219
	10:00–10:50 Th Lecture		MCS 219
	11:00–11:50 Th Lab		MCS 219
6120	12:00–1:50 M Lecture	Tyo, J.	H 4
	12:00–12:50 W Lecture		H 4
	1:00–1:50 W Lab		H 4
6123	1:00–2:50 M Lecture	Staff	ADM 207
	1:00–1:50 W Lecture		ADM 207
	2:00–2:50 W Lab		ADM 207
6125	1:30–3:20 T Lecture	Sutch, P.	H 3
	1:30–2:20 Th Lecture		H 3
	2:30–3:20 Th Lab		H 3
6126	1:30–3:20 T Lecture	Miller, W.	H 4
	1:30–2:20 Th Lecture		H 4
	2:30–3:20 Th Lab		H 4
6127	1:30–3:20 T Lecture	Gross, D.	H 6
	1:30–2:20 Th Lecture		H 6
	2:30–3:20 Th Lab		H 6
6128	1:30–3:20 T Lecture	Staff	MU 201
	1:30–2:20 Th Lecture		MU 201
	2:30–3:20 Th Lab		MU 201
6132	4:00–5:50 M Lecture	Gross, D.	H 6
	4:00–4:50 W Lecture		H 6
	5:00–5:50pm W Lab		H 6
6134	4:00–5:50 T Lecture	Barlock, R.	H 4
	4:00–4:50 Th Lecture		H 4
	5:00–5:50pm Th Lab		H 4

Evening Hours

6136	6:00–7:50pm M Lecture	Gross, D.	H 6
	6:00–6:50pm W Lecture		H 6
	7:00–7:50pm W Lab		H 6
6137	6:00–7:50pm M Lecture	McCallum, V.	H 3
	6:00–6:50pm W Lecture		H 3
	7:00–7:50pm W Lab		H 3
6138	6:00–7:50pm M Lecture	Fitch, J.	MU 201
	6:00–6:50pm W Lecture		MU 201
	7:00–7:50pm W Lab		MU 201
6140	6:00–7:50pm M Lecture	Norman, P.	ING ONE
	6:00–7:50pm W Lab		ING ONE
	8:00–11:50 S Lecture		ING ONE

Section 6140 meets for the SECOND NINE WEEKS: October 18–December 18, 1999, at the Inglewood One Stop, 110 S. La Brea, Inglewood. For more information, see the One Stop section of this schedule.

6141	6:00–7:50pm T Lecture	Barlock, R.	H 4
	6:00–6:50pm Th Lecture		H 4
	7:00–7:50pm Th Lab		H 4
6143	6:00–7:50pm T Lecture	Kai, F	H 1
	6:00–6:50pm Th Lecture		H 1
	7:00–7:50pm Th Lab		H 1
6145	8:00–9:50pm M Lecture	McCallum, V.	H 3
	8:00–8:50pm W Lecture		H 3
	9:00–9:50pm W Lab		H 3
6146	8:00–9:50pm T Lecture	Kai, F	H 1
	8:00–8:50pm Th Lecture		H 1
	9:00–9:50pm Th Lab		H 1

From El Camino College, *Schedule of Classes*, Fall 1999, p. 46.

Exercise 7B: Scanning

Scan the opposite page, taken from a typical college catalog, for answers to questions that most beginning students will encounter. Look for key words in the headings to help you scan more quickly.

1. If you do not officially withdraw from a class, what may the result be?

   _____

2. How many absences may cause you to be dropped from a class?

   _____

3. What may be the penalty for not attending the first meeting of a class in which you are enrolled? _____

4. Approximately how many hours of independent study will an instructor expect in exchange for one unit of credit? _____

5. Is a student allowed to add a class after the third week of classes? _____

Check your answers with the key, and record your scores below.

Scanning Time   _____

Number of Errors   _____

Attendance, Credit

Attendance at First Class

Students who enroll in class but do not attend the first scheduled class meeting may be dropped from the roster and their places given to waiting students who were unable to enroll at the time of registration.

Attendance Without Official Enrollment

Students will not be permitted to attend classes in which they are not enrolled. Exceptions may be allowed by the instructor for bonafide visitors.

Attendance During Semester

Regular attendance is expected of every student. A student may be dropped from class when absences from class exceed the number of units assigned to the course. This rule also applies to excessive absences due to illness or medical treatment. The student who has been absent due to illness or medical appointment must explain the absence directly to the instructor. The student who has been absent due to a communicable disease or quarantine must report directly to the Health Center for clearance before returning to classes.

Adding a Class

If space is available, students who have completed registration may add a class by going to the first meeting of the class and securing permission of the instructor. After the third week of classes in a semester, with instructor/dean approval, students may enroll in classes under extenuating circumstances.

Withdrawal from Class

Official withdrawal from class must be processed through the online system in the Admissions Office. Failure to complete this process may result in the assignment of a letter grade of A through F.

Independent Study

The following regulations govern Independent Study at El Camino College:

1. Independent Study projects will normally be for one unit of credit with a maximum of three units per semester and must be approved by the instructor and Dean of the Division.

2. Independent Study projects are normally undertaken in the Department or Division of the student's academic major. Exceptions to this rule must be approved by the Dean of the Division of the student's academic major.

3. To be eligible for Independent Study a student must:

A. Show evidence of competence or study in depth in the ECC curriculum of the academic major and the area in which the student proposes to do independent study.

B. Be concurrently enrolled in at least one other class at ECC. Exceptions to this rule may be made by the Division Dean.

4. As a guideline, instructors should expect 60 hours of independent study as criteria for the assignment of one unit of credit.

5. No faculty member should supervise more than three Independent Study students in any one semester.

From *1999–2000 El Camino College Catalog*, p. 10.

Exercise 7C: Skimming and Scanning

In these phrases, scan for each noun that represents an animate object (has human or animal life) and make a slash through it.

Example: the broken leg.

Some phrases have none; some have more than one. Skim the descriptive details to find the setting. (It is usually animate nouns that are most important in a story.)

1. small southern town
2. five hundred people
3. the courthouse square
4. magnolia trees on lawn
5. old men on benches
6. whittling and spitting
7. old pickup trucks
8. bird-splattered windshield
9. farmer walking into courthouse
10. to pay his taxes
11. farmer's wife shopping
12. six dry-goods stores
13. horse and wagon
14. causing traffic jam
15. coon dog scratching fleas
16. noonday sun shining
17. long, hot summer
18. spilled ice cream cone
19. on the pavement
20. flies buzzing around
21. teenagers lined up
22. outside the movie house
23. *Son of Swamp Monster*
24. store clerk rushing
25. back to work
26. shirtsleeves rolled up
27. perspiration on arms
28. college kids hanging around
29. the local dairy treat
30. waitress chewing gum
31. boy on motorcycle
32. roars up
33. waitress giggling
34. manager in front
35. shakes his fist
36. only bank in town
37. customers lined up
38. cashiers handling money
39. children in cowboy boots
40. scuffling on floor
41. mothers grabbing hands
42. holding on tight
43. sound of music
44. and marching feet
45. trumpets off-key
46. the high school band
47. around the courthouse square
48. hands waving
49. hearts beating
50. too much excitement

Time _____

Number of Errors _____

Check your answers with the key.

Exercise 7D: Skimming and Scanning

In these phrases, scan for each noun that represents an animate object (has human or animal life) and make a slash through it.

Example: the fat ~~finger~~.

Some phrases have none; some have more than one. Skim to follow the plot.

1. the overcast sky
2. high on a hill
3. towering stone mansion
4. howl of a coyote
5. a door creaking
6. the monkey's paw
7. the whistling wind
8. the chain clanking
9. sudden glimpse of mummy
10. candles snuffed out
11. a starving black rat
12. the mad doctor
13. in a dank, dark basement
14. blood on the coat
15. a twisted arm hanging
16. glaring bloodshot eyes
17. one foot sliding behind
18. sharpening of a blade
19. eyes on last victim
20. hoarse, croaking laugh
21. footsteps up the stairs
22. whining cries of a child
23. lightning outside a window
24. vultures hovering above
25. bat wings rustling in attic

26. bedroom on West Wing
27. pale sleeping girl
28. under a red velvet spread
29. the slim trembling hand
30. an eyelid fluttering
31. stirred by unknown fears
32. birds caught in a trap
33. steps coming closer
34. clawlike hand reaching
35. doorknob slowly turning
36. heavy door creaking open
37. frightened eyes piercing the dark
38. blade illuminated by lightning
39. shrill scream shattering quiet
40. desperate struggle beginning
41. knife near throat
42. lips looming near
43. yellow teeth bared
44. fangs piercing throat
45. not a drop wasted
46. body falling to floor
47. mad doctor dead
48. pink flush returning
49. to girl's pale cheeks
50. return of Vampira

Time _____

Number of Errors _____

Check your answers with the key.

Exercise 7E: Phrases

Scan for the phrase identical to the key phrase and make a slash through it.

Key Phrase

1. an open book   an open door   open a book   an open book
2. is always gay   is almost gay   is always gay   is another guy
3. pitches the tent   pitches the tent   pinches snuff   watches the rent
4. reading fiction   reading fiction   working fractions   reads nonfiction
5. built like a brick   like a built brick   built like a bat   built like a brick
6. very bruised ego   very bruised ego   very broken ego   very bruised skin
7. lovely green lamp   lovely green ramp   lovely green lamp   lovely damp stream
8. navy blue suit   navy blue blouse   blue-suited navy   navy blue suit
9. twice-seen film   twice-seen film   seen two films   wind the filmstrip
10. catches a ball fast   catches a ball fast   snatch ball fast   watches a ball fall
11. covers a bed   covers the bread   over the beds   covers a bed
12. estimates damage   estimates the profit   estimates damage   estimates danger
13. good baked potato   bake good potatoes   good baked potato   baked potatoes
14. snakes in a pen   snakes in a pen   snake in a pen   snakes in a bin
15. twists and shakes   twisted and shaken   twists a snake   twists and shakes
16. picks a pretty posy   picks a pretty rose   picks pertinent point   picks a pretty posy
17. turned page slowly   slowly turns page   turn cheek slowly   turned page slowly
18. hunts with hounds   hunts for pound   hunts with hounds   hunts without hound
19. a shattered pot   a shattered pot   shatter the pot   a flattened pot
20. the first circle   the first circus   the fast circuit   the first circle

Time _____

Number of Errors _____

Exercise 7F: Phrases

Scan for the phrase identical to the key phrase and make a slash through it.

Key Phrase

1. shoes and socks	socks and shoes	shoes and socks	shoe the horse
2. red schoolhouse	read schoolbook	red schoolhouse	red poolhouse
3. sat quietly there	sat quietly there	sits quietly here	sit quite quietly
4. a good purpose	a good purpose	a purple food	a hidden purpose
5. flying away now	flying away now	now flying away	flew that way
6. fields and streams	field that hit	streams and fields	fields and streams
7. big soft pillow	soften big pillow	big soft pillow	digs soft ridges
8. the quick defeat	the quiet defeat	the quick defeat	the queer defect
9. isolates the town	the brown insole	the round isobar	isolates the town
10. ate with relish	ate with relish	beat with relish	ate the radish
11. caught in a maze	caught in a maze	caught in a haze	caught with a mate
12. this superb dinner	this superb dinner	this inner stupor	this winning suburb
13. a conscious effort	a consecrated fort	a formed conscience	a conscious effort
14. strikes the knave	stroke the slave	strikes the knave	the grave knack
15. those precious few	these precise few	those precious few	these few luscious
16. reverses the trend	reverses the trend	reviews the trick	the reversed trend
17. the mangled body	mangle the body	the mangled body	the tangled web
18. that gentle person	fat genteel person	that genuine person	that gentle person
19. figures the fraction	figures the fraction	the figured fraction	punctures the fragment
20. throughout infinity	through infinity	thoroughly infirm	throughout infinity

Time _____

Number of Errors _____

The two readings in this chapter are longer than in earlier chapters and not meant to be read carefully. They are taken from newspaper articles that reflect our shrinking world.

Exercise 7G: Timed Reading   978 words

This reading, from *The World Paper*, discusses the international impact of what most of us think is an American staple—soap operas.

Preview: *Quickly survey the title, author's name, first paragraph, and last paragraph. Also read the underlined sentences and phrases, mostly topic sentences and related details, in the first three paragraphs. In the remaining sections, continue to underline at least one important point per section and a few related supporting details. Then write how you think this soap opera affected people in another country.*

Wait for a signal from your instructor before you begin reading. Then skim the article by rapidly reading the subheadings and focusing on the first couple of sentences under each subheading. Quickly reread the underlined sentences and phrases. Skip over minor details. Try to double or triple your usual reading speed. Circle your reading time when you have finished, and find your WPM.

Soap Operas and Social Change

Gregorio Lasota, in Caracas, Venezuela

Members of Venezuela's ruling elite call it "the snake." Its bite is said to have killed the career of former president Carlos Andres Perez. But every night more than two-thirds of the country's residents, rich and poor, head home to watch it.

Watched by Rich and Poor

What motivates people ranging from the richest country club dwellers to the poorest inhabitants of Caracas' Petare neighborhoods to spend an hour in front of their television sets? The answer is the soap opera *Por Estas Calles* (Along These Streets), which has run for almost two years.

"We have aired over 700 installments. Every day, at 9 p.m., 70 percent of television viewers tune into this soap opera," asserts Alberto Giarocco, the program's drama manager. That is some seven million Venezuelans.

Broke with Convention—Tackled Meatier Topics

The show's popularity stems from the fact that it broke with many of the old conventions binding television programs. Instead of the sentimental relationships usually portrayed in Latin American soap operas, the producers of this program chose to tackle meatier topics. Thus, they attracted a wider audience. As one television critic observed, "The authors and the producers skillfully took full advantage of the material provided by growing social conflicts, two failed coups and innumerable cases of corruption. Viewers identified the characters of this soap opera with <u>real-life characters</u>. They connected its plot with authentic political, financial and sexual scandals."

Introduced Real-Life Presidential Scandals into Plot

Among the events adopted by the authors of *Por Estas Calles* were the scandals surrounding Venezuela's last two presidents. Both men stand accused of stealing public funds and helping their lovers accumulate sizable fortunes. With their lovers, who also happened to be their secretaries, they then stashed the fortunes abroad. It was by utilizing real events like these that the show turned from pure entertainment into an instrument of social and political criticism. The authors created the extravagant character Don Lengua and gave him freedom to comment on such events as the presidential scandals. All this without disturbing the central plot of *Por Estas Calles*. Lengua, like his peers in Greek tragedies, has an editorial role. Only this time it is expressed in the language of television.

Characters—Not the Usual Victims

Normally, soap opera characters are ordinary people mistreated by life. But in *Por Estas Calles* the characters are anything but ordinary—and anything but victims. They include the likes of Don Chepe, a gubernatorial candidate, who is launching his campaign. Then there is Lucha, his ambitious lover. And Dr. Valerio, a family doctor married to the Governor's daughter. She owns a clinic and has made a fortune through dubious business dealings. Another is Natalio Vega, a chief of police who, frustrated with judicial inefficiency, takes justice in his own hands and kills two thugs. Finally, there is Mauro, a diabolical drug trafficker.

Of course, *Por Estas Calles* has kept the traditional elements of the melodrama. It still has the love Mauro professes for Euridice (a poor schoolteacher) and the passion of the naive and sensual Eloina for Valerio. But these subplots get buried under weightier issues. Thus, the soap opera—usually full of Cinderellas and Snow Whites—has in the case of *Por Estas Calles* become more credible. And it has done so without giving up the banalities that keep many viewers glued to the screen.

Soap Opera Called Factor in Fall of President Perez

While relatively new to Venezuelans, soap operas with a clear moral and educational message emerged in Brazil during the military dictatorship that ended in 1984. It is said that the generals promoted the moralizing. But they opposed political issues. The best Brazilian shows, even though different from their historical reality, seemed to have potential for being tools for social change. Venezuelans say that those in power frowned upon *Por Estas Calles* and pressured television management to soften the show's critical tone. The show had a great deal of influence on public opinion, expressing as it does the frustrations of a society sick and tired of the political structure. Members of Venezuela's ruling elite also suggest that this soap opera was a factor in the fall of President Carlos Andres Perez. . . .

More Worm Than Snake?

While the soap opera *Por Estas Calles* may be regarded by Venezuela's elite as "the snake," the United States Information Agency (USIA) sees it as more of a worm.

The USIA expressed its views in a recent memorandum titled, *"Por Estas Calles: Soap Opera or Subversion?"* The USIA finds that the show has some antiestablishment themes. But it dismisses the snake's bite. "A week's viewing leads to the conclusion that [the show] is basically a traditional soap opera with some populist commentary added for variety."

The USIA review, however, admits that the show does touch on many of the themes and issues affecting everyday life in Venezuela. These include the corruption that accompanied the influx of oil revenues, the poor state of public health facilities, and the cost of everyday staples such as food and shelter. The reviewer quotes several of the show's characters as examples. One is a hospital administrator who says, "When are people going to realize that in this country the poor don't have a right to get sick? They have to pay for it."

According to the reviewer, there is no doubt the show "depicts a modern-day Caracas as an anarchic den of iniquity where collective social values are nonexistent, the government is corrupt, and life is daily becoming worse for ordinary folk."

However, "To see the show as subversive is clearly stretching the point," concludes the USIA report. "Individual problems of unrequited love, cross-class marriages, surprise pregnancies, secret affairs, and murdered girlfriends are still more vital to the program than any notion of social justice. It is only a matter of time before one of the characters develops amnesia."

TIMING CHART	
min:sec	wpm
1:57	500
1:53	520
1:49	540
1:45	560
1:41	580
1:38	600
1:35	620
1:32	640
1:29	660
1:26	680
1:24	700
1:22	720
1:19	740
1:17	760
1:15	780
1:13	800
1:12	820
1:10	840
1:08	860
1:07	880
1:05	900
1:04	920
1:02	940
1:01	960
1:00	980
0:59	1000

Answer the five skimming questions without referring to the article.

1. What is the soap opera's name (in Spanish or English)? _____

2. Who watches this soap opera?
   (a) mostly the rich   (b) mostly the poor   (c) both

3. What makes this soap opera different from others?
   _____

4. How are the characters different from those in other soap operas?
   (a) less likely to be victims   (b) more likely to be victims

5. In a complete sentence, state the thesis of the article.
   _____
   _____

   [What is popular?   With whom?   Why?]

You may refer to the article to answer these scanning questions. Some are "complex" scanning questions that may require you to do some interpreting.

6. How many television viewers watch this show? _____

7. What made Venezuela's last two presidents a source for good drama?
   _____

8. What do the list of characters given have in common—other than not being ordinary? _____

9. What does the USIA mean by calling "the snake" more of a "worm"?
   _____

10. The quotation by the character of the hospital administrator, used in the USIA review, is meant to make the show look bad.   (a) true   (b) false

Check your answers with the key, and record your scores below and on the Progress Chart.

Words per Minute   _____

Percent Comprehension   _____

The last, much longer, reading, from *Freedom Review*, exposes a serious problem that affects our country more than we realize—child slavery in third world countries.

Preview: *Quickly survey the title, first paragraph, subheadings, and last paragraph. Write here any problems and solutions you anticipate the author will cover.*

_____

_____

 Wait for a signal from your instructor before you begin reading. Then skim the article by quickly reading a few sentences under each subheading. Try to read almost vertically in between subheadings, picking up topic sentences and related phrases as you move your eyes quickly down the page. Try to skim at double or triple your usual speed. Check your reading time when you have finished, and find your WPM.

from Outlawing the Crime of Child Slavery: Stolen Childhood

Robert A. Senser

"Who says slavery is dead? It is still very much alive. It survives especially among children—more than 200 million in the world, very many of them Asians."

The speaker is a charismatic Asian in his late thirties, a Brahmin by birth, an engineer by training, and a social activist by choice. Kailash Satyarthi has a simple message, one that he is spreading across the world, from the small villages of his native India to the power centers of Washington, London, and Frankfurt. The message: *It is time to liberate the millions of children now held in servitude.*

Protests Against Child Slavery

Satyarthi chairs the South Asian Coalition on Child Servitude. This is a network of more than sixty nongovernmental groups trying to free South Asian children from slavery and near-slavery. On September 18 of this year, Satyarthi escorted about 250 children, most of them aged from 6 to 12, in a march through the streets of New Delhi to protest the employment of children in sweatshops. The little marchers chanted, "We want freedom." They carried banners reading: "STOP BUYING AND SELLING PRODUCTS MADE BY CHILDREN," "REPLACE CHILDREN WITH MILLIONS OF UNEMPLOYED ADULTS," AND "LET THERE BE FREE, COMPULSORY EDUCATION FOR ALL." In a sitdown in front of the Labor Ministry, they displayed a few of the products Indian children make—glass bangles, household locks, brassware, and bricks.

Satyarthi introduced reporters to some of the marchers, including fourteen-year-old Devanandan, rescued from forced labor a few months earlier. Devanandan said he was coaxed to leave home in 1991 by promises of wages up to $100 a month for working at a loom two hours a day while going to school. Instead, he was forced to work, eat, and sleep locked in the same room, knotting carpets from 4 a.m. till late evening for pennies in pay.

The demonstration was part of the annual Day Against Child Servitude, observed in India since 1989. This date is the first anniversary of a Pakistani Supreme Court decision that led to releasing hundreds of children from bondage. Protests less dramatic than the one in New Delhi were held in other

South Asian cities, as well as in London and a few other European cities, according to the Anti-Slavery International of London. In the United States demonstrators picketed fourteen Wal-Mart stores nationwide. They were protesting the chain's record of purchasing garments from Asian suppliers notorious for employing girls and boys under 14 six and seven days a week.

The September 18 observances were a few recent public signs of a fledgling international movement against an ancient evil commonly called child labor. Although South Asia by no means has a monopoly on the labor of children, the worst and most numerous abuses are concentrated there, even in organized commercial industries making carpets, glassware, shoes, fireworks, locks, and other products. South Asians themselves are leading the crusade against the evil they call child servitude. Once dismissed as unrealistic dreamers, they have now won unprecedented national and international attention for their cause.

(Re)Enter the ILO: Improved Conditions Not Enough

The problem of child labor has gripped the International Labor Organization from its very founding at a conference in Washington, D.C., in 1919. Then, in an optimistic postwar mood, the delegates adopted a convention fixing a minimum age of 14 for employment in industry. An ILO convention adopted in 1973 raised the minimum age to 15. India was among the countries that adopted the new standard, but it has not enforced it.

According to the view that predominated until recently, child labor is so endemic in the developing world that realistically you can't abolish it. You can only improve the working conditions of children. Instead of striving to get children out of sweatshops, you make sure that, if they lose a finger on the job, they get proper medical care before they go back to work again in, perhaps, a safer environment.

A growing number of South Asian social activists now reject that approach. So does a new ILO initiative called the International Program on the Elimination of Child Labor. It was launched in early 1992, thanks partly to a five-year grant totaling $31 million from the German government. The program commits the organization "to a major effort to halt child labor in its more unacceptable forms and to begin reversing the trend toward reliance on child labor for economic support."

A few U.N. agencies are now rallying behind the same goal. Most notable is the U.N. Children's Fund (UNICEF). . . . Further, multinational corporations have become sensitive to media reports that some of their far-flung contractors and subcontractors around the world have boys and girls working for them. In 1992, the San Francisco–based Levi Strauss & Co. took the lead. It requires its 600 suppliers in fifty countries to adopt a code of conduct that includes a prohibition against the employment of children under 14.

Problem Growing Worse with Modern Technology

What accounts for this new international interest, which the ILO calls a "global offensive"?

Among the multiple reasons, the foremost has to be that the problem is not going away. It is worsening. Nobody has accurate global figures, particularly because few countries have accurate national figures. However, according to a 1992 ILO report, all indications are that the number of children at work around the world is growing. The number is growing, not just in totals, but proportionately in the same age groups.

Surprisingly, the trend is happening despite—or perhaps even *because of*—the modernizing process of international trade and investment. In 1984, when India exported $100 million worth of hand-knotted carpets, it had an estimated 100,000 children working fourteen to sixteen hours a day in the industry. Now, with the export figure reaching $300 million, child labor in the industry has reached more than 300 million. In China's booming coastal provinces, according to China's official media, children on a mass basis have dropped out of school in order to take jobs in new factories that have sprouted up both in urban and rural areas.

Abuse of Child Workers Common

Tragic signs of the trend periodically appear in the casualty figures of fires in factories devoted to export production. In Bangladesh, eleven children under the age of 16, three of them only 12 years old, were among the twenty-four workers who died on December 27, 1990, when a fire engulfed a Dhaka factory making garments for American and European consumers. In South China, twenty workers, most of them between 9 and 14 years old, died in an explosion in a fireworks factory on a Sunday in December 1992.

Contrary to a common impression, little children can be efficient at many unskilled and semi-skilled tasks, and can toil from dawn to dusk. In some cultures, particularly in Asia, children acquire discipline at work through physical punishment or the threat of it. In Bangladesh garment factories, for example, male supervisors punish children for miscounting and other errors by striking them or forcing them to kneel on the floor or stand on their head for ten to thirty minutes.

The abuses are even worse in India's carpet factories, which hold many low-caste children in bondage. A former Indian Chief Justice, P. N. Bhagwati, has publicly testified about discovering some "heart-rending" examples of boys working fourteen to twenty hours a day. "They are beaten up, branded [with red hot iron rods], and even hung from trees upside down."

Slavery by Any Other Name

Because of such abuses, the term "child labor" is too benign for the fate of most children working full-time in industry, certainly for carpet weaving and glassmaking in India. The term as commonly used covers two extremes. At one end is the suburban U.S. high school student who holds a part-time job in a fast food outlet and illegally works past 7 P.M. during a school day. And, at the other extreme, is the low-caste Indian boy, aged 10, kidnapped from his home, forced to work in a carpet sweatshop a hundred or more miles away, and beaten if he cries for his mother. Applied to such a wide range of different conditions, the same label implies that the harmful practices it covers are equally reprehensible, when they are not. However, the Anti-Slavery International of London argues that children conscripted into the full-time labor force before a certain age (say 14 or 15), and thus deprived of their right to an education, are suffering from a contemporary form of slavery. . . .

Child Labor Promotes Poverty

One rationale, popular even among Washington policymakers, is that no progress on eliminating child labor will occur until poverty declines. "But we argue the other way," Satyarthi said at a conference in Vienna. "Today in India we have 55 million children in servitude and an equal number of unemployed adults.

No government can scale down unemployment without curbing child labor," which he insists perpetuates poverty. . . .

Satyarthi never lets up on introducing the media to individual victims of such exploitation. As a result of this publicity, carpet manufacturers and exporters have found him an irritant. But, until recently, they could still dismiss him as a visionary, well meaning but not practical. They have argued, for example, that the industry needs child labor to survive in competition with the carpet industries in Pakistan, Nepal, Morocco, and other countries that have become heavily dependent on child workers.

U.S. Legislation

That was the situation before August 6, 1993, when Senator Tom Harkin introduced the Child Labor Deterrence Act. The Harkin bill, reintroduced in 1993, has become much more famous in India, Pakistan, and Bangladesh than anywhere else in the world, including the United States. In India it caused what James Ehrman, the labor attaché at the U.S. Embassy in New Delhi, calls a "sea change" in public concern about child servitude. . . .

The Harkin bill riveted people's attention because, unlike ILO conventions, unlike letters of protest from consumer groups, unlike appeals to conscience, it would have teeth in it. . . . The Harkin bill would ban the importation into the United States of any manufactured or mined goods produced in whole or in part by children under 15. That in itself is not radical. What gives the bill meaning is that it would back up its prohibition with enforcement, including civil and criminal penalties for violations. . . .

Work and Wealth

Contrary to Third World critics of the Harkin bill, who fear that it will cripple some industries of developing countries, Satyarthi predicts that, if passed with effective compliance procedures, it will give industries new life. The reason: employers will be induced to put adults to work. In India, as well as Nepal, some carpet manufacturers and exporters are now seriously considering that alternative. They are taking a new interest in an old proposal of SACCS: to certify and label carpets *not* made by children. This practice is similar to labeling some brands of tuna "dolphin safe."

With the help of an expert from the Indo-German Export Promotion, various interested parties in India—including carpet manufacturers and exporters—have developed a wordless "Smiling Carpet" label. The label is registered as a trademark to identify carpets untainted by child servitude. . . .

A century ago Americans didn't understand the implications of the new "national" economy. So until the 1930s the country considered child labor to be the exclusive concern of states. Today, the global economy faces a similar lag in adjusting to new horizons. The challenge is to adjust national and international rules on child labor to reach beyond the boundaries of individual nations.

At a union convention in Pittsburgh in 1881, the time when ending child labor was far from a national priority, Samuel Gompers vividly described the plight of boys and girls working in U.S. sweatshops, and issued a stirring appeal for change. Gompers' words need to reverberate throughout the global economy, wherever choices are made affecting child servitude. "Shame upon such crimes!" he cried. "Shame upon us if we do not raise our voices against them!"

TIMING CHART

min:sec	wpm
3:57	500
3:48	520
3:40	540
3:32	560
3:25	580
3:18	600
3:11	620
3:05	640
3:00	660
2:54	680
2:49	700
2:45	720
2:40	740
2:36	760
2:32	780
2:28	800
2:25	820
2:21	840
2:18	860
2:15	880
2:12	900
2:09	920
2:06	940
2:04	960
2:01	980
1:59	1000

Answer the five skimming questions without referring to the article.

1. According to the author, where do we find most forced child labor today?
   (a) Africa   (b) America   (c) Asia

2. What is the mission of Kailash Satyarthi?

   _____

3. The International Labor Organization and most reform groups are content with improving working conditions of children.   (a) true   (b) false

4. The most important reason for new international interest in child labor is that it is increasing.   (a) true   (b) false

5. Thesis: _____

   _____

   [Who is doing what?   Why?]

You may refer to the article to answer these scanning questions. Some are "complex" scanning questions that may require you to do some interpreting.

6. What is the contrast in what fourteen-year-old Devanandan was promised and what he found to be reality?

   Promise: _____

   Reality: _____

7. What has the ILO accomplished regarding child labor?
   (a) raised the minimum age twice   (b) abolished child labor

8. What is the ratio of children working to export dollars?

   _____ to $300 million

9. What is considered radical about the 1993 Harkin bill?

   _____

10. Why does Satyarthi believe eliminating child labor will help industries?
    (a) more adults working   (b) happier children   (c) increased productivity

Check your answers with the key, and record your scores below and on the Progress Chart.

Words per Minute _____

Percent Comprehension _____

Writing and Discussion Activities

1. Write a summary of the first Timed Reading. Your first sentence should give the author, title, and thesis. Your next sentences should include the first-level detail (see the headings) and additional detail from the underlined portion.

2. Now that we live in a "global village," what can you see as advantages and what can you see as disadvantages? Draw a line down the middle of a sheet of paper. To the left of the line, list the advantages. To the right of the line, list the disadvantages. Choose a point of view. (Stress the advantages or stress the disadvantages.) Then write a thesis statement with your point of view for the introduction of an essay.

Vocabulary Review, Chapter 7

Match the vocabulary word on the left with its definition on the right.

e 1. **coup**   (a) slavery

c 2. **caste**   (b) ban

a 3. **servitude**   (c) social class

b 4. **prohibition**   (d) fiendish

d 5. **diabolical**   (e) takeover

*Choose the best definition for each **boldfaced** word as it is used in its context.*

_____ 6. Studies show that children who have been abused by their parents often **perpetuate** the abuse when they have their own children.
   (a) prolong   (b) reverse   (c) lie about

_____ 7. Almost everyone's first experience of **unrequited** love feels like a tragedy.
   (a) required   (b) inappropriate   (c) not returned

_____ 8. The **banality** of the television show made Sharon change the channel to a show with more original dialogue.
   (a) clichéd nature   (b) indecent subject matter
   (c) frightening scenes

_____ 9. She searched the best shops for a purse made of **authentic** leather.
   (a) imitation   (b) genuine   (c) expensive

_____ 10. The consequences of **iniquity** are not always easy to see.
   (a) sin   (b) good judgment   (c) a virtuous life

*Mark each sentence to show whether the **boldfaced** word is used correctly.*

a = True   b = False

T 11. People who enjoy watching **melodrama** tend to prefer subtle, low-key movies.

T 12. Rosie realized that, to make ends meet, she needed either to spend less or have a larger **influx** of funds each month.

T 13. During the Vietnam War, many young men resisted being **conscripted** into the U.S. Army.

F 14. Governments best serve the needs of their people when they operate in an **anarchic** manner.

T 15. Being a member of the **elite** often brings with it not only privileges but also the envy of the less fortunate.

(Continued)

Choose the word from the box that fits the context of the following paragraph.
Write the letter of each choice on the blank lines to the left of the paragraph.

(a) **fledgling**	(b) **diversified**	(c) **launching**
(d) **reprehensible**		(e) **charismatic**

_____ 16.   For the successful __16__ of a political career, it's best if the __17__

_____ 17.   politician has not had a __18__ past. In addition, the would-be politi-

_____ 18.   cian could use a __19__ personality and a __20__ group of supporters.

_____ 19.

_____ 20.

% Correct _____

Comprehension Review, Chapter 7

1. In a complete sentence, define *skimming*.
   Skimming is reading for the general idea or
   the big picture.

2. In a complete sentence, define *scanning*.
   Scanning is looking for exact answers to
   specific questions.

_b_ 3. Which skill involves faster reading?   (a) skimming   (b) scanning

_b_ 4. Which skill involves more skipping?   (a) skimming   (b) scanning

____ 5. What is a reasonable long-term speed goal in skimming? _766 or 800_ .
     WPM

____ 6. Which of the following would *not* be a good situation for skimming?
   (a) sorting through your junk mail
   (b) rereading textbook material you have already studied
   (c) reading a textbook chapter for the first and only time you read it
   (d) selecting reference materials you might use for a term paper
   (e) reading the boring parts in a trashy novel

____ 7. When skimming nonfiction, the *preview* method is useful.
   (a) true   (b) false

____ 8. Which type of scanning is used for doing the Words in Context exercises in this book?
   (a) simple scanning   (b) complex scanning

____ 9. Which type of scanning is used for doing the Phrase Practice exercises in this book?
   (a) simple scanning   (b) complex scanning

Give two examples of situations in which you might use simple scanning *outside of this class. (Do not use examples from #6.)*

10. _Locating a certain street or town on a map._

11. _Finding a name in the fone book_

Give two examples of situations in which you might use complex scanning *outside of this class.*

12. _Looking in the movie ads or TV guid for "any_

13. _good show"_

Finding out when bus buses travel
between 2 cities

(Continued)

_____ 14. What is the best way to use skimming and/or scanning in connection to study-reading?

(a) as a replacement for study-reading

(b) as an aid to study-reading

(c) never to be used with study-reading

_____ 15. If you increase your skimming speed, is there a reasonable chance that your study-reading speed will increase as a side benefit?

(a) yes   (b) no

% Correct _____

VOCABULARY PREVIEW for Chapter 8

WORDS IN CONTEXT

Directions: *Examine the **boldfaced** word as it is used in the sentence and write your best guess of the word's meaning. Then look up the word in your dictionary and write the best definition for its context in the sentence.*

PRONUNCIATION KEY

a	cat	ā	made	ä	bar	k	cot, quit			adore
e	pet	ē	these	â	care	s	cent			travel
i	sit	ī	ride	è	term	z	beds	ə	{	horrify
o	rot	ō	note	ô	order	j	giant			pardon
u	nut	o͞o	rude	o͝o	foot	th	thank			circus
ù	put	yo͞o	use	o͞o	food	ᴛʜ	this			

from Practice 1(a) (p. 271)

1. **cloning**   (klōn′ ing)   *verbal (noun)*

   Congress should ban human cloning now.

   Your best guess: _____

   Best dictionary definition: _____

2. **draconian**   (dra kō′ nē ən)   *adjective*

   It should be **draconian**: the deliberate creation of headless humans must be made a crime.

   Your best guess: _____

   Best dictionary definition: _____

3. **barbarity**   (bär bar′ ə tē)   *noun*

   If we flinch in the face of this high-tech **barbarity**, we'll deserve to live in the hell it heralds.

   Your best guess: _____

   Best dictionary definition: _____

from Paragraph 8A (p. 277)

4. **white supremacist**   (hwīt′ sə prem′ ə sist)   *noun*

   A recent example [of people who shouldn't have guns] is **white supremacist** Buford O. Furrow, Jr.

   Your best guess: _____

   Best dictionary definition: _____

5. **felon** (fel′ ən)   *noun*

A convicted **felon**, he wasn't supposed to have a gun.

Your best guess: _____

Best dictionary definition: _____

from Paragraph 8B (p. 278)

6. **refute** (ri fyo͞ot′)   *verbal*

The notion that access to "handguns" or any other object causes violence is almost absurdly easy to **refute**.

Your best guess: _____

Best dictionary definition: _____

from Paragraph 8C (p. 279)

7. **dispatched** (dis pacht′)   *verb*

[Billy the Kid] murdered [his] first victim when he was 14 and had **dispatched** 20 more human beings by the time he reached voting age—all with a six-shooter.

Your best guess: _____

Best dictionary definition: _____

8. **prolific** (prō lif′ ik)   *adjective*

Imagine how **prolific** he [Billy the Kid] could've been with a semi-automatic.

Your best guess: _____

Best dictionary definition: _____

from Timed Reading 8F (p. 284)

9. **fodder** (fod′ ər)   *noun*

This does not stop people from taking this incident and using it as **fodder** for their own political views.

Your best guess: _____

Best dictionary definition: _____

10. **advocates** (ad′ və kəts)   *noun*

The first and most predictable reactors to this event were the gun-control **advocates**.

Your best guess: _____

Best dictionary definition: _____

11. **alleged** (ə lejd′)   *adjective*

The two **alleged** criminals also used explosive devices.

Your best guess: _____

Best dictionary definition: _____

12. **cant**   (kant)   *noun*

    The media dutifully reported this view, because they, as a rule, follow the **cant** of the political left.

Your best guess: _____

Best dictionary definition: _____

13. **bridles**   (brīd′ lz)   *verb*

    The political left **bridles** at the mere recitation of a single prayer in public schools.

Your best guess: _____

Best dictionary definition: _____

[Clue: Pick the verb definition, not the more common noun definition.]

14. **inculcating**   (in kul′ kāt ing)   *verbal*

    We can't have the public schools **inculcating** belief in something like that—and we don't.

Your best guess: _____

Best dictionary definition: _____

15. **lax**   (laks)   *adjective*

    Nobody shot up St. Matthew Elementary School while I was there—and back then gun-control laws were far more **lax** than they are now.

Your best guess: _____

Best dictionary definition: _____

16. **contemporary**   (kən tem′ pə rer′ ē)   *adjective*

    The simple fact is that the political left has assumed ownership of the rules of **contemporary** society.

Your best guess: _____

Best dictionary definition: _____

[Clue: This word was used as a "noun" in Chapter 6.]

17. **intervened**   (in′ ter vēnd′)   *verb*

    But nobody **intervened**, and evidently nobody told these two misguided kids that some things are objectively wrong.

Your best guess: _____

Best dictionary definition: _____

18. **purview**   (pėr′ vyo͞o)   *noun*

    Perhaps too many public schoolteachers do not view morals instruction as being within their professional **purview**.

Your best guess: _____

Best dictionary definition: _____

19. **accord** (ə kôrd')   *noun*

It is neither difficult nor particularly offensive to instruct children in the better reasons rather than casting them adrift to find the worse ones on their own untutored **accord**.

Your best guess: _____

Best dictionary definition: _____

[Clue: Pick the definition for the word used as an idiom.]

from Timed Reading 8G (p. 287)

20. **casualty** (kazh' o͞o əl tē)   *noun*

After the ribbons fade, after the dead are laid to rest, after reporters drift away, the last **casualty** of the ***massacre*** at Columbine High School may turn out to be the idea of public school.

Your best guess: _____

Best dictionary definition: _____

21. **massacre** (mas' ə kər)   *noun*

Your best guess: _____

Best dictionary definition: _____

[Note: See sentence #20 for context clues to **massacre**.]

22. **balkanized** (bôl' kə nizd)   *verbal (adjective)*

After Littleton, Colorado, who wonders about Yugoslavia? The most **balkanized** region of America may well be the high school.

Your best guess: _____

Best dictionary definition: _____

[Clue: Think about what the Balkan states represent; then add the verb suffix.]

23. **Goths** (goths)   *noun*

What we saw at Columbine—the **Goths** against the jocks—was a kind of ethnic cleansing.

Your best guess: _____

Best dictionary definition: _____

24. **parody** (par' ə dē)   *noun*

But then we started to see white kids emerge from the forests of rural America, their **parody** of big-city gangs, their murderous rage against parents and school.

Your best guess: _____

Best dictionary definition: _____

25. **anonymity**   (an′ ə nim′ ə tē)   *noun*

   Littleton, a middle-class suburb where nice people live and the streets are wide and the houses have separate bedrooms for everyone and a three-car garage—the domestic architecture of **anonymity**.

   Your best guess: _____

   Best dictionary definition: _____

26. **decipher**   (di sī′ fər)   *verb*

   A woman, a mother of teenagers, said to me this week that she began to "lose contact" with her children when they began to listen to a music she could not **decipher**.

   Your best guess: _____

   Best dictionary definition: _____

27. **diminish**   (də min′ ish)   *verb*

   In Twain's story of Finn, the "school marm" must play the villain, because it is she who intends to catch Huck and **diminish** his individualism by making him "speak regular."

   Your best guess: _____

   Best dictionary definition: _____

28. **sentimentality**   (sen′ tə men tal′ ə tē)   *noun*

   At a time when the American public school is open to all, many teachers settle for the **sentimentality** of "***multiculturalism***" . . . instead of insisting on a ***communal*** vision.

   Your best guess: _____

   Best dictionary definition: _____

29. **multiculturalism**   (mul′ ti kul′ chər ə liz′ əm)   *noun*

   Your best guess: _____

   Best dictionary definition: _____

30. **communal**   (kə myo͞o′ nl)   *adjective*

   Your best guess: _____

   Best dictionary definition: _____

31. **conformist**   (kən fôrm′ ist)   *adjective*

   It's [high school] always been the most **conformist** society of our lives.

   Your best guess: _____

   Best dictionary definition: _____

32. **impersonality**   (im pėr′ sə nal′ ə tē)   *noun*

They live surrounded by an architecture of **impersonality** and a technology of **solitude**—Web pages screaming in silence for attention.

Your best guess: _____

Best dictionary definition: _____

[Clue: Look at the definition for the adjective form of the word; then look up the noun suffix.]

33. **solitude**   (sol′ ə to͞od)   *noun*

Your best guess: _____

Best dictionary definition: _____

34. **parochial**   (pə rō′ kē əl)   *adjective*

Theodore J. Forstmann, a Wall Street financier-billionaire, and John Walton, the Wal-Mart heir, promised low-income children scholarships to private or **parochial** schools.

Your best guess: _____

Best dictionary definition: _____

35. **theological**   (thē′ ə loj′ ə kəl)   *adjective*

In spite of their **theological** **tribalism** [at private, religious schools], or maybe because of it, a student is grounded in a larger reality than his separate self.

Your best guess: _____

Best dictionary definition: _____

36. **tribalism**   (trī′ bə liz′ əm)   *noun*

Your best guess: _____

Best dictionary definition: _____

[Clue: Look at the adjective form of the word, then at the noun suffix.]

Exercise, Vocabulary Preview, Chapter 8

Directions: *Choose the best definition for each **boldfaced** word or phrase as it is used in its context.*

_C_ 1. The controversy about **cloning** is a complex issue; we must weigh the value of medical advancement and ability to prolong human life against the value of human individuality.

(a) vaccinating babies (b) clothing the poor (c) copying humans

_b_ 2. The **draconian** punishment, prison for life, did not fit the crime, which was stealing a loaf of bread.

(a) too mild (b) very severe (c) too public

_b_ 3. The **barbarity** of his crimes against children enraged the other inmates at the maximum security prison.

(a) strangeness (b) cruelty (c) inappropriateness

_a_ 4. For many, the stereotype of a **white supremacist** is an uneducated, unsophisticated "redneck" or hillbilly; however, the reality is that hatred and bigotry are found in all kinds of people.

(a) minority hater (b) Caucasian hater (c) king of whites

_b_ 5. A convicted **felon** loses some of his or her constitutional rights while in prison: for example, the right to vote.

(a) foreigner (b) criminal (c) juvenile delinquent

_c_ 6. The op-ed section of the newspaper is often a place for the "common man" to **refute** ideas and opinions held by politicians.

(a) support (b) prove (c) contradict

_a_ 7. A professional exterminator was called upon to **dispatch** the pests in and around our house quickly and efficiently.

(a) kill (b) protect (c) transfer

_a_ 8. Danielle Steele is a **prolific** writer; she publishes at least one novel per year and sometimes two.

(a) productive (b) talented (c) scary

_c_ 9. Minorities and poor whites were said to be used by the U.S. Armed Forces as "cannon **fodder**" during the Vietnam War.

(a) fire (b) trash (c) fuel

_b_ 10. Child **advocates** have had much cause for concern with the state of the foster care system in this country.

(a) opponents (b) supporters (c) competitors

_c_ 11. Joseph was the **alleged** perpetrator of the crime; in other words, the police suspected that he did it.

(a) alternate (b) proven (c) thought to be

_a_ 12. The school newspaper wrote such radical **cant** that Cecilia resented part of her tuition dollars being used for it.

(a) prejudiced statements   (b) elaborate style   (c) vulgar words

_c_ 13. My two-year-old daughter **bridles** at the mere suggestion of sleep; she would rather keep playing until she drops from sheer exhaustion.

(a) shows relief   (b) shows affection   (c) shows resentment

_b_ 14. The Quakers are known for **inculcating** high ideals and values in their children.

(a) noticing   (b) instilling   (c) discouraging

_c_ 15. As a society, we have become **lax** in our manners, especially those involving simple courtesy.

(a) strict   (b) picky   (c) permissive

_a_ 16. In **contemporary** literature, as in current movies, more violence is being used as a dramatic device.

(a) modern   (b) Old English   (c) futuristic

_c_ 17. When Casey's brother **intervened** on her behalf with the neighborhood bully, she was furious with him for butting in.

(a) fought   (b) lied   (c) interfered

_____ 18. While the **purview** of schoolteachers has expanded to include many aspects of character education, they are somehow expected to instill character, without instilling judgment.

(a) range of motion   (b) range of responsibility   (c) driving range

_____ 19. Fran learned to eat healthier of her own **accord** instead of giving in to the nagging of her mother, who was also a nutritionist.

(a) voluntarily   (b) greed   (c) for money

_____ 20. The latest **casualties** of the Vietnam War may be the children of the survivors; the psychological injuries of the fathers may have helped to create a generation of emotionally confused young adults.

(a) news   (b) heroes   (c) victims

_____ 21. Before there were any laws regulating the killing of whales, animal-rights activists would routinely protest the annual **massacre** of migrating whales.

(a) roundup   (b) sightings   (c) slaughter

_____ 22. In any newly **balkanized** region, the differing factions must find it difficult at first to remember which of their neighbors they are not speaking to.

(a) divided   (b) liberated   (c) defeated

_____ 23. Each generation of teenagers has had its own version of **Goths**, adopting dark clothes and a gloomy, aggressive manner they associate with the Germanic tribes, who repeatedly attacked the Roman Empire.

(a) scholarly nerds   (b) ancient invaders   (c) pitiful losers

_____ 24. Many badly written television shows are an unintentional **parody** of the movies on which they are based, making viewers laugh when they are supposed to cry.

(a) plagiarism   (b) award-winning show   (c) comic imitation _b_ 25. It is often all too easy to find **anonymity** in a large city such as Los Angeles or New York City; one can go days and days without having a personal conversation or being recognized by another human being.

(a) sophistication   (b) being lonely   (c) being unknown

_b_ 26. In order to **decipher** the code, Mr. Johnson presented it to his advanced math class as their weekly challenge problem.

(a) send out   (b) figure out   (c) receive

_a_ 27. As adults, I think we tend to **diminish** our children with our impatience, rushing to make assumptions instead of listening to what they have to say.

(a) minimize   (b) increase   (c) bully

_c_ 28. Most people seem to view an upcoming high school reunion with either dread or indifference or with **sentimentality**, weeping and gushing over every reminder.

(a) revenge   (b) happiness   (c) excess emotion

_____ 29. Textbook publishers make an effort to satisfy the demand for **multiculturalism** by including stories about every ethnic group.

(a) one culture   (b) many cultures   (c) no culture

_b_ 30. Charlotte's mother kept suggesting a **communal** living situation, in which the entire family would live together in a grouping of homes and share the responsibilities of living and raising children.

(a) hippie   (b) shared   (c) rural

_b_ 31. While Rolf's father had been considered a rebel by the government, Rolf's mother was a strict **conformist**, never questioning or disagreeing with any public policies.

(a) disciplinarian   (b) accepting authority   (c) defying authority

_a_ 32. People seeking houses with character and charm stay away from the **impersonality** of new housing developments.

(a) boring sameness   (b) modern conveniences   (c) great perks

_b_ 33. Patrick searched for **solitude** in the remote mountain regions of Utah.

(a) happiness   (b) seclusion   (c) sunshine

_c_ 34. More and more parents who are not religious are choosing **parochial** schools because of the discipline and higher standards not found in public schools.

(a) church   (b) business   (c) private

_c_ 35. In spite of their **theological** differences, the Methodist minister and the priest worked well together on the project for the homeless shelter.

(a) ethnic   (b) cultural   (c) religious

_a_ 36. The **tribalism** found in gang members is often stronger than their ties to their own families.

(a) group loyalty   (b) blood ties   (c) cannibalism

Number of Errors _____

Chapter 8
Reading Critically

I. How to Understand More

Reading Critically

What does it mean to read *critically*? You probably recognize the word "critic" as the root of "critical." When you read as a critic, you question what you read. You evaluate the merits and faults of what an author is saying. You learn to see if the author presents the subject in a fair and trustworthy way. You also learn to read "between the lines" and notice the things an author hints at or implies instead of saying directly. In other words, you learn to infer and draw conclusions, skills that are important in every job or social activity.

As your ability to read critically grows, you reap three rewards. First, you recognize and better understand ideas that are well presented. Second, you gain a valuable ability to question those main ideas that are not fairly or accurately supported. Thus you can protect yourself against misleading claims or ideas. Third, you have a tool that you can use in your own writing and speaking, so you will sound informed and believable.

Decide Author's Purpose

The first thing a good critical reader does is determine the author's purpose for writing. Usually a writer's purpose is one of these three possibilities:

1. **To inform**—most textbook chapters, news articles, and instructions explain or inform.
2. **To persuade**—most advertising and newspaper editorials argue a particular point of view. They want to convince or persuade you to agree.
3. **To entertain**—this is the main purpose of many stories, humorous essays, and biographies. But sometimes writers want to entertain at the same time they try to persuade and inform you, so these purposes can overlap.

You need to know a writer's purpose so you can judge how well facts and opinions are used. Writers who inform usually have the most facts and opinions from experts. Writers who persuade might misrepresent facts and opinions. Writers who entertain usually have less need of facts and expert opinions.

Practice 1   In each of the following three paragraphs, decide the author's purpose: to inform, to persuade, to entertain.

(a) [President] Clinton banned federal funding of human-cloning research, of which there is none anyway. He then proposed a five-year ban on cloning. This is not enough. Congress should ban human cloning now. Totally. And regarding one particular form, it should be draconian: the deliberate creation of headless humans must be made a crime, indeed a capital crime. If we flinch in the face of this high-tech barbarity, we'll deserve to live in the hell it heralds.

CHARLES KRAUTHAMMER, FROM "OF HEADLESS MICE . . . AND MEN," TIME, SEPT. 19, 1998

Author's Purpose: _____

(Practice 1 continued on next page)

(b) In reading, a "fixation" is the point along the line of print at which the eyes stop for a fraction of a second. The eyes now actually "see" the letters. We read when the eyes fixate. Fixations take up about 90 percent of our reading time. The more words we can see at each fixation, the fewer we need to make along the line. And the less we strain our eye muscles.

Author's Purpose: _____*Information*_____

(c) Oliver, being left to himself in the undertaker's shop, set the lamp down on a workman's bench and gazed timidly about him with a feeling of awe and dread, which many people, a good deal older than he, will be at no loss to understand. An unfinished coffin on black trestles, which stood in the middle of the shop, looked so gloomy and deathlike that a cold tremble came over him every time his eyes wandered in the direction of the dismal object. He almost expected to see some frightful form slowly rear its head, to drive him mad with terror.

CHARLES DICKENS, FROM OLIVER TWIST

Author's Purpose: _____*entertain.*_____

Is It Fact or Opinion?

A mistake some inexperienced readers make is thinking an opinion is a fact, especially when they read it in print. We need to know the difference between facts and opinions because we evaluate them in different ways. *Factual statements can be proved to be true or false. An opinion is someone's personal judgment.* Opinion often shows someone's approval or disapproval about something.

The following *facts* may provoke "opinions," but they can be proved true or false.

■ According to the U.S. Bureau of Justice Statistics, 75 percent of reported rape victims are female.

■ In California in 1999, only one in five eligible families collected any child support at all.

■ Eight out of ten low-income fourth graders in America cannot read.

[Note: Remember a fact can be proved true or false. A statement that can be proved false is still a fact. It is simply a false fact. Actually, the accurate number is six out of ten, so the sentence is a false fact, not an opinion.]

Some of the following *opinions*, may be convincing statements, with which you agree, but they cannot be proved true or false.

■ Although it is too late to stop global warming entirely, it is not too late to slow it down.

■ Open admission to community college should not mean tolerating goof-off students who don't attend class and don't study.

■ Since prisons are filled with women and men who can barely read, it is obvious that better reading training would decrease the prison population.

Practice 2 On the lines below, first write two *facts*, then two *opinions*:

Facts:

(a) ______________________________

(b) ______________________________

Opinions:

(a) ______________________________

(b) ______________________________

Practice 3 **Apply what you have just learned about fact and opinion to the following statements. Place a checkmark before the statements that are facts. You do not have to know if a fact is true or false. Decide if it's possible for someone to prove the statement [or "it"] true or false.**

____ (a) The capital of Arkansas is Little Rock.

____ (b) Only fools fall in love.

____ (c) A sound foundation in phonics will solve America's reading problem.

Some sentences can't be quickly identified as either fact or opinion. Sometimes sentences are a mixture of both. The facts in the sentences below are underlined once. The opinions are underlined twice.

- Art Buchwald said in his syndicated column, "Most people who own semiautomatics use them to shoot rabbits and squirrels and soup cans in their back yards."
  [It is a *fact* that he said this, but the actual quotation is not provable and is meant to make fun of the NRA.]
- Because of the higher number of non-English-speaking students, California and Hawaii ranked last in the latest federal assessment of fourth-grade reading skills.
  [The ranking of the states is provable *fact*, but the reason is an *opinion*.]

Practice 4 **Analyze each of the following sentences. Underline the *fact* once and the *opinion* twice in each one.**

(a) Author Anne Fadiman's father helped start America's Book-of-the-Month Club; this influenced his daughter to love books all her life.

(b) The Texas school board once banned *The Tropic of Cancer* from its school libraries because it is a dirty book, unsuitable for young minds.

(Practice 4 continued on next page)

(Practice 4 continued from previous page)

    (c) The Stanford 9 test scores in 1999 show a big plunge in reading scores, but not in math between the eighth and ninth grades, proving that students like math more than they like reading.

    (d) Eleanor Roosevelt once made this statement about decreased funding for black children: "How stupid we are. We're all going to go ahead together, or we're all going to go down together."

Once you are able to tell the difference between a fact and an opinion, you can start to judge how well a writer is using each. In other words, you can start to evaluate the kind of support writers use for their main ideas.

Evaluate the Support

Learning to judge a writer's (or speaker's) support takes awareness, training, and practice. It can be hard when you are just starting to inform yourself about a particular topic. You may feel you just don't know enough to judge a writer's use of facts and opinions. Still, you can begin your training by learning to ask certain key questions.

Ask these questions about facts:

1. *Are they recent?* In some fields, such as computers, new developments occur constantly, so facts from even three years ago may be outdated. Name two other fields in which new developments can take place rapidly.

    _____   _____

2. *Are the facts from a reliable source?* When you get more knowledge of your field, you will learn which sources you can trust. With your instructor or class, you may wish to decide the organizations and publications whose facts you would trust in various fields. Consider the following questions.

    To what extent is your college newspaper reliable? _____
    Your city's daily newspaper? _____
    The radio and television news programs you tune in? _____
    Do you consider a university's published research in science reliable? _Yes_
    A word-of-mouth report from your neighbor? _N_
    Word-of-mouth from a radio phone-in talk show? _N_
    Word-of-mouth from a political lobbyist? _N_

Ask these questions about opinions:

1. *Are they reliable*—meaning do they come from an expert in the field? When you see baseball players talking about car insurance or famous actors talking about health, some advertiser has found a way to catch your attention. But those actors and baseball players are probably not experts in the areas of car insurance or health. Can you recall an advertisement you recently saw or heard in which a famous person was advertising something outside his or her area of expertise? _____

2. *Are these opinions based on any facts?* _____

Now you are ready to put together the three critical reading skills you have practiced in this chapter.

Practice 5   Read the passages below and answer the questions about each.
The first one has been done to show you how.

(A) "the new Volvo C70 coupe. the blissful marriage of safety and sensually-sculpted beauty."
[From an advertisement for a Volvo car, *Newsweek*, June 15, 1998.]

1. What is the writer's purpose in this statement? _to persuade_

2. What is the implied main idea? _You will be safe and look_
   sexy, beautiful, and maybe married, if you buy this car.

3. Analyze the support for this idea.
   (a) Are there any facts? _no_
       If yes, are the facts recent? _____ and from a reliable source? _____
   (b) Are there any opinions from experts? _no_

4. Overall, I judge the support for the main idea to be
   (a) poor   (b) fair   (c) good
   because _there are no reliable facts, and no opinions_
   from experts, to persuade me to buy this automobile.

(B) The Labor Department reported that, in 1998, almost two-thirds of American high school graduates attended college. Out of the 2.8 million high school graduates that year, 65.6 percent continued to college. The unemployment rate for students who dropped out of college rose from 20 percent in 1997 to 28 percent in 1998. Labor Secretary Alexis M. Herman said, "The message to America's young people is clear: What you learn has a direct and significant impact on what you earn."

1. What is the writer's purpose? _____

2. What is the main idea? _____
   _____

3. Analyze the support for the paragraph.
   (a) Are there any facts? _✓_
       If yes, are the facts recent? _✓_ and from a reliable source? _✓_
   (b) Are there any opinions from experts? _M. Herman_

4. Overall, I judge the support for the main idea to be
   (a) poor   (b) fair   (c) good
   because _____
   _____

[Clue: Think of the writer's purpose. How well do the statements accomplish the purpose?]

Learning these three critical reading skills takes time. If you start to read a lot about a topic that is important to you, your base of knowledge will start to grow. Through reading and questioning, you will get a better sense of how to evaluate what you read or hear.

Study Outline

Complete the sentence outline below.

_____

[title, Ch. #]

Introduction:

A. _____

[Explain reading critically.]

B. _____

[*Why* read critically?]

I. Decide what _____ (three possibilities).

   A. To _____, as in _____

   B. _____, as in _____

   C. _____, as in _____

II. Tell facts from opinions.

   A. The test for a fact is that it _____

      1. Example: _____

[Use your own example.]

   B. An opinion is _____

      1. Example: _____

[Use your own example.]

III. _____ the _____

   A. Ask these questions about facts.

      1. _____

      2. _____

   B. Ask these _____.

      1. _____

      2. _____

Conclusion:_____

[Paraphrase last paragraph in Study Unit.]

A More Violent America

As you read the three paragraphs on the problem of growing violence in America, continue to look for the main idea. Look also for the author's purpose, and notice facts and opinions. How reliable are they? Do they fit the author's purpose? After answering the questions for each paragraph, check the key.

Exercise 8A: Paragraph

"May you live in interesting times," says the old Chinese curse. When it comes to time periods, the most interesting ones are clearly marked by controversy and tension. The end of the twentieth century may be remembered for its violence against children by people who weren't supposed to have guns. A recent example is white supremacist Buford O. Furrow, Jr. As a convicted felon, he wasn't supposed to have a gun, but he brought five assault weapons to Los Angeles on August 10, 1999, looking for Jews to kill. He wounded a 68-year-old receptionist, a teenager, and three children at a Jewish community center. Then he shot and killed a non-white postman with an Uzi semi-automatic, Glock handgun. Perhaps more frightening examples are the teenage, and even pre-teen, boys who terrorized their schools with guns. Earlier this year, Dylan Klebold, 17, and Eric Harris, 18, killed thirteen people and wounded 23 others at Columbine High School in Colorado. They had a handgun, a sawed-off shotgun, and a semi-automatic rifle. Then they shot themselves. Last year at a school in Jonesboro, Arkansas, 13-year-old Mitchell Johnson and 11-year-old Andrew Golden killed four students and a teacher and wounded ten others. They broke into a locked gun case and stole two rifles and a Smith and Wesson revolver. They weren't supposed to have guns either, but they got them.

BASED ON "AMERICA UNDER THE GUN," NEWSWEEK, AUGUST 23, 1999

1. What is the writer's main purpose in this paragraph? _____

2. In your own words, write a complete sentence that states the main idea.

_____

_____

[Clue: Paraphrase the topic sentence.]

3. Analyze the support for the paragraph.
   (a) Are there enough facts? _____
       If yes, are the facts recent? _____ and from a reliable source? _____
   (b) Are the opinions convincing? _____

4. Considering the choice of examples given, is the author more likely to be *for* gun control or *against* gun control? _____
   because _____

Exercise 8B: Paragraph

The notion that access to "handguns" or any other object causes violence is almost absurdly easy to refute. In the District of Columbia, handguns have been essentially banned since 1977. Virginia adjoins the District and has been criticized for its "easy access" to handguns. (A one-handgun-a-month law was passed in Virginia in 1993.) Using official FBI crime statistics, Gun Owners of America compared the murder statistics in Virginia and the District. The comparison was for the period of 1976 (just before the District's ban went into effect) to 1991. The Virginia murder rate decreased over this 15-year period, while the District's went up by approximately 200 percent.

DAN PETERSON, WASHINGTON, D. C., LAWYER, FROM GUNS MAGAZINE, JANUARY 1994

1. What is the author's purpose? _____

2. In your own words, write a complete sentence stating the main idea.

   _____

   _____

3. Analyze the support for the paragraph.
   (a) Are there enough facts? _____
   (b) If yes, are the facts recent? _____ and convincing? _____
   (c) What are some opposing opinions not mentioned [other reasons why violence in the District may have increased]? _____

   _____

4. Considering where the paragraph was first published, is the author more likely to be *for* gun control or *against* gun control? _____

Exercise 8C: Paragraph

William H. Bonney . . . [Billy the Kid] murdered his victim when he was 14 and had dispatched 20 more human beings by the time he reached voting age—all with a six-shooter. Imagine how prolific he could've been with a semi-automatic. Which leads us to the single most effective, violence-reducing strategy we can undertake in the short term: restricting kids' access to firearms. Just a few decades ago, bloodbaths such as Littleton and Jonesboro would have ended as schoolyard beatings or, at worst, stabbings. There is simply no reason for an 11-year-old to know how to speedload, as did Andrew Golden, one of the Jonesboro, Ark., killers. We do a reasonably good job of enforcing access to another class of potentially lethal machinery: motor vehicles. There's no reason not to apply similar restrictions to guns. Further, parents whose children violate weapons laws should be subject to criminal and civil prosecution.

JONATHAN KELLERMAN, CHILD PSYCHOLOGIST AND NOVELIST, FROM "VIOLENCE DOESN'T BEGIN IN THE THEATER," THE WALL STREET JOURNAL, JUNE 9, 1999

1. What is the author's purpose? _____persure_____

2. In your own words, write a complete sentence that states the main idea.

   _____

   _____

3. Analyze the support for the paragraph.
   (a) Is the paragraph mostly fact or mostly opinion? _opinion_
   (b) How many facts are in the paragraph? _1_
   (c) Is the source reliable? _Yes_
   (d) Are the opinions convincing? _Yes_

4. Overall, I judge the support for the main idea to be
   (a) poor   (b) fair   (c) good
   because _____

II. How to Read Faster

Within any reading passage, it is natural to speed up on some easier parts, like dialogue or action. It is natural to slow down on harder parts, like long abstractions (example: philosophizing). If you are stuck in a slow, word-by-word speed, you may need to force your speed up in some practice sessions. Expect to lose some comprehension until you get used to the faster speeds.

Use a Pacing Device

As they push to build speed when they read or skim, many students find it helpful to use some type of pacing device. A pacing device is like the pace car at an auto race. It determines the speed that the other cars go. When you use a pacing device while reading or skimming, you hurry to keep up with the "pace car." The pacing device improves your concentration and, with frequent use, your speed.

You can easily make your own pacing device with a tape recorder. Decide if you wish to read in five-minute or ten-minute sets. A *set* is the period of time you will sit and read with no interruptions. Then, with a watch in hand, record your voice on the tape. Every minute—or half-minute, if the print in your book is large—say into the recorder, "Turn the page." The goal is to force yourself to cover the page faster than is comfortable for you. Continue to record your voice giving the "turn the page" order until the five or ten minutes have passed.

Note: The Learning Centers or Reading Rooms of some colleges already have these pacing or timing tapes prepared. You may also have a friend pace you through a few sets. Or your instructor may wish to pace you in class, especially for your first time.

Keep a Pacing Chart

Once you have your pacing or timing tape, you are ready to keep a pacing chart by following these steps.

1. Choose an easy paperback novel (fiction) for practice. Make sure it interests you.

2. Calculate the average number of words on a typical page in your book. To do this, pick any typical "full" page and count all the words. (*Short cut:* count the words in three full lines and divide by three; then multiply that number by the number of full lines on the page.) Write the average number of words per page here. _____

3. Preview your book. Read the front and back covers and the first page.

4. Now you are ready to start the tape recorder and read—or skim, if that is what you are practicing. Try to turn the page each time the pacing device tells you. Do not stop until the set is finished.

5. Keep a record of how many pages you are reading in each set. As soon as you finish a set, fill in the pacing chart on the next page. Do several sets each time you use the pacing device, trying to improve your WPM each time. You may want to alternate a paced and an unpaced set. Contrast your first and last sets.

Pacing Chart

Before beginning any pacing chart, prepare by previewing the book. That is, read the back and front covers and first page. Be sure to record all five numbers for each set.

Practice Set
Average Words per Page _____
× Pages Read   _____
= Average Words Read   _____ ÷ _____ min. (Reading Time) = **WPM** _____

Set #1
av. words per p. _____
× pp. read   _____
= av. words   _____ ÷ _____ min. = _____
                                                    WPM

Set #2
av. words per p. _____
× pp. read   _____
= av. words   _____ ÷ _____ min. = _____
                                                    WPM

Set #3
av. words per p. _____
× pp. read   _____
= av. words   _____ ÷ _____ min. = _____
                                                    WPM

Set #4
av. words per p. _____
× pp. read   _____
= av. words   _____ ÷ _____ min. = _____
                                                    WPM

Set #5
av. words per p. _____
× pp. read   _____
= av. words   _____ ÷ _____ min. = _____
                                                    WPM

Set #6
av. words per p. _____
× pp. read   _____
= av. words   _____ ÷ _____ min. = _____
                                                    WPM

Set #7
av. words per p. _____
× pp. read   _____
= av. words   _____ ÷ _____ min. = _____
                                                    WPM

Set #8
av. words per p. _____
× pp. read   _____
= av. words   _____ ÷ _____ min. = _____
                                                    WPM

Set #9
av. words per p. _____
× pp. read   _____
= av. words   _____ ÷ _____ min. = _____
                                                    WPM

Set #10
av. words per p. _____
× pp. read   _____
= av. words   _____ ÷ _____ min. = _____
                                                    WPM

Set #11
av. words per p. _____
× pp. read   _____
= av. words   _____ ÷ _____ min. = _____
                                                    WPM

Set #12
av. words per p. _____
× pp. read   _____
= av. words   _____ ÷ _____ min. = _____
                                                    WPM

Exercise 8D: Phrases

Scan for the phrase identical to the key phrase and make a slash through it.

Key Phrase

1. plush velvet lining	lush velvet lining	plush velvet lining	very plush living
2. speaking to group	speaking to group	speeding to place	reaching group
3. pasting gold parts	pasting partial gold	pasting gold parts	partial gold paste
4. holding hands high	holding hands high	holding high hands	holding high hand
5. says nothing to him	nothing said to him	says more to him	says nothing to him
6. long slender legs	long spending days	along slender lines	long slender legs
7. place for dinghy	place for dinghy	place for dimple	a dingy place
8. eating good jerky	eating food jerkily	wearing good jerseys	eating good jerky
9. left-handed batter	left-handed batter	left-handed batters	right-handed batter
10. dealing with pathos	dealing with pathos	dealing with bathos	dealing with patience
11. has the button	has the butter	was the button	has the button
12. spoken with candor	spoken with candor	spoken candidly	poked the canine
13. that pungent odor	punctured motor	that pungent odor	the pungent odor
14. an obscure person	an obsessed person	an obscure person	an observed person
15. two in the dark	two in the dark	ten in the dark	two in the park
16. one forlorn girl	one forlorn curl	one foreign girl	one forlorn girl
17. sleeping dogs lying	sleeping dogs lying	the dogs lying	creeping dogs lying
18. taking out garbage	taking out garbage	taking out baggage	taking in garbage
19. more narrow minds	more national binds	more narrow minds	more rational minds
20. carrying crates	carrying crates	parrying cracks	raising rates

Time _40 sc_

Number of Errors _1_

Exercise 8E: Phrases

Scan for the phrase identical to the key phrase and make a slash through it.

Key Phrase

1. eating ice cream	making ice cream	eating ice cream	heating ice cream
2. picking up sticks	picking up sticks	picking dead sticks	packing up stacks
3. gnawing the bone	gnawing the bones	throwing the stone	gnawing the bone
4. the empty basket	emptied waste basket	two empty baskets	the empty basket
5. filling the tooth	filling the tooth	filling the teeth	filing the tooth
6. shoes all shined	sun all shining	shores all shiny	shoes all shined
7. the Monkey Trial	the Monkey Trial	the Monkey Trail	the Monkey's Trial
8. a chilling frost	a chilled frosting	a chilling frost	a killer frost
9. pen on the table	pen in the table	pencil on the table	pen on the table
10. news of the week	news of the weak	blues of the bleak	news of the week
11. sat in the sun	sat in the sun	seat with your son	not in the sun
12. drinking the coffee	drinking the coffee	drinking the Coke	blinking an eye
13. viewing a bad film	viewing a sad film	viewing a bad film	viewing bad films
14. under milkwood	under milkwoods	under milkworm	under milkwood
15. spared a dime	spared a dime	a spared dime	a dim space
16. lightning flash	lightning splash	lighter flash	lightning flash
17. my older brother	my old mother	my old brother	my older brother
18. peace with honor	peaceful honor	peace with honesty	peace with honor
19. evaded the draft	evaded the draft	avoided the draft	invaded the draft
20. different drummer	diffident drummer	different drummer	difficult drummer

Time _42_

Number of Errors _3_

A More Violent America

The two timed readings are editorials by well-known authors. They present different angles on the problem of teenage violence and were prompted by the much-publicized shooting at Columbine High School in Colorado in 1999. As you read, consider the authors' purpose. Examine the validity of their facts, often fewer in an editorial, and the credibility of their opinions.

Exercise 8F: Timed Reading   *997 words*

This article by best-selling novelist Tom Clancy first appeared as what is called a "column-right" (more conservative) editorial in the *Los Angeles Times* in April 1999. Be aware of whether this knowledge influences you as you read.

Preview: *Quickly survey the title, subheadings, first sentence of a few paragraphs, and last paragraph. What does the author seem to be blaming for the shooting?* _____ *And what is he "not" blaming?* _____

Wait for a signal from your instructor before you begin reading. Remember to read critically. Do not skim, but do not slow down to study-read either. Circle your reading time when you have finished, and find your WPM.

Moral Absolutes, Not More Gun Laws

Tom Clancy

Almost exactly eight years ago I was at Walt Disney World in Florida, pushing a wheelchair occupied by a little boy of seven years who had already lost a leg to cancer and would, on August 1 of that year, lose his life. I say this to let the reader know that I am aware of the fact that, if there is something worse than the death of a child, I have yet to encounter it.

Fourteen kids and one adult are dead, and for no good reason. The horrid events in Littleton, Colorado, last week cause us all first to wince, then to feel the loss of other parents and, last of all, to ask why it had to happen.

This last question cannot ever be answered with certainty. To look into another human heart is something none of us can really do. We can only guess and hope that something like this stays a long way away from our own families. This does not, however, stop people from taking this incident and using it as fodder for their own political views.

The first and most predictable reactors to this event were the gun-control advocates. It had to be the guns' fault, they said even before the last sad echoes faded. (The two alleged criminals also used explosive devices; why not do away with chemistry class in addition to toughening up gun-control laws?) The media dutifully reported this view, because they, as a rule, follow the cant of the political left, because for the news media the Constitution starts and ends with the 1st Amendment and not even all of that.

"Congress," this part of the Constitution says, "shall pass no law respecting an establishment of religion," and then it goes on to protect the press, freedom of speech and assembly. This first entry in the Bill of Rights is taught to kids in school as freedom *of* religion. Yet current political culture twists it into freedom *from* religion. The political left bridles at the mere recitation of a single prayer in public schools. Why? Well, it offends some of those among us who choose not to believe in God, and since those people may be offended (especially the noisy ones), this small minority is able to impose its views on the majority, and to do so with the blessing—nay the advocacy—of the "progressive" elements of our political culture.

I suppose my first reaction is, what's the big deal? If atheists don't believe, what possible interest could they have in the words of those who do? Oh, yeah, the kids of parents who choose not to believe can't be exposed to a contrary outlook, lest they be polluted by it. We can't have the public schools inculcating belief in something like that—and we don't.

Instead we have schools promoting "value-neutral" cant. Modern school books tell kids that stealing, for example, is wrong, not because it's "wrong," but rather because after stealing you might feel bad about it later on. Better, isn't it, to let kids mush along with their own help of rap music and Web sites about Adolf Hitler?

I never attended public schools. My parents sent me to Catholic ones, where education in religion was part of the curriculum, and along with that came a few simple rules: killing and stealing were out. Why? Because they were wrong. A simple bit of advice for a child to absorb, and evidently effective. Nobody shot up St. Matthew Elementary School while I was there—and back then gun-control laws were far more lax than they are now. Crime was also a far more rare event.

There's a lot more to it than that, of course, but the simple fact is that the political left has assumed ownership of the rules of contemporary society. They have replaced right and wrong with something else, and one result of this is that there were no people to take the two adolescent shooters in Littleton aside and say, "Hey, guys, this Hitler chap you talk about, he was not much of a role model, and by the way, whatever problems you may have with your schoolmates, we can work on that, and maybe if you change a little, they will, too, and whatever feelings of rejection you have will fade away in a relatively short period of time."

But nobody intervened, and evidently nobody told these two misguided kids that some things are objectively wrong. Perhaps too many public schoolteachers do not view morals instruction as being within their professional purview. Perhaps their union disapproves of prayers and morality-teaching as much as the ACLU does. Maybe it was their parents' fault, maybe the fault of many segments of society. The final score is dismally simple: These two boys did what they did because nobody told them convincingly that to do so was horribly wrong.

So maybe, just maybe, we can allow public schools to tell kids that some things are just plain wrong? The problem with that is that our ideas of right and wrong ultimately come from a source higher than government. And to say such a thing would offend atheists. But if you remove something and fail to replace it with something else, there will be a downstream effect.

These two kids used guns and some homemade explosives. In the former case, let's try to remember that guns are inanimate objects. They do not leap up and operate on their own accord. A person, misguided or not, has to do that. The person may be motivated by greed, hatred, or madness, and in some cases there is nothing we can do about the wishes of that human heart. But in some cases we can, if we think a little about what ideas we trouble ourselves to teach our children. It is neither difficult nor particularly offensive to instruct children in the better reasons rather than casting them adrift to find the worse ones on their own untutored accord.

TIMING CHART

min:sec	wpm
04:59	200
04:32	220
04:09	240
03:50	260
03:34	280
03:19	300
03:07	320
02:56	340
02:46	360
02:37	380
02:30	400
02:22	420
02:16	440
02:10	460
02:05	480
02:00	500
01:55	520
01:51	540
01:47	560
01:43	580
01:40	600
01:36	620
01:33	640
01:31	660
01:28	680
01:25	700
01:23	720
01:21	740
01:19	760
01:17	780
01:15	800

Answer the following recall questions without referring to the article.

1. What is the purpose of the seemingly unrelated example in the first paragraph of the author pushing a little boy in a wheelchair?
   (a) to raise awareness of more children dying of cancer than by shooting
   (b) to show how aware he is of the impact of a child's death
   (c) to show that he knows one of the children injured in the shooting
   (d) to gain sympathy for the author

2. What seems to be the author's stand on gun control?
   (a) for   (b) against

3. What seems to be the author's stand on religion in schools?
   (a) for   (b) against

You may refer to the article to answer the following questions.

4. What is the author's main purpose in the article?
   (a) to inform   (b) to persuade   (c) to entertain

5. Thesis: _____

   _____

   [the author believes what?   about what?]

Check your answers with the key, and record your scores below and on the Progress Chart.

Words per Minute _380_

Percent Comprehension _____

The second editorial, by Pulitzer Prize-winning essayist and poet Richard Rodriguez, examines some overlooked issues related to violence in high schools.

Preview: *Quickly survey the title, subheadings, first sentence of a few paragraphs, and last paragraph. What does the author seem to be blaming for the shooting?* _____

Wait for a signal from your instructor before you begin reading. Remember to read critically. Do not skim, but do not slow down to study-read either. Circle your reading time when you have finished, and find your WPM.

The Unmentioned Victim at Columbine High School

Richard Rodriguez

After the ribbons fade, after the dead are laid to rest, after the reporters drift away, the last casualty of the massacre at Columbine High School may turn out to be the idea of public school.

Public school. We used to know what that concept meant. Earlier generations understood, in a nation as individualized as ours, that we needed an institution, a school, where children would learn to regard themselves as people in common.

After Littleton, Colorado, who wonders about Yugoslavia? The most balkanized region of America may well be the high school—inner city or rural, also suburban, middle class. In the cafeteria, the teenagers of America segregate themselves, each group with its own: jocks, skinheads, blacks, surfers, Latinos, nerds, etc. What we saw at Columbine—the Goths against the jocks—was a kind of ethnic cleansing.

More than a century ago, Mark Twain created Huck Finn, a kid who, in the company of a runaway slave, left his small town to risk the great American river. The nonfictional reality today is much less romantic.

At that very time—season we call adolescence—when we expect our children to leave home, to grasp their independence, American teenagers instead are looking for home or a tribe.

Inner-city kids, for example, speak of their gang as "family," "blood." Because school is not the center of existence for the big-city gangsta, ethnic cleansing, East L.A.-style, tends to be accomplished through drive-bys, on street corners.

We have known for some time that brown and black inner-city kids kill one another, to establish their sense of belonging in gangs, in the city of strangers. We are sorry for them, but as long as we stayed out of their line of fire, we thought we were safe.

But then we started to see white kids emerge from the forests of rural America, their parody of big-city gangs, their murderous rage against parents and school.

Now the nightmare moves closer to America's heart and hearth, to Littleton, a middle-class suburb where nice people live and the streets are wide and the houses have separate bedrooms for everyone and a three-car garage—the domestic architecture of anonymity.

We look at photographs of those split-level suburban homes where Eric Harris and Dylan Klebold lived. Steven Spielberg, our modern Twain, would doubtlessly romanticize the warm, golden light coming from within. The other

Stephen—King, the writer whom many teenagers read—imagines teenagers in the basement, plotting to blow up the junior prom while several televisions blare upstairs.

An Italian friend of mine shakes his head. He says we Americans are always flattering ourselves by announcing our "individualism" to the world. But, my Italian friend says, you cannot be truly individualistic unless you have a strong sense of family or village. You can't become an "I" without a strong sense of "we."

For all our American talk of individualism, my Italian friend says, we are merely the loneliest people on Earth. Our divorced and womanizing politicians keep yearning for "family values." The rest of us settle for chat rooms or support groups or a cafeteria table with people just like ourselves.

Have you ever been to Littleton? There are hundreds of Littletons in America now, from Silicon Valley to North Dallas to Long Island. The main employers are high-tech firms; many homeowners have college degrees; and there is a preference on Saturdays for soccer, not football.

But Littleton is a town built on restless ambition. Most people arrive from elsewhere, and most will probably end up moving away.

A psychologist on one of the networks this week estimated that 20% of American teenagers today should seek psychological help. But, all week, I kept thinking of the parents of the two "monsters."

A woman, a mother of teenagers, said to me this week that she began to "lose contact" with her children when they began to listen to a music she could not decipher. Before that, they had their televisions. Now, of course, they have their own computers. "They live in their own world."

This, of course, is where the teacher comes in. We send our children who are innocent of intimacy to Columbine High School. But look at the place! The building has the charm and scale of an office building alongside the interstate.

It falls to the teacher, underpaid and overworked, to teach the children of Littleton what public-school teachers have always tried to teach children, that they belong to a culture in common, speaking a common tongue, carry a common history that connects them to Thomas Jefferson and Malcolm X.

The ideal of public education is an extraordinary one, especially because America is a country that otherwise prizes its unruly soul. (In Twain's story of Finn, the "school marm" must play the villain, because it is she who intends to catch Huck and diminish his individualism by making him "speak regular.")

In fact, for many decades, in many parts of America, our public schools betrayed their role by being racially segregated. Today, on the other hand, at a time when the American public school is open to all, many teachers settle for the sentimentality of "multiculturalism" (celebrate diversity!) instead of insisting on a communal vision.

There are doubtlessly good teachers at Columbine. (One teacher died last week, trying to protect the lives of his students.) But imagine the task of today's public-school teacher. Every day facing too many faces to know by name. Body-builders, pierced noses, shaved heads, brown skin, Calvin Klein blues, black trench coats.

At such a school, can we be surprised to learn that a sad little tribe, the Trench Coat Mafia, dressed like the Blues Brothers, published an ad in the yearbook that announced, "Insanity's healthy"? No one on the faculty apparently noticed or had the time to remark.

It turns out, something not nice was going on at Columbine High School. One father told CBS News that a football player used to look for his son in the hallways, pick on his son–a Jew–for being different. Meanwhile, elsewhere along the school hallway, two boys in black trench coats murmured Nazi tags to each other about football players.

You will say, of course, that high school is high school. It's always been the most conformist society of our lives. What is different now is that increasing numbers of high-school students come from families and neighborhoods that barely exist. They live surrounded by an architecture of impersonality and a technology of solitude–Web pages screaming in silence for attention.

All last week, child psychologists dispensing sound bites spoke about ways to "identify" the kid who might mean big trouble. Listening to them, I remembered how, after Timothy J. McVeigh's arrest in the Oklahoma bombing, a newspaper reporter, talking to his high-school teachers, found that none of them could remember the boy.

As my Italian friend would say, you cannot become a true individual if you do not come from a "we." You merely end up a loner, looking for a tribe. The white-supremacist dreams of a cabin on the edge of America, where he might be with his own kind. The street thug kills to prove that he is tough enough to earn his place in the gang.

Now we know that there are borderlines in the middle-class high school as murderous as any in Kosovo.

[4]Lost in the news from Colorado this week was an education story not unrelated. Theodore J. Forstmann, a Wall Street financier-billionaire, and John Walton, the Wal-Mart heir, who have promised low-income children scholarships to private or parochial schools, announced that they had received replies from more than a million families.

[3]The rich, of course, long ago abandoned our public schools. Now the poor want out. For many poor families, the best hope for what we might call a "public" education may be private, religious schools. In spite of their theological tribalism, or maybe because of it, a student is grounded in a larger reality than his separate self, call it a faith.

[2]After Littleton, the middle-class parent may well decide that the public-school library is too dangerous a place for her daughter or son.

[1]But the question for America is larger than the safety of any one of our children. The question, now, is whether or not Americans will be able to embrace the idea of a public life–our responsibility to all children–at a time when we feel so foreign to our own, sitting in front of their computer screens or playing in the basement.

Answer the following five recall questions without referring to the article.

1. What does the author consider to be "the unmentioned victim at Columbine High School"?

   (a) surviving students   (b) public schools   (c) teachers

2. The author's Italian friend is critical of what aspect of American life?

   (a) violent society   (b) angry teenagers   (c) so-called individualism

3. The author is critical of Littleton as a town.   (a) true   (b) false

4. The author is more critical of which of the following?
    (a) unaware teachers   (b) racist teenagers   (c) large, impersonal schools

5. Name one of the objects in a middle-class home that isolates teenagers from their parents. _____

You may refer to the article to answer the following questions.

6. How is Mark Twain's character Huck Finn contrasted to today's adolescent?
   _____

7. When the author claims that we took notice only when violence emerged from rural America, he is suggesting that we have become immune to inner-city kids killing each other.   (a) true   (b) false

8. If the main purpose of this article is to persuade, as well as to inform, what is the author's underlying advice to parents?
    (a) Don't send your children to a public school.
    (b) Reestablish family and community ties.
    (c) Send your troubled children to a psychologist.
    (d) Vote for stricter gun-control laws.

9. How do the facts in the fourth-to-the-last paragraph help support the thesis?
   _____
   _____

10. Thesis: _____
    _____
    [the author believes what?   about what?]

Check your answers with the key, and record your scores below and on the Progress Chart.

Words per Minute _____

Percent Comprehension _____

Writing and Discussion Activities

1. What is your position on any controversial issue, like gun control or causes of violence? Write a paragraph, stating your position in a topic sentence. Then support your belief with opinions and facts. Underline any facts.
2. Cut out an article from the opinion page of your local newspaper.
    (a) Underline all the facts.
    (b) State the author's main purpose. Is it to inform, persuade, or entertain?

Vocabulary Review, Chapter 8

Match the vocabulary word on the left with its definition on the right. Write the letter of the answer on the short blank to the left.

c 1. **lax**   (a) very severe

d 2. **parochial**   (b) productive

e 3. **alleged**   (c) permissive

b 4. **prolific**   (d) private

a 5. **draconian**   (e) thought to be

*Choose the best definition for each **boldfaced** word as it is used in its context.*

b 6. the **anonymity** of the city
   (a) being distracted   (b) being unknown   (c) being entertained

a 7. having a **theological** argument
   (a) about God   (b) about the court system   (c) about medicine

c 8. grew tired of the **cant** in political speeches
   (a) overly long talk   (b) confusing statistics
   (c) prejudiced or insincere statements

b 9. see a **parody** of the sports figures and their high salaries
   (a) questioning attitude   (b) comic imitation   (c) impressive goal

c 10. **inculcating** a love of reading and literature
   (a) discouraging   (b) missing out on   (c) instilling

*Mark each sentence to show whether the **boldfaced** word is used correctly.*

a = True   b = False

a T 11. Because she likes **solitude**, Wanda moved to a house far out in the country.

b F 12. Putting "**felon**" on a resume is an asset in getting most jobs.

a T 13. The diplomat had lived in several different countries and developed an interest in **multiculturalism**.

a 14. Professors often find it hard to **decipher** the handwriting of their students.

a 15. Fortunately, there were quite a large number of **casualties** from the train accident.

(Continued)

Choose the word from the box that fits the context of the following paragraph.
Write the letter of each choice on the blank lines to the left of the paragraph.

to make sth   kiềm chế   ủy hộ.   bác bỏ lại   xen vào, can
| smaller.

(a) **diminish**   (b) **bridle**   (c) **advocates**   (d) **refute**   (e) **intervene** thiệp vào

b 16.   The issue of cloning is highly controversial in our society. Those

a 17. against it __16__ with fear or anger. They believe cloning will __17__

e 18. the value and miracle of life. They also believe it is wrong to __18__ in

c 19. a natural process in such a manner. But the __19__ of cloning support

d 20. the advances of science and __20__ the argument that cloning is

against the laws of nature.

% Correct _____

Comprehension Review, Chapter 8

1. Explain what it means to *read critically*.
   [Clue: How is it different from the other reading you have been doing in this book?]

   Read critically means you learn to infer and draw conclusions, skills that are important in every job or social activity.

   List the three purposes (discussed in this chapter) that an author might have for writing.

   2. To inform
   3. To persuade
   4. To entertain.

5. Explain the difference between *factual* statements and *opinion* statements.

   Factual statements can be proved to be true or false. Opinion statements are someone's personal judgments

   Write F (for fact) or O (for opinion) for each of the following statements.

   O   6. William Jefferson Clinton is a good president but an immoral person.

   F   7. Abraham Lincoln was president during the Civil War.

   F   8. Dr. Martin Luther King, Jr., was killed by a knife wound in 1964.

   O   9. The best president of the United States was George Washington because he never told a lie.

10. List one way you might evaluate the credibility of an editorial essay, printed in your local newspaper, about a controversial subject like abortion or gun control.
    [Clue: Your answer should not include a discussion about abortion or gun control.]

    New Gun Control Politics : A Whimper, Not a Bang

Read the two paragraphs below and answer the questions about them.

A. It's the devil you know, not the devil you don't know, that you should fear. We warn our students, our children, our younger brothers and sisters, our grandchildren not to talk to strangers. We don't warn them that they are more likely to be in danger from people they know. Of the one in five children sexually abused in America, 90% of them are abused by someone they know. One-fourth of the children who are raped say their attacker was a father or stepfather or another relative. Eighty percent of child prostitutes (approximately a quarter of a million in America) report that they were abused sexually at home. In a national study, 62% of pregnant teenagers reported that they had been abused, either sexually or

(Continued)

physically, at home. And one-fourth of these teenagers said they had been abused when they were five or younger. A final tragedy is that all too frequently the abused then becomes the abuser.

CHLOE EICHENLAUB, PRINCIPAL, THE OAKS [ELEMENTARY SCHOOL], HOLLYWOOD, CA, AUG. 1999
[SOURCE: U.S. DEPT. OF JUSTICE STATISTICS, 1997 AND 1998]

11. What is the author's purpose? _inform and persuade_
    If a secondary purpose were "to persuade," what advice might the author give to parents? _Be careful with people they know_

12. In your own words, write a complete sentence that states the main idea. _the readers & parent_
    The information about are given to tell its be careful with
    So people they know because they can a bused their
    children
    parents and their children [Clue: Paraphrase the topic sentence.]

13. Analyze the support for the paragraph:
    (a) How many sentences are mostly facts? _5_
    (b) Are the facts from a reliable source? _Yes_
    (c) Are the opinions from a reliable source? _Yes_

B. If we really want to combat extreme violence perpetrated by the young, we need to stop wasting time on yet more commissions and instead channel our energies and tax dollars into identifying and treating youngsters at risk for violence as early as possible. Studies suggest that if a seriously aggressive and antisocial kid isn't changed by age 12, the chances of rehabilitation are slim to none.

JONATHAN KELLERMAN, FROM "VIOLENCE DOESN'T BEGIN IN THE THEATER,"
THE WALL STREET JOURNAL, JUNE 9, 1999

14. What is the author's purpose? _persuade_
15. Are there any facts in the paragraph? _No_

% Correct _____

⟨11⟩ The author advise parents that they should warn their children be careful with people they know because they can be ~~dangero~~ in danger

VOCABULARY PREVIEW for Chapter 9

WORDS IN CONTEXT

Directions: *Examine the **boldfaced** word as it is used in the sentence and write your best guess of the word's meaning. Then look up the word in your dictionary, and write the best definition for its context in the sentence.*

PRONUNCIATION KEY

a	cat	ā	made	ä	bar	k	cot, quit		adore
e	pet	ē	these	â	care	s	cent		travel
i	sit	ī	ride	ė	term	z	beds	ə {	horrify
o	rot	ō	note	ô	order	j	giant		pardon
u	nut	o͞o	rude	o̯o	foot	th	thank		circus
u̇	put	yo͞o	use	o͞o	food	ŦH	this		

from Practice 4 (p. 306)

1. **oppressively** (ə pres' iv lē)　　　*adverb*

   The clouds hung **oppressively** low in the heavens.

   Your best guess: _____

   Best dictionary definition: _____

   [Clue: Look up the definition for the adjective form, then the suffix.]

2. **insufferable** (in suf' ər ə bəl)　　　*adjective*

   I know not how it was, but, with the first glimpse of the building, a sense of **insufferable** gloom filled my spirit.

   Your best guess: _____

   Best dictionary definition: _____

3. **mere** (mir)　　*adjective*

   I looked upon the scene before me—upon the **mere** house and the simple landscape.

   Your best guess: _____

   Best dictionary definition: _____

4. **bleak** (blēk)　　*adjective*

   I looked upon the **bleak** walls, upon the vacant, eyelike windows.

   Your best guess: _____

   Best dictionary definition: _____

5. **unnerved**   (un nėrvd')   *verb*

What was it that so **unnerved** me about the House of Usher?

Your best guess: _____

Best dictionary definition: _____

from Paragraph 9A (p. 309)

6. **empathy**   (em' pə thē)   *noun*

She wants **empathy**, but he thinks she wants solutions.

Your best guess: _____

Best dictionary definition: _____

from Paragraph 9B (p. 310)

7. **furor**   (fyo͞o' ôr)   *noun*

I thought that my apology would end the **furor** over my politically incorrect statement.

Your best guess: _____

Best dictionary definition: _____

8. **harassment**   (har' əs mənt)   *noun*

If they don't stop this sexual **harassment**, I intend to take legal action.

Your best guess: _____

Best dictionary definition: _____

from Timed Reading 9F (p. 315)

9. **unicorn**   (yo͞o' nə kôrn')   *noun*

Once upon a sunny morning a man . . . looked up . . . to see a white **unicorn** with a gold horn quietly ***cropping*** the roses in the garden.

Your best guess: _____

Best dictionary definition: _____

10. **cropping**   (krop' ing)   *verbal*

Your best guess: _____

Best dictionary definition: _____

[Note: See sentence #9 for context clues to **cropping**.]

[Clue: Look for the verb definition, not the more common noun definition.]

11. **gloat**   (glōt)   *noun (usually a verb)*

She was very excited and there was a **gloat** in her eye.

Your best guess: _____

Best dictionary definition: _____

12. **subduing** (səb dōō′ ing)   *verbal*

 They had a hard time **subduing** her, for she put up a terrific struggle.

Your best guess: _____

Best dictionary definition: _____

from Timed Reading 9G (p. 317)

13. **hazing** (hāz′ ing)   *verbal (used as a noun)*

 There are words we use to describe what happens all too often on the school playground or the shop floor. We call it "**hazing**."

Your best guess: _____

Best dictionary definition: _____

14. **roustabout** (roust′ ə bout′)   *noun*

 This is how it worked at its worst for one **roustabout** named Joseph Oncale on an oil rig in the waters off Louisiana.

Your best guess: _____

Best dictionary definition: _____

15. **belittled** (bi lit′ ld)   *verbal (used as an adjective)*

 In a phrase that must be a classic understatement, he said, "I feel **belittled**."

Your best guess: _____

Best dictionary definition: _____

16. **dusky** (dus′ kē)   *adjective*

 This is one of those moments when the unusual case . . . can throw light on a **dusky** corner of the law.

Your best guess: _____

Best dictionary definition: _____

17. **quid pro quo** (kwid′ prō kwō′)   *Latin phrase (noun-preposition-noun)*

 The **quid pro quo**—no sex, no job—is now discrimination.

Your best guess: _____

Best dictionary definition: _____

18. **heterosexual** (het′ ər ə sek′ shōō əl)   *adjective*

 Some [courts] have ruled against homosexual supervisors harassing **heterosexual** employees.

Your best guess: _____

Best dictionary definition: _____

19. **fare** (fâr)   *verb*

 I have no idea how Joseph Oncale will **fare** if he goes to trial.

Your best guess: _____

Best dictionary definition: _____

20. **dweeby**   (dwē′ bē)   *adjective (slang)*

   I don't know if this story fits into what Franke calls the "**dweeby** guy" category or whether some other dark ***dynamic*** was in play on that oil rig.

   Your best guess: _____

   Best dictionary definition: _____

21. **dynamic**   (dī nam′ ik)   *noun*

   Your best guess: _____

   Best dictionary definition: _____

Exercise, Vocabulary Preview, Chapter 9

Directions: *Choose the best definition for each **boldfaced** word or phrase as it is used in its context.*

_____ 1. Aunt Rosie's cheap perfume was **oppressively** strong when she bent over us to kiss us goodnight.

    (a) slightly (b) overwhelmingly (c) amazingly

_____ 2. The preteen boy's **insufferable** rudeness made him unfit for polite society.

    (a) guilty (b) unbearable (c) funny

_____ 3. After the booming voice told me to come in, I was shocked when a **mere** slip of a girl came to meet me at the door.

    (a) huge (b) insignificant (c) scantily clad

_____ 4. The desert landscape looked **bleak** before the developers planted palm trees and grass and constructed two-story houses.

    (a) barren (b) lovely (c) expensive

_____ 5. While taking out the garbage in the dark, Samuel was **unnerved** by the sight of a huge, vicious dog springing out of the bushes.

    (a) angered (b) bored (c) alarmed

_____ 6. Julie preferred friends who gave her **empathy**, or who really seemed to share her feelings, instead of friends who gave her only sympathy.

    (a) understanding (b) chocolate (c) advice

_____ 7. When the students heard that the class they had enrolled in was canceled, they raised a **furor** that could be heard across the campus.

    (a) doubt (b) firecracker (c) commotion

_____ 8. The **harassment** by Jodie's boss became so upsetting to her that she developed a stomachache every day at the thought of going to work.

    (a) smoking (b) amount of work (c) mistreatment

_____ 9. For some reason, the **unicorn**, an animal from mythology, has always held a special fascination for little girls.

    (a) goat with single horn (b) horse with single horn
    (c) lion with two horns

_____ 10. Sharon caught her son, Christopher, with her sewing scissors, busily **cropping** his sister's hair as she slept.

    (a) cutting (b) combing (c) planting

_____ 11. The little boy had a **gloat** in his eye as he watched his younger sister put her hand in the cookie jar and pull it out with horror when she touched the cold, wet spaghetti he had placed there.

(a) silly glow   (b) self-satisfied gleam   (c) quiet tear

_____ 12. **Subduing** the suspect was not easy, for he was very strong and highly motivated.

(a) confronting   (b) convincing   (c) controlling

_____ 13. On many college campuses, the practice of **hazing** has been prohibited due to its often violent and humiliating nature.

(a) toga parties   (b) cruel initiation   (c) date rape

_____ 14. The **roustabouts** did most of the heavy lifting when the circus was setting up in the small town.

(a) unskilled laborers   (b) clowns   (c) professionals

_____ 15. Johnny had **belittled** his wife for so many years, that she began to believe that she really was worthless and stupid.

(a) adored   (b) ignored   (c) ridiculed

_____ 16. Lucy was afraid to venture into the **dusky** corners of her closet.

(a) dangerous   (b) bright   (c) dark

_____ 17. Much of the criminal justice system works on a **quid pro quo** basis, where something is given or received for something else: for example, less time in jail in exchange for a written statement of guilt.

(a) equal trade   (b) client privilege   (c) hourly billing

_____ 18. Homosexual couples are now demanding the same legal rights and protections that **heterosexual** couples have.

(a) not happy   (b) not young   (c) not gay

_____ 19. Kate was concerned that Holly would not **fare** well at preschool since she had never been separated from her mother.

(a) share   (b) get along   (c) develop

_____ 20. Laura refused to date the **dweeby**-looking guy from her building even though she knew he was a genius and owned his own software company.

(a) ugly   (b) suspicious   (c) nerdy

_____ 21. Renee couldn't tell if George was simply tired of her or if there were a more complicated **dynamic** at play that might explain his strange behavior.

(a) force   (b) short fuse   (c) game

Number of Errors _____

Chapter 9
Drawing Inferences

I. How to Understand More

Drawing Inferences

Chapter 8 introduced you to the practice of critical reading. In this chapter, you will continue that training as you practice a related skill: reading for *inferences*. This skill requires you to read *beneath the surface*.

An inference is an idea that readers get when they draw a conclusion or read between the lines. Readers draw an inference when writers do not directly state their point. Instead, writers *imply*—suggest—an idea, indirectly, through their words, through supporting details. This *implication* writers make is similar to the "implied main idea" in a paragraph without a topic sentence. Readers *infer* that idea from the details given.

Infer from Actions

These inferences and implications are also made through actions, not just through the written word. Sometimes an implication is obvious and simple. For example, a door slammed in your face quickly tells you someone is angry with you. A simple situation such as "a street maintenance crew working in front of the college on the first day of a new school year" implies "a traffic jam" and that implies "many students late to class." An action such as an invitation to dinner implies that you are pleasant company. If you don't telephone to say that you can't keep an appointment, that implies you don't care about the person who is stood up.

Practice 1   What can you logically *infer* from the following actions?

(a) A metal detector is placed at the entrance of the college bookstore.

_____

(b) The parents of a fourteen-year-old girl won't let her visit a friend's house unless a parent is at home.

_____

(c) It is the fourth week of the semester, and the student still hasn't bought the textbook.

_____

Infer from Words

Verbal implications may be less obvious. Examples that require you to be very aware of inference are a political speech, an advertisement, a law, a novel, and a movie. In these cases, you will have to read more deeply or listen more carefully. You will have to be alert to the implications, not only in deeds and gestures, but in words, too.

Connotations

You may have heard the saying, "The pen is mightier than the sword." This statement recognizes the power words have. We have all been in situations in which words, written or spoken, have moved us to fight, cry, run, laugh, even fall in love. This power does not come from the *literal* meaning alone of the words. It comes from the power of words to suggest or *imply*. *These underlying meanings of words, with the feelings or ideas they suggest, are called their connotations.*

We associate some words with situations in which they are often used. For example, suppose your professor asked you to come see her this afternoon about an essay you wrote. Would you say you have a *date* or a *meeting* with your professor? Which word is more *neutral*, less charged? The word "date" obviously has other associations. Those other associations are the word's *connotations*. Connotative words carry a negative or positive charge. For example, a *fat* neck carries a negative charge, and a swanlike neck carries a positive charge.

Practice 2 How do the following pairs of words differ in their *connotations*? Circle the item in the pair that has the stronger connotation. Then write on the line whether the stronger connotation is negative or positive.

negative or *positive*

(a) plump ■ obese: _____

(b) wanderer ⬤ tramp: *negative* _____

(c) my ball and chain ■ my wife: _____

(d) horse ■ steed: _____

Neutral—or Unbiased—Language

In the setting where you probably most often find yourself—a college classroom—the kind of language that is preferred is neutral language. *The terms "neutral" and "unbiased" describe language that doesn't take sides or doesn't have strong connotations.* A "meeting" is more neutral than a "date." It's true a date might be nothing more than an appointment. But the word is often used for a meeting that has romantic possibilities—a much different situation. So the word "date" in this context is not as neutral as the word "meeting" because of its romantic connotations.

The ability to recognize and use neutral language is important in many fields, such as journalism, law, business, academic writing, and science. It is also important if you wish to avoid insulting people and to keep the peace in your relations with family and friends.

Practice 3 How good are you at recognizing neutral language? Circle the word or phrase in each list that seems to be the most neutral, that is, without strong connotations—neither negative nor positive.

(a) Professor Higginbothom, the results of the biology experiment were (inconclusive) (a real letdown) (a big flop).

(Practice 3 continued on following page)

(Practice 3 continued from previous page)

    (b) My friends say I am (stubborn) (opinionated) (firm).

    (c) She is from a wealthy family, but her husband's family is (low-income) (low class) (starving).

    (d) Without furniture, the house looks (barren) (spacious) (empty).

Infer Tone

The style or manner in which people use words creates the tone of their speaking or writing. We can't speak to others without revealing a bit of ourselves and our attitudes, no matter what we say. We are experienced at reading a speaker's attitude, or in other words, *tone.* A speaker gives us clues like facial expressions and gestures. Writers also reveal themselves, sometimes unconsciously, in the way they choose their words. From the way they put their ideas into words, we can often *infer* meanings beyond or even different from what is actually stated.

Speakers and writers often deliberately use language that is *not* neutral. Why? They may wish to use the rich connotations of words to:

1. Set a mood, as in a story or a speech
2. Inspire you to action, as in a religious sermon or a political campaign
3. Plant ideas in your mind, as in advertising, literature, and yes, romance
4. Entertain you, as in good conversation or literature

Many different words are used to describe tone, probably as many as can describe a person's nature. Someone's tone can be informal or formal, serious or comic, solemn or playful, bitter or forgiving, cynical or idealistic, and so on. When Shakespeare's Macbeth says that life ". . . is a tale / Told by an idiot, full of sound and fury, / Signifying nothing," we know he is feeling bitter and cynical.

Certainly the *connotation* of words, which you just studied, affects the tone of a written statement. Tone is also influenced by other elements that make up language and give it personality. Other elements can be the length of the sentence, the use of repetition, and the context. Tone can also be created through the use (or avoiding) of slang and other special forms of diction, as well as references the author may make to arenas such as politics, history, literature, music, or other writing.

Below are three famous quotations. Notice how word choice (*connotation*) and other elements create the tone.

- May the force be with you.—from *Star Wars*

  [The word *may* sets the tone, making the statement more formal, a command. The use of *be with you* is also formal. The tone is that of both a command and an official blessing that gives power.]

- Mother died today. Or maybe yesterday, I don't know.—from Albert Camus's novel *The Stranger*

  [The words *or maybe* shock us with their uncertainty about such an important even as the date of a mother's death. The casual tone here is also emphasized by the way the words *or maybe* sound tacked on to the first statement like an afterthought, not particularly important. The tone reflects the speaker's indifference.]

- I shall return.—spoken by General Douglas MacArthur upon leaving the Philippine Islands in World War II

  [The word *shall* connotes a stronger commitment than the word *will* would have. The fact that the sentence is so short and so simple also gives it a more forceful tone, that of a solemn promise.]

Use your imagination as you experiment with *tone* in these situations.

1. You borrowed $20 from your best friend, promising upon your life to pay it back by today. Alas, you're flat broke and have to tell your friend you don't have the money. Example of *fearful* tone:

   I'm afraid I don't have the money. Please don't hurt me. I'll get it for you.

   Example of *matter-of-fact* tone:

   _____

2. You just found out that you didn't pass your composition class and will have to repeat it next semester. You tell your friends what happened. . . .

   Example of *sad* tone:

   _____

   Example of *bitter* tone:

   _____

Infer Irony

Verbal Irony

Another way writers and speakers often express tone is through verbal irony. *Verbal irony is the technique of saying one thing and meaning the opposite.* Suppose your friend says he has to write a term paper during spring break instead of going to the beach. You say, "What fun!" Your sarcasm is a form of verbal irony; you actually mean just the opposite of what you're saying. A humorist like Art Buchwald may write, "I'm sure glad this country doesn't have a foreign policy because, if it did, I'd have to explain it to my relatives." He's not really glad, and, in spite of his playful touch, there's a sharp poke at the government in his remark. The difference between verbal irony and lying is *intent*. With irony, you intend for your audience to understand that you mean the opposite.

Here are some more examples of *verbal irony*.

- You come rushing into the room, your hair a mess, your clothes wrinkled and mismatched. Your friend says, "Oh, don't you look nice."

- Oscar Wilde, the English poet and playwright, wrote, "Ah! Don't say that you agree with me. When people agree with me, I always feel that I must be wrong."

- Can you and your classmates think of an example? _____

  _____

Situational Irony

Another kind of irony that authors use to imply their ideas or feelings is found in *situations that contain an unexpected twist*. A classic example takes place in the Oedipus story:

When Oedipus is born in the city of Thebes in ancient Greece, a prophecy fore-tells that the boy will one day kill his father and marry his mother. His parents, the king and queen, give him to a shepherd who is supposed to kill him. Instead, the shepherd gives him to a couple in the city of Corinth. The boy lives to become a man and one day hears the prophecy that he will kill his father and marry his mother. Determined to avoid that fate, Oedipus leaves Corinth and flees to Thebes. On the road, he gets into a fight with a man and kills him, not realizing the man is his real father. When he gets to Thebes, the city is under the spell of a terrible curse and can't be freed until someone can answer the famous Riddle of the Sphinx. Oedipus answers the riddle, and, for his reward, he receives the hand of the newly widowed queen in marriage. And by now, you must have guessed—although Oedipus doesn't—that the queen is his very own mother. The irony lies in the fact that, in trying to escape his fate, Oedipus made it happen.

A common example of *situational irony* in real life can be found in men or women who are obsessed with work. They neglect their health, while driving themselves to provide security for their old age. Then, as soon as they retire, they drop dead of a heart attack. The irony lies in their sacrificing their lives for a future they never have.

Can you and your classmates think of a different example of situational irony? _____

Practice 4   Be aware of *connotation* and *tone* as you read the following pas-sage. Notice the *narrator's mood* and the *words that connote that mood*.

It was a dull, dark, and soundless day in the autumn of the year. The clouds hung oppressively low in the heavens. I had been passing alone, on horseback, through a dreary tract of country. I finally found myself, as the shades of the evening drew on, within view of the melancholy House of Usher. I know not how it was, but, with the first glimpse of the building, a sense of insufferable gloom filled my spirit. . . . I looked upon the scene before me—upon the mere house and the simple landscape. I looked upon the bleak walls, upon the vacant, eyelike windows, upon a few rank plants, and upon a few white trunks of decayed trees. I felt an utter depression of soul which I can compare to no earthly sensation. There was an iciness, a sinking, a sickening of the heart, an unredeemed dreari-ness of thought. What was it—I paused to think—what was it that so unnerved me about the House of Usher?

–Edgar Allan Poe, from "The Fall of the House of Usher"

(a) What is the *tone* of the paragraph—or in this case, what is the narrator's mood?

   1. cheerful   2. gloomy   3. matter-of-fact

(b) What are some *connotative* details that suggest that mood?

_____

_____

(Practice 4 continued on following page)

(Practice 4 continued from previous page)

(c) What *unstated inference* might be drawn about how the narrator feels about the House of Usher? _____

_____

(d) What deeper inference, or logical conclusion, might be drawn about the House of Usher? _____

_____

(e) Try to think of some *unsupported inferences* (or guesses that go too far):

Example: *The narrator feels he will be locked up in the house*
and tortured. _____

Again, the ability to draw inferences depends first on a correct literal understanding of what's been written or said. Then you must interpret the implications carefully. Remember from earlier chapters, *the parts must fit the whole* for inference, as well as for main idea.

Study Outline

Finish the topic outline below, using your own examples.

_____
[title, Ch. #]

Introduction (definitions):

A. To *infer* = _____

B. *Inference* = _____

C. To *imply* = _____

D. *Implication* = _____
[Paraphrase the author's words]

I. Inferring from actions

   A. Sample action: _____

   B. Inference from the above action: _____

II. Inferring from words

   A. Definition of *connotation*: _____

      1. Sample word (with connotation): _____

      2. Its connotation(s): _____

   B. Definition of *neutral* or *unbiased language*: _____
_____

      1. Sample words (neutral): _____

III. Inferring tone

   A. Definition of *tone*: _____
_____

   B. Examples of tone:

      1. Example of cheerfulness: _____

      2. Example of _____ : _____
[your choice]

IV. Inferring irony

   A. Definition of *verbal irony*: _____
_____

   B. Definition of *situational irony*: _____
_____

Conclusion: _____

The Gender Gap

"Anatomy is destiny," said Sigmund Freud, sometimes referred to as the father of modern psychology. Women and men in the twentieth century struggled to go beyond Freud's view of traditional gender roles, but we are still struggling. And the struggle creates unexpected conflicts.

Read the following paragraphs carefully, continuing to look for the main idea and the logic patterns. Also be alert to the implied *ideas, the* inferences, *which can be revealed through the author's* tone *and* connotations. *Look beneath the surface for* unstated ideas *as well as for stated details. After answering the questions for each paragraph, check the key.*

Exercise 9A: Paragraph

[1]The most frequently expressed complaint women have about men is that men don't listen. [2]Either a man completely ignores her when she speaks to him, or he listens for a few beats, assesses what is bothering her, and then proudly puts on his Mr. Fix-It cap and offers her a solution to make her feel better. [3]He is confused when she doesn't appreciate this gesture of love. [4]No matter how many times she tells him that he's not listening, he doesn't get it and keeps doing the same thing. [5]She wants empathy, but he thinks she wants solutions. [6]The most frequently expressed complaint men have about women is that women are always trying to change them. [7]When a woman loves a man she feels responsible to assist him in growing and tries to help him improve the way he does things. [8]She forms a home-improvement committee, and he becomes her primary focus. [9]No matter how much he resists her help, she persists—waiting for any opportunity to help him or tell him what to do. [10]She thinks she's nurturing him, while he feels he's being controlled. [11]Instead, he wants her acceptance.

—JOHN GRAY, FROM MEN ARE FROM MARS, WOMEN ARE FROM VENUS

1. The main logic pattern in this paragraph is obviously contrast. What is the most important contrast?

   _____ vs. _____

2. The *irony* comes from expectations being different from reality for both men and women. What kind of irony is this?   (a) verbal   (b) situational

3. What *connotation* does the use of "his Mr. Fix-It cap" (in sentence #2) have?
   (a) positive   (b) negative   (c) neutral

4. This paragraph has two topic sentences: sentences _____ and _____.
   What *implied* main idea can you *infer* from these two sentences?

   _____

   _____

Exercise 9B: Paragraph

¹In the February 3 issue of the [college newspaper], I publicly apologized for calling one of my female colleagues "dear." ²I thought that my apology would end the furor over my politically incorrect statement. ³On the contrary, women everywhere have now decided to get even with me by calling me "dear" every time they get a chance. ⁴Let me tell you this is a terrible ordeal I have to go through. ⁵I wake up in the middle of the night trembling and in a sweat seeing all those women smiling at me and saying, "Hi, dear," "How are you, dear?" ⁶"Can we do anything nice for you, dear?" ⁷Yes, they certainly can do something nice for me. ⁸First, they can stop smiling at me. ⁹Second, they can stop calling me "dear." ¹⁰If they don't stop this sexual harassment, I intend to take legal action. ¹¹In fact, I have already contacted Gloria Allred [feminist lawyer]. ¹²I keep asking myself, why does it have to be me who is the subject of this rude behavior? ¹³Sometimes I think that my wife is one of the few people who knows how to act politically correct. ¹⁴She quit smiling at me and calling me "dear" about two days after we got married.

—Dr. Stan Fitch, Professor of Psychology, from "Letters to the Editor"

1. What is the *unstated detail* that caused the author to write his February 3 letter to the editor? Why would he apologize for calling someone "dear"?

   _____

2. What is the author's *tone* in the letter?
   (a) angry   (b) playful   (c) matter-of-fact
   What is the *tone* of the women who are calling the author "dear"?
   (a) angry   (b) playful   (c) matter-of-fact

3. We may *infer* the author is making fun of which group?
   (a) the women calling him "dear"
   (b) the women who called him "politically incorrect"

4. The paragraph has what kind of *irony*?
   (a) verbal   (b) situational   (c) both

5. In a complete sentence, state the *implied* main idea of the paragraph.

   _____

   _____

   [who? is pretending what? why?]

Exercise 9C: Paragraph

[1]Women are winning big from sexual harassment suits! [2]Ever since the court ruling, eight years ago, that the 1964 Civil Rights Act protects workers from being sexually harassed, women have gone from being taken advantage of to taking advantage. [3]According to *USA Today* [Oct. 15, 1992] women have filed 66 percent more complaints of sexual harassment in 1992 than in 1991. [4]And they are winning—$2.4 million more in 1992 than in 1991. [5]If this trend continues, a woman will profit more from her boss giving her a compliment than from giving her a raise. [6]Even college gals may find an easier way to pay their way through school than working. [7]At Antioch College, students now are required to get a verbal agreement for every move they make on their dates—from hand-holding to kissing to sex. [8]Move too quickly and risk getting expelled. [9]Men, beware! [10]You may lose more than your shirt on a date.

—BRICK MANFULL, FROM HOLLYWOOD INTRUDER

1. The reader may *infer* that the author is more likely to be
   (a) male   (b) female
   and that the reading audience is more likely to be
   (a) male   (b) female.

2. What word in the paragraph is not politically correct?

   _____

3. (a). Do the facts in the paragraph make the author's opinions reliable?

   _____

   (b). What are some serious, underlying issues that are not being acknowl-edged?

   _____

4. In your own words, write a complete sentence that states the *implied* main idea of the paragraph.

   _____

   _____

   [who?   is warning whom?   about what?]

II. How to Read Faster

To continue to read faster, review this list of suggestions, some of which were made in earlier chapters. Choose the tips that fit your situation, and practice on the lighter material you read as part of your daily reading habit.

Practical Suggestions for Reading Faster

1. To reduce eye fixations and increase eye span, put dots or x's above two- and three-word phrases in a paragraph, and fix your eyes on the dots or x's while reading and rereading the paragraph.

2. Use a metronome with suggestion #1. Set the beeps as a signal to move the eyes to the next dot or to the next line.

3. Draw a straight line down the middle of a narrow newspaper column, and try to read vertically.

4. For more efficient rapid reading, fix your eyes on key words (nouns, verbs, and transition words) and pick up lesser words (articles, prepositions, and modifiers) with your peripheral vision.

5. To avoid number blindness (distraction by numbers), concentrate on the main idea of a paragraph and round numbers off to the nearest 50 or 100. It is usually more important to recognize the significance of the number than to memorize the exact number.

6. To avoid word blindness (distraction by specific words), again, try to follow the main idea of the paragraph or article by reading in phrases (groups of related thoughts). In general, don't stop to look up words you don't know. Try to determine each word's meaning through context and look it up after finishing the selection.

7. If you have access to a speed-reading program on computer (or the older Controlled Reader or Guided Reader), run one article twice. The first time, run the article at double your usual speed. Do not tune out because you think it is too fast; try to follow the main idea. Then run the same reading a second time, slower, but at about 100 WPM faster than your usual speed. This speed should seem slow after reading at the faster rate. Continue increasing speeds with each session.

8. For a variation of the above method, begin an article at your usual speed (for example, 250 WPM), and gradually increase speed to the maximum (750–900 WPM). Run the article again, beginning at the fastest speed and gradually decreasing the speed to 100 WPM faster than your usual speed (at least 350 WPM). Again, this rate should seem slow after attempting to read at the faster rates. Try to increase both speeds with each session.

Exercise 9D: Phrases (Variation)

Each column of twenty items has only one key phrase (in italics). Scan for each repeated phrase and mark it. Work through both columns vertically before checking your time.

Key Phrase	Key Phrase
livid with fear	*singed his finger*
lived with fear	sings his finger
livid with fear	singed his fins
loved with fear	signals his finish
loved with tears	signing his finish
living with fear	signals the swingers
living with fears	singed his finger
livery of fear	singed his fingers
lively with wear	signed the singers
livid with fear	singed two fingers
alive with fear	singed her finger
livid ears	singer's fingers
lively ears	singed my fingers
in living color	singing of fingers
livid with fear	unhinged with anger
living on fear	singing of anger
lived without fear	singed his finger
lives with fear	signs this finger
livid with fear	signed with fingers
alive with fleas	singed his finger
liquid with fear	Band-aid, please!

Time _____

Number of Errors _____

Check the Answer Key to see how many times each key phrase is repeated.

Exercise 9E: Phrases (Variation)

Each column of twenty items has only one key phrase (in italics). Scan for each repeated phrase and mark it. Work through both columns vertically before checking your time.

Key Phrase	Key Phrase
tract of land	*curries favor*
track of land	curries favors
track landing	carries favors
attracts land	famous curry
tractor on land	carries flavor
traction on land	the cur you favor
tract of land	cherry flavor
trace of land	carrying favors
traced island	cured favorite
tract of land	cursory favor
traced inland	curries flavoring
traces the island	curries favor
tract or land	savors the curry
races for land	hurries the favor
track the landing	curious favor
tract of land	curry for four
tracing the hand	crawls for favors
trance of mind	cans a favor
raced to land	cares for few
tract of land	curries favor
contract for land	furry favors

Time _____

Number of Errors _____

Check the Answer Key to see how many times each key phrase is repeated.

The Gender Gap

The two Timed Readings are about as different from each other as they can be in tone and style. Perhaps this is because the sources are so different: the first is a classic fable written in 1940 and the second is a modern newspaper column. What they have in common is gender conflict.

Exercise 9F: Timed Reading   *534 words*

This first reading, by a famous American humorist, is on the surface a tale about a man seeing a unicorn. Read beneath the surface and draw some *inferences* about traditional male-female relationships. Look for the *connotations* of words that might justify why the author has sometimes been called a "misogynist" (women-hater).

Preview: *Quickly survey the title, first paragraph, and last paragraph (plus "Moral"). Look for "who," "what," "when," "where." Then write what you think is the main conflict in the story.* _____

Wait for a signal from your instructor before you begin reading. If you practice speed-reading this story, you will find it worth rereading just for pleasure later. Circle your reading time when you have finished, and find your WPM.

The Unicorn in the Garden

James Thurber

Once upon a sunny morning a man who sat in a breakfast nook looked up from his scrambled eggs to see a white unicorn with a gold horn quietly cropping the roses in the garden. The man went up to the bedroom where his wife was still asleep and woke her. "There's a unicorn in the garden," he said. "Eating roses." She opened one unfriendly eye and looked at him. "The unicorn is a mythical beast," she said, and turned her back on him.

The man walked slowly downstairs and out into the garden. The unicorn was still there; he was now browsing among the tulips. "Here, unicorn," said the man, and he pulled up a lily and gave it to him. The unicorn ate it gravely. With a high heart, because there was a unicorn in his garden, the man went upstairs and roused his wife again. "The unicorn," he said, "ate a lily." His wife sat up in bed and looked at him coldly. "You are a booby," she said, "and I am going to have you put in the booby-hatch." The man, who had never liked the words "booby" and "booby-hatch," and who liked them even less on a shining morning when there was a unicorn in the garden, thought for a moment. "We'll see about that," he said. He walked over to the door. "He has a golden horn in the middle of his forehead," he told her. Then he went back to the garden to watch the unicorn, but the unicorn had gone away. The man sat down among the roses and went to sleep.

As soon as the husband had gone out of the house, the wife got up and dressed as fast as she could. She was very excited and there was a gloat in her eye. She telephoned the police and she telephoned a psychiatrist; she told them to hurry to her house and bring a strait-jacket. When the police and the psychiatrist arrived, they sat down in chairs and looked at her, with great interest. "My husband," she said "saw a unicorn this morning." The police looked at the psychiatrist and the psychiatrist looked at the police. "He told me it ate a lily," she said. The psychiatrist looked at the police and the police looked at the psychiatrist. "He told me it had a golden horn in the middle of its forehead," she said. At a solemn signal from the psychiatrist, the police leapt from their chairs and seized the wife. They had a hard time subduing her, for she put up a terrific struggle, but they finally subdued her. Just as they got her into the strait-jacket, the husband came back into the house.

"Did you tell your wife you saw a unicorn?" asked the police. "Of course not," said the husband. "The unicorn is a mythical beast." "That's all I wanted to know," said the psychiatrist. "Take her away. I'm sorry, sir, but your wife is as crazy as a jay bird." So they took her away, cursing and screaming, and shut her up in an institution. The husband lived happily ever after.

Moral: Don't count your boobies until they are hatched.

Answer the following recall questions without referring to the article.

1. What action does the wife take in response to her husband's story about the unicorn?

   (a) She shares his pleasure in watching the unicorn.

   (b) She tries to drive the unicorn from the garden.

   (c) She calls the police and a psychiatrist.

2. The husband tries to stop the police from taking his wife to the booby-hatch.   (a) true   (b) false

You may refer to the article to answer the following questions.

3. The ending (the wife being taken off to the booby-hatch instead of the husband) represents what kind of *irony*?   (a) verbal   (b) situational

4. List some descriptive words that *connote* the author's negative *tone* toward the wife.

   _____

5. In your own words, write a complete sentence that states the thesis (or *theme*) in this story.

   _____

   _____

   [who?   does what?   why?]

Check your answers with the key, and record your scores below and on the Progress Chart.

Words per Minute   _____

Percent Comprehension   _____

min:sec	wpm
2:14	240
2:03	260
1:54	280
1:47	300
1:40	320
1:34	340
1:29	360
1:24	380
1:20	400
1:16	420
1:13	440
1:10	460
1:07	480
1:04	500
1:02	520
0:59	540
0:57	560
0:55	580
0:53	600
0:52	620
0:50	640
0:49	660
0:47	680
0:46	700
0:45	720
0:43	740
0:42	760
0:41	780
0:40	800

TIMING CHART

This second selection, written by a syndicated columnist, looks at a less-publicized view of sexual harassment. It reinforces what you just learned about the *connotation* of words.

Preview: *Quickly survey the title, author's name, and first and last paragraphs. Write here what you think is the author's thesis.*

_____

 Wait for a signal from your instructor before you begin reading. Try to finish in a minute, if you can. Circle your reading time when you have finished, and find your WPM.

It's Not about Sex, but Power

Ellen Goodman

There are words we use to describe what happens all too often on the school playground or the shop floor. We call it "hazing." Or "horseplay." We describe it as "crude locker-room behavior." We say, "Boys will be boys."

It's a vocabulary that often trivializes the cruel ways many men keep each other in line. It's a language that dismisses the way one man makes another pay if he falls outside some standard of masculinity.

This is how it worked at its worst for one roustabout named Joseph Oncale on an oil rig in the waters off Louisiana. The trouble began, he says, with a supervisor taunting him, "You know, you got a cute little ass. I'm going to get you." It ended with threats of rape from this boss and two co-workers who held him down in a shower and forced a bar of soap between his buttocks.

Who knows why they went after Oncale. All of these men are heterosexuals. Was it because Oncale, the father of two, was small? Or because he was new? In any case, in a phrase that must be a classic understatement, he said, "I feel belittled."

But Oncale didn't call it hazing. He called it harassment. When Sundowner Offshore Services Inc. refused to help when he was forced from work, he charged sexual harassment. Same-sex sexual harassment. And when a federal appeals court denied him the right to a trial, saying that harassment between men was not covered by Title VII of the Civil Rights Act, he appealed this ruling to the Supreme Court.

There, on Wednesday, a skeptical group of justices seemed ready to overturn the appeals court. "A Jew could discriminate against a Jew. An African American against an African American," so why couldn't a man discriminate against a man? asked Justice Stephen Breyer.

But even if Oncale gets his day in court, even if same-sex harassment is a permissible charge, it is by no means the end of the matter. This is one of those moments when the unusual case, the man-bites-dog case or straight-man-harasses-straight-man case can throw light on a dusky corner of the law.

When women first claimed that sexual harassment was a form of gender discrimination, they were dismissed with the familiar arguments. It was just locker-room stuff, boys will be boys, it's the price you pay for breaking into the boys' club.

Gradually the law changed. The quid pro quo—no sex, no job—is now discrimination. The creation of a hostile work environment—taunts, pinups, pinches—is illegal.

Courts have ruled against men harassing women, women harassing men. Some have ruled against homosexual supervisors harassing heterosexual employees. But underlying this is a certain confusion, a notion that sexual harassment is connected to sexual attraction. What then about a case of same-sex harassment when all parties are heterosexual and presumably not "attracted" to each other?

The Oncale case forces us to the heart of the matter. And at its heart, sexual harassment is not about sex but about power. Just as rape is not about sex but about violence.

As Katherine Franke of Fordham Law School describes it, "Sexual harassment is a way of enforcing gender norms in the workplace." As such, she says, it's a form of discrimination against men or women, opposite sex or same sex.

As an example, Franke says, a man may harass a woman because he thinks of her as an object of sexual attention, not as a co-worker. A man may harass another man because of the "kind of" man he is. "It's a way of saying you aren't the kind of man we want working here." They are both victims of separate but equal stereotypes, different but equal discrimination.

I have no idea how Joseph Oncale will fare if he goes to trial. I don't know if this story fits into what Franke calls the "dweeby guy" category or whether some other dark dynamic was in play on that oil rig. But I do know it should be heard.

Men do discriminate against each other "on account of sex." If anything, we vastly underestimate the ways some men enforce rules of masculinity and terrorize those who deviate. Joseph Oncale is not telling a different story than one heard from a million women. He's telling the rest of the story.

Answer the following recall questions without referring to the article.

1. What is the location for the incident about which Joseph Oncale complains? _____

2. Which type of harassment is the Joseph Oncale incident:
   (a) male harassing female
   (b) heterosexual male harassing heterosexual male
   (c) female harassing male
   (d) homosexual male harassing homosexual male

3. What does "quid pro quo" mean in sexual harassment cases?

   _____

4. The author speculates that Oncale might have been the object of harassment because of
   (a) his size and newness on the job   (b) his female characteristics
   (c) his loudness

5. Oncale's charge of harassment under Title VII of the Civil Rights Act was at first denied.   (a) true   (b) false

   You may refer to the article to answer the following questions.

6. The role reversal (harassment of a man instead of a woman) is what kind of irony?   (a) verbal   (b) situational

TIMING CHART	
min:sec	wpm
03:01	240
02:47	260
02:35	280
02:25	300
02:16	320
02:08	340
02:01	360
01:54	380
01:48	400
01:43	420
01:39	440
01:34	460
01:30	480
01:27	500
01:23	520
01:20	540
01:17	560
01:15	580
01:12	600
01:10	620
01:08	640
01:06	660
01:04	680
01:02	700
01:00	720
00:59	740
00:57	760
00:56	780
00:54	800

7. Explain the *connotation* of "harassment," as opposed to "hazing," being used to describe what happened to Oncale.

_____

_____

8. What is the author's *tone* toward the people charged with harassing Oncale?   (a) negative   (b) positive   (c) neutral

9. Explain the *implication* of Franke's statement: "Sexual harassment is a way of enforcing gender norms in the workplace." _____

_____

10. Thesis: _____

_____

[what?   represents what?]

Check your answers with the key, and record your scores below and on the Progress Chart.

Words per Minute   _____

Percent Comprehension   _____

Writing and Discussion Activities

1. Write a paragraph describing a time in your life when you were expected to act or think a certain way simply because of your gender. (Examples: You were expected to fight someone because you were a male even though you weren't angry. Or, as a female, you were expected to smile and agree when you did not agree.) Explain why you think this situation was unfair.

2. Discuss whether or not you agree with the point of view expressed in any of the selections in this chapter. Write a paragraph with a topic sentence that sums up your opinion. Expand on your topic sentence with first and second level details.

Vocabulary Review, Chapter 9

Match the vocabulary word on the left with its definition on the right. Write the letter of the answer on the short blank to the left.

_c_ 1. **insufferable**   (a) alarmed

_e_ 2. **dusky**   (b) not gay

_d_ 3. **dweeby**   (c) unbearable

_d_ 4. **unnerved**   (d) nerdlike

_b_ 5. **heterosexual**   (e) dark

*Choose the best definition for each **boldfaced** word as it is used in its context.*

_c_ 6. Dissatisfied with her appearance, each week she kept **cropping** her hair until she had a crew cut.
   (a) experimenting with color   (b) hiding under a hat
   (c) cutting shorter

_a_ 7. The senator agreed to vote for the other senator's bill, but he wanted a **quid pro quo**.
   (a) something in exchange   (b) deeper explanation
   (c) general election

_b_ 8. The economics professor said he would talk about the many **dynamics** that influence the stock and bond markets.
   (a) war zones   (b) forces   (c) powerful leaders

_c_ 9. The college placed a ban against fraternities that conduct **hazing**.
   (a) cheating schemes   (b) binge drinking   (c) cruel initiations

_b_ 10. **Subduing** a classroom of kindergarten children is not easy, but an experienced teacher can do it.
   (a) teaching creativity to   (b) controlling and calming
   (c) filling with enthusiasm

*Mark each sentence to show whether the **boldfaced** word is used correctly.*

a = True   b = False

_b_ 11. The wife had a **gloat** in her eye when her husband proved to her that she was once again wrong about how to operate the VCR.

_b_ 12. You can recognize a **unicorn** in pictures by its gold hooves and wings.

(Continued)

_a_ 13. Knowing how to write clearly and in an organized way will help you **fare** well in most careers.

_b_ 14. When a circus comes to town, the **roustabouts** are essential to setting it up and taking it down.

_b_ 15. In many parts of the world, there are famous winds, **oppressively** hot, known for their ability to calm and relax people.

Choose the word from the box that fits the context of the following paragraph. Write the letter of each choice on the short lines to the left of the paragraph.

(a) **belittled** (b) **insignificant** (c) **furor** (d) **harassment** (e) **empathy**

_d_ 16.   Thirty years ago, the concept of sexual __16__ was considered too

_a_ 17. __17__ to take seriously. Few people had __18__ for a woman—or a

_e_ 18. man—who might dare to report having been __19__ because of

_c_ 19. unwanted sexual advances or comments made at work or on

_b_ 20. campus. But, by the 1990s, the issue had become a __20__. It was the

topic of books, movies, lawsuits, and a famous hearing on the suitability of a current Supreme Court justice.

% Correct _____

Comprehension Review, Chapter 9

_b_ 1. An idea that writers or speakers suggest indirectly through details but do not state openly is an

   (a) inference   (b) implication

_a_ 2. An idea that readers or listeners understand by drawing a conclusion is an

   (a) inference   (b) implication

_a_ 3. Who is more likely to *infer*?   (a) reader   (b) writer

_b_ 4. Who is more likely to *imply*?   (a) reader   (b) writer

From each pair of similar words, pick the word with the stronger connotation.
[Clue: The connotation can be either negative or positive. Which one is *not* neutral.]

a _b_ 5. (a) filthy rich   (b) wealthy

_b_ 6. (a) nice looking   (b) gorgeous

_b_ 7. (a) thin   (b) anorexic

Match the term on the left with its definition on the right.

_e_ 8. connotation   (a) the attitude or mood created by the way a writer uses words

_c_ 9. neutral   (b) saying one thing and meaning the opposite

_a_ 10. tone   (c) unbiased—describes language that doesn't take sides

_b_ 11. verbal irony   (d) an unexpected twist in life; a reversal of fate

_d_ 12. situational irony (e) words with underlying meanings or feelings

Read the following two passages and answer the questions about them.

   A. It was a blonde [woman], a blonde to make a bishop kick a hole in a stained-glass window.

   —FROM RAYMOND CHANDLER, FAREWELL, MY LOVELY, *1940.*

13. Explain how language is used in this line to create the author's *tone* toward the blonde character.

   [Clue: A bishop doesn't *really* kick a hole through a window.] It

   The author wanted to write in his own way.
   Use his own the la

   The author wanted the readers to infer his ideas
   He wanted to set a mood in his the *(Continued)*
   ohara his story.

B. She was created to be the toy of man, his rattle, and it must jingle in his ears whenever, dismissing reason, he chooses to be amused.

—FROM MARY WOLLSTONECRAFT, A VINDICATION OF THE RIGHTS OF WOMEN, *1792*.

[Clue: "Vindication" means a justification or a defense against opposition.]

14. Which of the following statements best expresses what the author is suggesting about male-female relationships?
    (a) Little boys should never play with Barbie dolls when they want to have fun.
    (b) Men treat women like brainless toys.
    (c) A woman should make herself pleasing to a man in order to soothe his tired brain.

15. Which *connotative* words from Wollstonecraft's line best support your choice of answers for #14?
    the toy of man

% Correct _____

*tuan
0909154916*

VOCABULARY PREVIEW for Chapter 10

WORDS IN CONTEXT

Directions: *Examine the **boldfaced** word as it is used in the sentence and write your best guess of the word's meaning. Then look up the word in your dictionary, and write the best definition for its context in the sentence.*

from Passage 10A (p. 338)

1. **idiocy** (id' ē ə sē)   *noun*

   The damned little brat must be protected against her own **idiocy**.

   Your best guess: _____

   Best dictionary definition: _____

2. **operatives** (op' ə rə' tivz)   *noun*

   But a blind fury, a feeling of adult shame, bred of a longing for muscular release are the **operatives**.

   Your best guess: _____

   Best dictionary definition: _____

3. **membrane** (mem' brān)   *noun*

   And there it was—both tonsils covered with **membrane**.

   Your best guess: _____

   Best dictionary definition: _____

from Poem 10B (p. 339)

4. **mandrake** (man' drāk)   *adjective*

   Get with child a **mandrake** root.

   Your best guess: _____

   Best dictionary definition: _____

5. **cleft** (kleft)   *verb*

   Tell me . . . who **cleft** the devil's foot.

   Your best guess: _____

   Best dictionary definition: _____

6. **thou** (Ŧhou)   *pronoun (archaic)*

   If **thou** be'st born to strange sights . . . .

   Your best guess: _____

   Best dictionary definition: _____

7. **befell** (bi fel')   *verb*

Thou, when thou return'st, wilt tell me / All strange wonders that **befell** thee.

Your best guess: _____

Best dictionary definition: _____

8. **fair** (fâr)   *adjective*

No where / Lives a woman true and **fair**.

Your best guess: _____

Best dictionary definition: _____

[Clue: Look for a less common definition, relating to appearance.]

9. **pilgrimage** (pil' grə mij)   *noun*

Such a **pilgrimage** were sweet.

Your best guess: _____

Best dictionary definition: _____

10. **ere** (er)   *conjunction*

Yet she / Will be / False, **ere** I come, to two or three.

Your best guess: _____

Best dictionary definition: _____

from Passage 10C (p. 340)

11. **braille** (brāl)   *noun*

You had to do it by **braille**, unscrewing unseen screws.

Your best guess: _____

Best dictionary definition: _____

from Timed Reading 10F (p. 344)

12. **putter** (put' ər)   *verbal*

He likes to fix motors, to **putter** with his car, or take apart the lawn mower.

Your best guess: _____

Best dictionary definition: _____

13. **noblesse oblige** (nō bles' ō blēzh')   *noun-adjective (French)*

Elizabeth . . . reminded him with extravagantly good-natured **noblesse oblige** to please change the bulb before they got home from their picnic.

Your best guess: _____

Best dictionary definition: _____

14. **emaciated**   (i mā′ shē ā′ tid)   *adjective*

   Rosie with her *Seventeen* . . . staring solemnly at page after page of **emaciated** beauty.

   Your best guess: _____

   Best dictionary definition: _____

15. **solar plexus**   (sō′ lər plek′ səs)   *adjective-noun*

   There was a sudden pinch in Elizabeth's **solar plexus**, a sinking feeling, a rage at James.

   Your best guess: _____

   Best dictionary definition: _____

16. **dereliction**   (der′ ə lik′ shən)   *noun*

   But because of James's **dereliction**, it was a mess.

   Your best guess: _____

   Best dictionary definition: _____

17. **lurching**   (lėrch′ ing)   *verbal*

   She found herself **lurching** here and there, tripping, knocking things over, ***smoldering*** with resentment.

   Your best guess: _____

   Best dictionary definition: _____

18. **smoldering**   (smōl′ dər ing)   *verbal*

   Your best guess: _____

   Best dictionary definition: _____

   [Note: See sentence #17 for context clues to **smoldering**.]

19. **parody**   (par′ ə dē)   *noun*

   They read their magazines and ate their mandarin oranges by flashlight and candles, a **parody** of an elegant dinner party.

   Your best guess: _____

   Best dictionary definition: _____

20. **improvisation**   (im′ prov ə zā′ shən)   *noun*

   Good cheer and **improvisation** were ***burbling*** again in the visible world, but a ***roiling*** feeling had begun in her gut.

   Your best guess: _____

   Best dictionary definition: _____

21. **burbling**   (bėr′ bling)   *verb*

   Your best guess: _____

   Best dictionary definition: _____

22. **roiling** (roi' ling) *verbal (adjective)*

Your best guess: _____

Best dictionary definition: _____

23. **hunkered** (hung' kərd) *verb*

She felt tired and short in her chair, as if she and Rosie were **hunkered** down in a cave.

Your best guess: _____

Best dictionary definition: _____

24. **pathetic** (pə thet' ik) *adjective*

"How **pathetic**," she said to Elizabeth. "Men can be such slobs."

Your best guess: _____

Best dictionary definition: _____

25. **gothic** (goth' ik) *adjective*

Rosie was up in bed with her latest teenage **gothic**.

Your best guess: _____

Best dictionary definition: _____

26. **troll** (trōl) *adjective (usually a noun)*

Smells, growths, moss and mold, furry mold like **troll** hair, fuzz with fur on it.

Your best guess: _____

Best dictionary definition: _____

27. **embossing** (em bôs' ing) *verbal*

She could feel the [toilet] seat **embossing** her butt.

Your best guess: _____

Best dictionary definition: _____

28. **livid** (liv' id) *adjective*

James was still not home at ten, by which time she was **livid**.

Your best guess: _____

Best dictionary definition: _____

29. **overt** (ō vėrt') *adjective*

Straightening her knees would be too **overt**.

Your best guess: _____

Best dictionary definition: _____

30. **invective** (in vek' tiv) *noun*

Who knew what might burst out—tears, **invective**, ***molten*** fury.

Your best guess: _____

Best dictionary definition: _____

31. **molten** (mōlt′ n)   *adjective*

Your best guess: _____

Best dictionary definition: _____

32. **bunker** (bung′ kər)   *noun*

She felt like she was in a **bunker**, and she listened to him sigh, clearly now getting that she was annoyed, punishing him.

Your best guess: _____

Best dictionary definition: _____

33. **smote** (smōt)   *verb*

He **smote** his forehead, gripped his head as if being pierced with migraine.

Your best guess: _____

Best dictionary definition: _____

[Clue: This word is the past tense of "smite."]

34. **martyr** (mär′ tər)   *noun*

And the jacket was always waiting in the closet, the jacket of being a **martyr** and a bitch, the jacket she was now wearing.

Your best guess: _____

Best dictionary definition: _____

35. **glowered** (glou′ ərd)   *verb*

Elizabeth **glowered** at the paper.

Your best guess: _____

Best dictionary definition: _____

36. **gawked** (gôkt)   *verb*

She **gawked** at him.

Your best guess: _____

Best dictionary definition: _____

37. **flourish** (flėr′ ish)   *noun*

He turned it [the light bulb] back on with a **flourish**, and then off.

Your best guess: _____

Best dictionary definition: _____

Exercise, Vocabulary Preview, Chapter 10

Directions: *Choose the best definition for each **boldfaced** word or phrase as it is used in its context.*

_b_ 1. Julia thought it was **idiocy** for the school board to vote to lengthen the school day when the students were already riding the school bus in the dark for most of the winter months.

(a) bad planning (b) obvious stupidity (c) good thinking

_c_ 2. A healthy diet, with fewer calories, and regular exercise are the **operatives** for losing weight and keeping it off.

(a) doctor's advice (b) old-fashioned way (c) working plan

_b_ 3. Garter snakes have a form of live birth instead of laying eggs; the baby snakes mature inside the mother and are then born with a **membrane** covering them.

(a) thick shell (b) thin layer (c) shiny scales

_c_ 4. The herbalist suggested that Mollie try **mandrake** root in her tea to help her sleep, then put the root under her pillow to make her fertile.

(a) Chinese powder (b) dwarf tree (c) man-shaped

_a_ 5. In the fable, the pig's hoof was **cleft** when he tried to cross the wooden bridge and remains that way until this very day.

(a) split (b) caught (c) broken off

_a_ 6. When Juliet asks, "Wherefore art **thou** Romeo?" she doesn't mean, "Where are you?" but "Why is your name Romeo?"

(a) you (b) she (c) him

_b_ 7. Terrible things **befell** Joanna after she threw away the chain letter in disgust.

(a) fell off (b) happened to (c) watched

_c_ 8. He had searched all his life for a **fair** young maiden to marry, but fell in love with a plain, middle-aged woman.

(a) smart (b) talented (c) beautiful

_a_ 9. Every summer the Kennedy family made a **pilgrimage** back to Ireland, the country of their ancestors.

(a) sacred journey (b) phone call (c) long vacation

_c_ 10. "I vow these lips will not smile again, Marianna, **ere** they touch your lips," swore Sir Thomas to his true love.

(a) since (b) after (c) before

_a_ 11. Helen Keller eventually learned to read **braille**, which opened up a whole new world of books and ideas for her.

(a) writing for the blind (b) shorthand (c) advanced vocabulary _b_ 12. Pamela's father liked to **putter** in his garden, doing a little planting, watering, and weeding.

(a) work hard   (b) do casually   (c) meditate quietly

_b_ 13. Queen Elizabeth of England treats her subjects with **noblesse oblige** on formal occasions.

(a) serious looks   (b) honorable behavior   (c) rude manners

_c_ 14. The **emaciated** models that look out at us from the pages of fashion magazines look more like starving refugees than healthy, wealthy young women.

(a) pleasingly plump   (b) too made-up   (c) sickly thin

_a_ 15. When Sean was punched in the **solar plexus**, all his breath was forced out, and he had to lie on the ground for a while to recover.

(a) pit of the stomach   (b) knee cap   (c) back of the head

_c_ 16. Roderick was suspended for **dereliction** of duty; in other words, he wasn't doing his job.

(a) making mistakes   (b) being silly   (c) neglecting work

_b_ 17. After being hit by the car, the dog was **lurching** along the side of the road before disappearing into the woods.

(a) hurrying   (b) staggering   (c) crawling

_b_ 18. Dan thought it safe to leave the fire **smoldering** overnight because, with rain forecast, there wasn't much danger of it flaring back up.

(a) blazing   (b) smoking   (c) unattended

_c_ 19. The *Saturday Night Live* television show did a **parody** of the president that must have embarrassed him and his family.

(a) harsh criticism   (b) bad joke   (c) ridiculing imitation

_a_ 20. Many acting instructors use **improvisation** to keep the students creative and thinking on their feet.

(a) scenes without script   (b) live audiences   (c) video cameras

_c_ 21. **Burbling** with laughter, Joan lifted the spirits of everybody at the dull party.

(a) holding back   (b) hiding   (c) bubbling

_b_ 22. The **roiling** in her stomach couldn't be contained a moment longer, so she hurried to the bathroom.

(a) milk shake   (b) stirring up   (c) heaviness

_a_ 23. Carsen **hunkered** down behind the chair, trying to hide from her cousins.

(a) crouched   (b) stretched out   (c) jumped

_a_ 24. Eddie made a **pathetic** attempt to talk with his ex-girlfriend, showing up at her work, unshaven and unwashed.

(a) pitiful   (b) aggressive   (c) persuasive

_c_ 25. The **Gothic** novel is very popular with teenage girls because it appeals to their need for escape and drama.

(a) light mystery   (b) serial killer   (c) dark romance

_b_ 26. Little Lisa liked to read fantasy books with **troll**-like characters, all shrunken and misshapen.

(a) fairy princess   (b) dwarflike   (c) tall and evil

_a_ 27. She wanted to try **embossing** her own Christmas ornaments, using a small tool that looked like an ice pick on some sheets of tin.

(a) imprinting   (b) painting   (c) decorating

_c_ 28. Tinker Bell was **livid** when Wendy wanted to give Peter Pan a kiss.

(a) hysterical   (b) tearful   (c) furious

_b_ 29. Rachel was hoping that licking her fingers might be **overt** enough to let him know she wanted a bite of his chocolate cake.

(a) subtle   (b) obvious   (c) hungry

_b_ 30. The angry student shouted every **invective** he knew at the stunned teacher before stomping out of the room.

(a) hard-luck story   (b) abusive insult   (c) false excuse

_c_ 31. The melted lead spilled out of the vat like **molten** lava, destroying everything in its path.

(a) cool liquid   (b) warm, watery   (c) hot and liquid

_a_ 32. The townspeople were furious to find out that their elected officials had built themselves a secret **bunker** beneath the courthouse to save themselves in case of nuclear war.

(a) protective chamber   (b) sports center   (c) heated pool

_c_ 33. He **smote** his own forehead with the heel of his hand in utter disgust.

(a) rubbed softly   (b) pinched   (c) struck sharply

_c_ 34. His mother had always played the **martyr**; she used her pain and sacrifices to manipulate family members and control them.

(a) sentimental songs   (b) overbearing boss   (c) constant sufferer

_b_ 35. Angela **glowered** at her brother when he walked into her room, unannounced and uninvited.

(a) beamed   (b) glared   (c) grinned

_a_ 36. The teenage boys **gawked** at the bikini-clad girls strolling by.

(a) openly stared   (b) trembled with desire   (c) turned away

_c_ 37. As always, the former actress left the room with a **flourish**, her skirt swirling, bracelets jangling, and long hair flying.

(a) bouquet of flowers   (b) modest smile   (c) dramatic show

Number of Errors _____

Chapter 10
Interpreting Literature

I. How to Understand More

Interpreting Literature

Interpreting literature is a matter of using all the reading skills you have learned thus far. You find the main idea (or *theme*). You connect the details and see a pattern emerge. You read between the lines (or draw *inferences*).

The word "literature" comes from the Latin *littera*, which means "letter." In the most general sense, then, literature means anything written. But, in the way you most often hear the word used, literature refers to poetry, novels, short stories, and plays.

Interpreting literature means appreciating literature; but, to appreciate it, you must first understand it. In this chapter, we will study three of the most common aspects of literature: *character, conflict*, and *theme*. Understanding these three basic elements of literature will help you appreciate and enjoy it more.

Observe Character Traits

The *character* who usually interests us the most in a story is the main character. The most entertaining main characters are often the most real, even though they are fictional. They have a mixture of personality traits, some good, some not-so-admirable, just as real people do. Characters who are realistic in this way we call *rounded*. They have been fully developed. They change, or often grow up, during the story. Characters who are one-sided and unrealistic we often call *flat* or *stereotyped*.

To help you understand character better, choose someone from your family. Then make a list of his or her personality traits on the lines below. So that your list gives a picture of a rounded, not a flat, person, include some of the person's unusual, or contrasting, traits.

good traits	*bad traits*
_____	_____
_____	_____
_____	_____

Identify the Conflict

Without *conflict*, there is no story, no play, and often no poem. What is conflict? It is the central problem or group of problems the main character has. Conflict is often what keeps us fascinated when we read a story or watch a play or film. We want to see how main characters handle or *resolve* the conflicts they are struggling with. Conflict can take many forms.

Physical Conflict. The main character's conflict or problem can be a physical one. For example, the character may have to fistfight another character. Or the character may have to wrestle a deadly snake or fight a serious disease. The character might even fight a force of nature, such as an earthquake or hurricane. We see this kind of physical conflict in adventure and action stories. Give a brief example of this type of conflict. You might use the same family member whose personality traits you described previously. _____

_____

Psychological Conflict. The best stories have conflict on a deeper level. It might be a conflict of emotion against emotion. It might be a struggle with another character. Psychological conflict can appear in two types: *external* or *internal* (or both at once).

In *external psychological* conflict, characters struggle with each other to be understood or to get their way. Stories about conflicts between friends, lovers, or parents and children usually fall into this category of conflict. Give a brief example of this kind of conflict. _____

_____

With *internal psychological* conflict, characters struggle within their own hearts and souls. For example, characters struggle against their bad habits or real desires. Characters who are tempted to cheat or steal might struggle against this desire. Give a brief example of this kind of conflict. _____

_____

Mixture of Conflicts. Often all three types of conflict—physical, external psychological, and internal psychological—will overlap. Characters may face all three types in the same story. A 21-year-old son may struggle so hard to prove himself to his father (an external psychological conflict) that he and his father may actually come to blows (physical conflict). And one of the reasons the son may find it so hard to gain his father's respect is that the son is constantly struggling to conquer his own hot temper (an internal psychological conflict). Characters who face a mixture of conflicts are usually the most realistic, the most like us. They are the ones the reader or viewer can relate to more. Give a brief example of a mixture of conflicts, perhaps using the same family member for whom you listed contrasting traits earlier. _____

_____

Practice 1   **Now identify the type of conflict in each of these mini-stories.**

(a) A couple spreads a blanket on the desert floor for a romantic springtime picnic when the wild flowers are in bloom. As a rush of water and rocks suddenly rounds the bend up ahead, they realize they've had the bad luck to make their picnic in a dry riverbed. A flash flood must have just struck somewhere in the mountains above.

Type of conflict: _____

(b) The same situation as above. However, when the woman sees the churning water coming their way, she first wants to grab her purse. It has their car keys. The man yells, "Are you crazy? No time! Let's go." She yells back, "You're calling me crazy? You, you, you bossy b-b-bull!" she sputters. "Stop telling me what to do all the time!"

Type of conflict: _____

(c) The same situation. But the man thinks to himself, "She may be right. I *am* always trying to tell her what's best." He wonders if he's right to take charge always.

Type of conflict: _____

(Practice 1 continued on following page)

(Practice 1 continued from previous page)

(d) The same situation. Meanwhile, the water and rocks continue to draw near at a frightening speed. For an awful second, time seems to stand still as the woman glares at the man, the man tries to look sorry, and the water and rocks are dangerously near.

Type of conflict: _____

As you read a story or novel, look for the main character's conflict or problem. Notice whether it is physical, external psychological, internal psychological—or a mixture. Then notice the way the main character resolves or handles the conflict. How the main character resolves the conflict can lead you to the theme.

Infer the Theme

The theme is similar to an implied main idea. It is the generalization or statement that we can make about life based on what happens in a particular story, poem, or work of art. For example, Shakespeare's play *Othello* is about a man who strangles his wife because he believes—wrongly—that she has been unfaithful to him. One possible theme is "We sometimes kill what we love the most." Or a more obvious theme is "Unproven jealousy can lead to tragic results." Even more so than main idea, theme can have more than one interpretation.

Practice 2 Let's return for a moment to our couple in the not-so-dry riverbed. Think about each of these possible endings to the story and how each *implies* a different *theme*, or point of view, by the author.

(a) The woman continues to glare at the man. He continues to hesitate about what to do. Then the rush of water slams into them. Their lives pass before their eyes as the two of them are washed away forever.

Possible theme (think of an implied main idea for the whole story, with this ending): _____

_____

(b) At the last possible moment, the woman shouts, "You're right! You're right! I guess I was getting as bullheaded as you." She grabs him by the hand. "Let's go," she yells, and they scramble out of the riverbed together. The raging waters swirl over their picnic. Her purse with the car keys is last seen bobbing down-stream next to an old beer can.

Possible theme (think of an implied main idea for the whole story, but with this second ending): _____

_____

(Practice 2 continued on following page)

(c) At the last possible moment, the man says to himself, "Nuts with being sensitive." He yanks her by the arm and with a mighty shove pushes her out of the riverbed. At the last minute, just before he leaps to safety, he reaches back and grabs her purse.

Possible theme: _____

_____

Seldom in literature do authors conveniently state their themes for us. Instead, they imply the theme by the kind of characters and conflict they create and by the way the characters resolve those conflicts and by whether the characters learn from their experiences. We readers must infer the author's dominating idea or theme, but our inference is always a guess. We should be ready to change our idea of the theme as we understand the work of literature better.

An effort to examine character, conflict, and theme can make reading literature more rewarding because it forces us to put ourselves in the writer's mind. Just as with other kinds of reading, seeing how the parts fit together helps us understand the whole—whether it's the theme or the thesis.

Study Outline

_____

[title, Ch. #]

Introduction: Literature is _____

_____

I. Observe the types of characters.

   A. _____ characters are _____

   B. _____ or _____ characters are _____

_____

II. Identify the types of _____.

   A. _____

   B. _____

   C. _____

   D. _____

[include explanations of A, B, C, D]

III. Infer the _____.

   A. Definition: _____

   B. Theme is not stated, but _____.

   C. Ask: "What has the main character learned from _____?"

Conflicts in Literature

The selections in this chapter, all by well-known writers, give you a sampling of literature and let you practice your interpretive skills. The three passages, from a short story, a poem, and a novel, are meant to be read carefully. Consider character, conflict, and theme as you read. After answering the questions for each passage, check the key.

Exercise 10A: Passage (from a short story)

This excerpt is from a short story set in the 1930s during a diphtheria epidemic. It was a time when doctors still made house calls.

Aren't you ashamed, the mother yelled at her. Aren't you ashamed to act like that in front of the doctor?

Get me a smooth-handled spoon of some sort, I told the mother. We're going through with this. The child's mouth was already bleeding. Her tongue was cut and she was screaming in wild hysterical shrieks. Perhaps I should have desisted and come back in an hour or more. No it would have been better. But I have seen at least two children lying dead in bed of neglect in such cases, and feeling that I must get a diagnosis now or never I went at it again. But the worst of it was that I too had got beyond reason. I could have torn the child apart in my own fury and enjoyed it. It was a pleasure to attack her. My face was burning with it.

The damned little brat must be protected against her own idiocy, one says to one's self at such times. Others must be protected against her. It is social necessity. And all these things are true. But a blind fury, a feeling of adult shame, bred of a longing for muscular release are the operatives. One goes on to the end.

In a final unreasoning assault I overpowered the child's neck and jaws. I forced the silver spoon back of her teeth and down her throat till she gagged. And there it was–both tonsils covered with membrane. She had fought valiantly to keep me from knowing her secret. She had been hiding that sore throat for three days at least and lying to her parents in order to escape just such an outcome as this.

—WILLIAM CARLOS WILLIAMS, FROM "THE USE OF FORCE"

1. What is the *physical conflict* in the passage?

   _____

2. What is the doctor's *external psychological conflict*?

   _____

3. What is the doctor's *internal psychological conflict*?

   _____

4. Which character is telling the story?
   (a) the mother   (b) the little girl   (c) the doctor

   How does the identity of the narrator affect the reader's attitude toward the doctor's unreasonable anger? (Does knowing the identity help excuse the behavior?)

   _____

Exercise 10B: Poem

This poem, "Song," was written by John Donne, a seventeenth-century British poet. (It is important that you study the words for this exercise in the Vocabulary Preview before you read the poem.) Consider each stanza as if it were a well-developed paragraph, each with an implied topic sentence, and all three working together to make a main point, or "theme." Read the poem at least twice and, in the blanks to the right, try to summarize it in your own words before you answer the questions.

Your Summary

Go and catch a falling star,
  Get with child a mandrake root,
Tell me where all past years are,
  Or who cleft the devil's foot:
Teach me to hear mermaids singing,
  To keep off envy's stinging,
    And find
    What wind
Serves to advance an honest mind.

Stanza 1: _____

If thou be'st born to strange sights,
  Things invisible go see,
Ride ten thousand days and nights
  Till Age snow white hairs on thee;
Thou, when thou return'st, wilt tell me
All strange wonders that befell thee,
    And swear
    No where
Lives a woman true and fair.

Stanza 2: _____

If thou find'st one, let me know;
  Such a pilgrimage were sweet.
Yet do not; I would not go,
  Though at next door we might meet.
Though she were true when you met her,
And last till you write your letter,
    Yet she
    Will be
False, ere I come, to two or three.

Stanza 3: _____

1. In the first stanza, the poet assigns someone seven tasks to perform. What do all these tasks have in common? _____

2. In Stanza 2, what is the final and most difficult task assigned? _____

3. Explain the sudden dramatic shift in the third stanza. Why does the poet change his mind about going on the pilgrimage himself? _____

4. What is the poet's tone toward women?
   (a) romantic (b) cynical (c) neutral

Exercise 10C: Passage (from a novel)

The following excerpt is the first paragraph of a chapter (used as the Timed Reading) from a modern novel, Crooked Little Heart, *by Anne Lamott. Notice how quickly and clearly the timeless conflict between male and female is established.*

Elizabeth asked James to change the light bulb in the kitchen one morning in late May, because she had so many things to do to get ready for the picnic with Rae and Rosie that day. He sat at the table still reading the paper. She was doing half a dozen things at once, trying to get everyone ready for the day, and besides, she hated changing light bulbs in this one particular fixture. You had to do it by braille, unscrewing unseen screws that held the glass globe in place, while your arm started to fall off and your neck got stiff. And then, when the screws finally came off, there were all those dead flies glued by sticky dust to the underneath brim. She felt like she was doing almost everything around the house but this one thing that would illuminate her work area so she could do even more for everyone else. James, sitting there reading the paper, could see just fine and so did not think to leap up and change the bulb. But Elizabeth knew that by the early evening the room would be filled with shadows, and preparing dinner would be hard and annoying, and so she said this to James, who said with slight irritation that he was going to change the light bulb in a minute.

1. List Elizabeth's three kinds of *conflict*.

   (a) *physical:* _____

   (b) *external psychological:* _____

   (c) *internal psychological:* _____

2. List some details given that justify, or explain, Elizabeth's reluctance to perform the simple task of changing a light bulb. _____

   _____

3. What is the narrator's *tone* in the sentence, "James, sitting there reading the paper, could see just fine and so did not think to leap up and change the bulb"?

   (a) sarcastic   (b) loving   (c) neutral

4. What may the reader *infer* will happen after James said he would "change the light bulb in a minute"?

   (a) He changes the light bulb in the next minute and Elizabeth is happy.

   (b) He postpones changing the light bulb and Elizabeth is not happy.

II. How to Read Faster

As you near the end of this book, now is the time to take stock of the reading techniques or strategies you have learned in this course of study. We hope by now these strategies for reading faster and understanding more have become a habit. The checklist that follows will let you know. (Your instructor may ask you to turn in the checklist.)

Review Your Reading Habits*

Choose the answer that fits your reading habits at this point in the course. On the line next to each item, write A *for always,* U *for usually,* S *for sometimes,* R *for rarely.*

_____ 1. Before I start to read, I preview the reading material for title, author, thesis, logic patterns, headings, lists, and other graphic aids.

_____ 2. In an article or chapter, I can tell where the introduction ends, the body begins and ends, and the conclusion begins.

_____ 3. I look first in the introduction of an article or chapter for the thesis or main idea for the whole piece.

_____ 4. Each time I read a paragraph, I am looking for a sentence that states the main idea for that paragraph.

_____ 5. If I do not see a topic sentence in a paragraph, I try to infer the main idea.

_____ 6. I try to determine the logic pattern for each paragraph and tell first-level details from second-level and third-level details.

_____ 7. I look for transitional words or phrases that writers use as signposts to guide the reader from one idea to the next.

_____ 8. I do not regress when reading easy material.

_____ 9. I read phrases at one glance, instead of pausing on each word, and I avoid margin reading.

_____ 10. I use a different method, like skimming, when reading for pleasure than when reading difficult material or for study purposes.

_____ 11. When I am studying or reading difficult material, I stop to tell myself in my own words what I have just read.

_____ 12. I determine whether an author's purpose is to inform, persuade, or entertain.

_____ 13. I am aware of an author's tone. In other words, I can tell when a writer is being sarcastic, bitter, gentle, playful, or ironic.

_____ 14. I make a constant effort to learn the meaning of new words from their context and from word analysis.

_____ 15. I have made a commitment to read something every day for pleasure.

Compare your list with "Preview Your Reading Habits," page xvi, for improvement. Notice how you can still improve.

---

*Partly based on the Leedy Reading Habits Inventory.

Exercise 10D: Phrases (Variation)

Each column of twenty items has only one key phrase (in italics). Scan for each repeated phrase and mark it. Work through both columns vertically before checking your time.

Key Phrase	**Key Phrase**
bears in mind	*the right station*
bear in window	the eighth station
bears in mind	the bright station
bears in the wind	the richest station
bear in winter	the right stanchion
bare in mind	the right state
beer in mind	the right station
bears in mind	the mighty station
bearing minds	the right station
mindless bear	the rigged station
barring minds	the right states
bears in mind	the station's right
bear in midwinter	the right stallion
bears in mind	tight little station
bears on your mind	the right station
hears in mind	the straight station
hears in the wind	the fight station
reads your mind	the night station
bears in mind	the fighting station
reads and minds	the night station
bearing in mind	the right station

Time _____

Number of Errors _____

Check the Answer Key to see how many times each key phrase is repeated.

Exercise 10E: Phrases (Variation)

Each column of twenty items has only one key phrase (in italics). Scan for each repeated phrase and mark it. Work through both columns vertically before checking your time.

Key Phrase	Key Phrase
copes with life	*a slow drawl*
cop-out from life	a low trawler
copes with strife	a low shawl
copes with life	a low drawling
copper has life	as low a drawl
coping with life	a lower drawl
cape with knife	a slight brawl
winning cop's life	a slow down
copes with light	a slow drawl
cops with lifer	a slow crawl
copes with life	as slowly crawl
comes with life	a southern drawl
runs from life	a slow draw
copes within	as slow a draw
coping with line	a slow drowning
copes with line	a slow howl
coping wins life	a low drawl
cold without life	a slow drawl
copes with life	a loud drawl
copes with knife	our slow drawl
pokes with knife	a slow drawl

Time _____

Number of Errors _____

Check the Answer Key to see how many times each key phrase is repeated.

This chapter ends with just one timed reading—an entire chapter from a national best-selling novel about a modern family living in northern California. *Newsweek* magazine says that author Anne Lamott is "armed with self-effacing humor and ruthless honesty—call it a lower-case approach to life's Big Questions."

Exercise 10F: Timed Reading   *2014 words*

As you read, look for different layers of *conflict*, as well as for *tone* and *irony*, in this 1990s love story.

Preview: *Quickly survey the title, the first paragraph, and the first sentence of a few other paragraphs. When you preview fiction, imagine yourself a reporter: look for* who *is in the story,* where *the story takes place,* when *it is happening, and* what is going on. Then write what you think the conflicts will be. _____*

_____

Wait for a signal from your instructor before you begin reading. Literature is not meant for speed-reading, but it is useful to know what your speed is. Circle your reading time when you have finished, and find your WPM.

from *Crooked Little Heart*

Anne Lamott

Elizabeth asked James to change the lightbulb in the kitchen one morning in late May, because she had so many things to do to get ready for the picnic with Rae and Rosie that day. He sat at the table still reading the paper. She was doing half a dozen things at once, trying to get everyone ready for the day, and besides, she hated changing lightbulbs in this one particular fixture. You had to do it by braille, unscrewing unseen screws that held the glass globe in place, while your arm started to fall off and your neck got stiff. And then, when the screws finally came off, there were all those dead flies glued by sticky dust to the underneath brim. She felt like she was doing almost everything around the house but this one thing that would illuminate her work area so she could do even more for everyone else. James, sitting there reading the paper, could see just fine and so did not think to leap up and change the bulb. But Elizabeth knew that by the early evening the room would be filled with shadows, and preparing dinner would be hard and annoying, and so she said this to James, who said with slight irritation that he was going to change the lightbulb in a minute.

"Please will you just do it now?"

"You want me to leap up onto my little stepladder with my toolbox and coveralls and change it? Right this very second?"

Elizabeth nodded.

He sighed and wandered off, and she thought he would return in a moment with the ladder. She watched him out in the front yard on his way out to his shed to get the bulb. But first he stopped to unscrew something on the manual lawn mower, and amazingly, he got distracted. She swallowed her annoyance; he would eventually get around to the lightbulb. He liked to fix motors, to putter with his car, or take apart the lawn mower. He liked to do things outdoors, in his manly domain. It was part of his hunger-gatherer legacy. He didn't like to change lightbulbs. Don Knotts could change lightbulbs. It occurred to Elizabeth, as she prepared the picnic basket, that she liked to put things away, while James liked to haul things out and create huge projects over which he could then look so serious; it seemed to her that James liked projects that, as someone had once said about artichokes, looked like there was more when they were done with than when they were begun.

He finished with the lawn mower, and went out to his shed, and still had not reappeared by the time Rae stopped by to pick up Elizabeth and Rosie. Elizabeth, for everyone's sake, had stopped by the shed on the way out, and reminded him with extravagantly good-natured noblesse oblige to please change the bulb before they got home from their picnic.

They had the loveliest day at the national park, stretched out on towels on the banks of the creek, reading, talking, wading, eating, dozing again, and Elizabeth tried not to think about the morning. But when she and Rosie walked into the kitchen that evening and she threw on the light switch, holding her breath, nothing happened. She looked at Rosie, who shook her head.

"Men," she said to Rosie.

Rosie rolled her eyes. "Should me and you do it?" she asked.

Elizabeth considered this. "You and I," she said. "Let's not let him off the hook so easily. Besides, it's too dark in here to do it now."

"Then how will he do it when he gets home?"

"That's not our problem. Our problems are blood sugar and world peace."

They were both tired and hungry and yet so wanted to continue the sweetness of the day that they set about good-naturedly in the dimness to make themselves a simple meal. They sat down together at the table to leftover soup and bread and cheese and ate by candlelight.

"Mama? Do you mind if I read my new magazine while we eat?"

"By what, flashlight?"

Rosie shrugged and nodded.

And so they ended up together, Rosie with her *Seventeen*, Elizabeth with a book, reading in silence with flashlights. The only sound was the turning of pages, like waves lapping the shore. Elizabeth looked up from time to time to study her strange silky daughter in the candlelight, staring solemnly at page after page of emaciated beauty, with the baby finger of her free hand hooked over her bottom lip just as she had when she had read fairy tales at eight in the window seat, horse stories at ten, Nancy Drew mysteries at eleven, and now advice on weight control and boys.

A moment later, there was a horrible sizzle and stink; Rosie, slumping, had gotten a bit of hair singed in the candle flame. There was a sudden pinch in Elizabeth's solar plexus, a sinking feeling, a rage at James. He must have assumed that she was going to change the bulb herself; he must see her as his mother, his nag of a mother. It was all hopeless. It meant that there was something really wrong with the relationship.

Elizabeth opened a can of mandarin oranges for dessert and knew that the syrup was spilling down the side of the can and onto the counter, as she tried by flashlight to spoon some into two bowls. It would be sticky soon and bring on ants, and all she wanted was to clean everything up and go to bed. She had lost her bearings in the dark. The kitchen was her territory, and it was supposed to be appetizing. But because of James's dereliction, it was a mess. She found herself lurching here and there, tripping, knocking things over, smoldering with resentment.

"Mommy? Why don't you sit down?"

They read their magazines and ate their mandarin oranges by flashlight and candles, a parody of an elegant dinner party. Good cheer and improvisation were burbling again in the visible world, but a roiling feeling had begun in her gut. She felt tired and short in her chair, as if she and Rosie were hunkered down in a cave.

They carried their dishes to the sink. Rosie, in bare feet, could feel crumbs and stickiness.

"How pathetic," she said to Elizabeth. "Men can be such slobs." And she wandered off to the ruins of her room.

After a while Elizabeth went upstairs to read but found herself back in the kitchen two hours later, still waiting for James to come home. Rosie was up in bed with her latest teenage gothic. Elizabeth peered down into the empty can of mandarin oranges, holding a flashlight on them with one hand, spearing segments one by one with a fork in the other. She hated leaving a mess for the morning; it always felt like part of you was still outside your body. Besides the threat of a bug invasion, there was the fear that the mess, the stickiness and crumbs and dirty dishes, could grow by themselves in the dark. Smells, growths, moss and mold, furry mold like troll hair, fuzz with fur on it. It could start composting. A miasma of smells would rise.

She shuffled around the house, went back to the dark sink, where she closed her eyes in the dark, and then went back upstairs, where she sat miserably for a while on the toilet. She could feel the seat embossing her butt. It was one of the stations of despair.

James was still not home at ten, by which time she was livid. She got in bed and read for a while, and eventually turned off the light. A little while later, she heard him tiptoe in.

"Are you awake?" he whispered in the dark. She grunted softly. "I want to hear about your day; I want to tell you about mine. It was so great. Please don't be asleep." But she lay there like a smoldering log as he took off his clothes and dropped them softly on a chair. She heard him yawn, heard and felt him crawl into bed.

"Are you really asleep?" he asked. She yawned, made the smallest possible sound. He put his knees in the crook of her knees, and where there was usually a yielding, she was stiff. Straightening her knees would be too overt. He flung his arm over her, as he did every night in the presleep position, in that fitting together, the key in the hole. But she pretended to be asleep, breathing as shallowly as possible, trying to breathe out as little as possible; otherwise, who knew what might burst out—tears, invective, molten fury. If he didn't offer anything, she wasn't about to. "You always . . .," she wanted to cry out. "You never . . ." You don't listen to me, you don't care—you only care about yourself. She felt like she was in a bunker, and she listened to him sigh, clearly now getting that she was annoyed, punishing him, but he didn't want to blow his day or his sleep.

And when he was asleep, Elizabeth lay in the dark for two hours, her eyeballs as rigid as her body, listening to his soft snore; then she got up and read in the living room until nearly four in the morning, and finally, finally she fell asleep.

James was reading the paper and drinking coffee when she got up at nine. "Hi!" he said.

She could barely look at him. There were crumbs and snail tracks of stickiness on the table. He had not bothered to wipe it all up before sitting down to read.

"What is it, Elizabeth?"

"Remember the lightbulb?"

"Ah!" He smote his forehead, gripped his head as if being pierced with migraine, beat the table. "Oh, I'm so sorry," he implored. "Sit down; let me get you some coffee."

"Just change the fucking lightbulb."

"Do you want me to do it now?" he asked, surprised. She nodded. "I will. But have some coffee, let me finish mine."

"No."

"No, you don't want any, or no, I can't finish mine."

"No, you can't finish yours."

James stood there, as sullen as one of the teenage boys on the tennis tour. Elizabeth cleaned off the table, poured her own coffee, and sat down with the paper. There was always that feeling in her soul that the bottom could drop out of their marriage. There were so many areas where things could go irreparably wrong. And the jacket was always waiting in the closet, the jacket of being a martyr and a bitch, the jacket she was now wearing.

James worked with great concentration, as if changing the dressing on a burn instead of a lightbulb, and when he was done, he walked to the wall switch and turned it on. The kitchen was flooded with golden light. "Watson," he cried, "come quickly. I need you." Elizabeth glowered at the paper. James turned the light off. She gawked at him. He turned it back on with a flourish, and then off. Elizabeth looked away. He turned the light back on with a gasp, a happy intake of air, like a child playing peekaboo. And then he turned it off. Elizabeth buried her face in her hands. The light went on again, and then, a moment later, off. Finally she smiled, and he turned the light on and left it.

That night when he bent his knees into the crook of hers, she yielded, melting into him, and they made love. Life was normal again, life was good—Bosnia to Paris in twenty-four hours.

He turned over with a big schlumpy male plop, now out of the presleep position and getting ready to drift off. He rearranged himself like a gull, shimmying his ruffled feathers back into place after landing.

Answer the following five recall questions without referring to the story.

1. Why is Elizabeth unwilling to change the lightbulb herself?
   (a) She is too lazy.
   (b) She is too busy.
   (c) She doesn't like the inconvenience and mess.
   (d) She wants to punish James for something else he did wrong.

2. List one thing Elizabeth says James would rather do than change light bulbs. _____

3. Despite her anger at James, Elizabeth enjoys herself at the picnic.
   (a) true   (b) false

4. What *inference* can be drawn from James' exaggerated actions while changing the bulb? _____

5. When does James finally change the bulb? _____

TIMING CHART	
min:sec	wpm
08:10	240
07:32	260
07:00	280
06:32	300
06:07	320
05:46	340
05:27	360
05:09	380
04:54	400
04:40	420
04:27	440
04:16	460
04:05	480
03:55	500
03:46	520
03:38	540
03:30	560
03:23	580
03:16	600
03:10	620
03:04	640
02:58	660
02:53	680
02:48	700
02:43	720
02:39	740
02:35	760
02:31	780
02:27	800

You may refer to the story to answer the following questions.

6. What is the author's *tone* toward both Elizabeth and James?
   (a) understanding and humorous   (b) bitterly critical
   (c) gently disapproving

7. The story has which kind of *conflict*?
   (a) physical   (b) external psychological
   (c) internal psychological   (d) mixture

8. Explain the *irony* in this passage: *"How pathetic," she [Rosie] said to Elizabeth. "Men can be such slobs." And she wandered off to the ruins of her room.*

   _____

   _____

9. What kind of *character* is Elizabeth?   (a) rounded   (b) flat

10. In a complete sentence, state the *theme* (implied thesis) of the story.

    _____

    _____

    [what?   represents what in life?]

Check your answers with the key, and record your scores below and on the Progress Chart.

Words per Minute   _____

Percent Comprehension   _____

Writing and Discussion Activities

1. Use the *character* traits for the family member you described earlier in this chapter, and write a paragraph of description or comparison and contrast.

2. Write a one-paragraph summary of the chapter you just read from *Crooked Little Heart*. Start your summary with a sentence that states the author, title, and the chapter's topic. The next sentences say *who* the main characters are, *where* they are, and *when* the story is taking place. Next, write a sentence or two giving a few of the traits for each of the main characters. Then state their *conflict*. Tell how the conflict gets resolved. Finally, end your summary by giving a possible *theme* for the chapter. (Remember: a summary is objective. It does not include your feelings about what you read.)

3. Point out the examples of humor in the chapter from *Crooked Little Heart*.

Vocabulary Review, Chapter 10

Match the vocabulary word on the left with its definition on the right. Write the letter of the answer in the short blank to the left.

_e_ 1. **livid**   (a) beautiful

_c_ 2. **overt**   (b) sickly thin

_a_ 3. **fair**   (c) obvious

_b_ 4. **emaciated**   (d) pitiful

_d_ 5. **pathetic**   (e) furious

*Choose the best definition for each **boldfaced** word as it is used in its context.*

____ 6. Although he wasn't very good at it, Bob liked to **putter** with gourmet cooking.
(a) earn a living   (b) do casually   (c) impress his girlfriends

____ 7. The would-be burglars **hunkered** in the dark, waiting for the family to leave the house.
(a) crouched   (b) looked in the window   (c) whispered

____ 8. The religious faithful went on a **pilgrimage** each year to their holy places.
(a) total fast   (b) sacred journey   (c) vacation

____ 9. The devil is often pictured in old paintings as having a **cleft** hoof.
(a) red-hot   (b) enlarged   (c) split

____ 10. The art student admired the beautiful **embossing** on the wedding invitation.
(a) wording   (b) paper quality   (c) imprinting

*Mark each sentence to show whether the **boldfaced** word is used correctly.*

a = True   b = False

_a_ 11. "Don't worry about me. I'll manage by myself somehow," whined the mother, playing the **martyr**.

_b_ 12. The war hero earned a Medal of Honor for his **dereliction** of duty.

_b_ 13. Practicing **noblesse oblige**, the factory owner refused to lend his worker money for his baby's emergency heart surgery.

_b_ 14. The young starlet was determined to find a husband with the best qualities—hardworking, successful, **troll**-like, and handsome.

_a_ 15. Toward the end of World War II, Adolf Hitler tried to protect himself by staying in his **bunker**.

(Continued)

Choose the word from the box that fits the context of the following paragraph.
Write the letter of each choice on the blank lines to the left of the paragraph.

(a) **smoldering**	(b) **glowered**	(c) **flourish**
(d) **invective**		(e) **gawked**

___ 16.   Dressed in an aluminum foil jumpsuit and cape, the famous

___ 17. wrestler entered the ring with a __16__ of his cape, as his fans shouted

___ 18. and __17__ at him. He __18__ fiercely at his opponent, as was expected,

___ 19. and let loose at him a few words of __19__, just to put him in his

___ 20. place and please the crowd. Then he gave __20__ looks to all the

ladies in the first row, as they blew him eager kisses.

% Correct _____

Comprehension Review, Chapter 10

1. Define a *rounded* character.

   Main Characters who are realistic have a mixture of personality traits, some good,

2. Define a *flat*, or *stereotypical*, character. *Some not so admirable*
   Characters who are 1 sided and unrealistic

3. Which type is more likely to be the main character in a story?

   (a) flat (b) rounded

4. The term *implied main idea* used in nonfiction would be called a ___the theme___
   in literature.

   Read the following passages and answer the questions for each.

   A. *Ghetto Pedagogy*

   "Dad?"
   "Yes?"
   "Why do black men always kill each other?"
   "Practicing."

   WALTER MOSLEY, FROM BLACK BETTY.

5. What *inference* may be drawn from the last line, "Practicing"? _____
   _____

6. What is the author's *tone* in the passage?

   (a) neutral (b) cynical (c) cheerful

   B. It must have caved his whole face in. I guess I pulped his nose and
   smashed both cheekbones. Jarred his little brain around real good. His legs
   crumpled and he hit the floor like a puppet with the strings cut. Like an ox
   in the slaughterhouse. His skull cracked on the concrete floor.

   LEE CHILD, FROM KILLING FLOOR.

   (Continued)

7. Explain the *connotation* of the following words, as they are used in Paragraph B.

   (a) caved . . . pulped . . . smashed _____

   (b) puppet with the strings cut _____

   (c) ox in the slaughterhouse _____

8. What is the *tone* of the narrator (or person telling the story) toward the person he is fighting?

   (a) neutral   (b) gloating   (c) pitying

9. Which type of *conflict* is used in this paragraph? _____

10–15. Finish the mapping outline by filling in the dotted lines. In the ovals, use examples from a novel or story you have read in this or another book—or from a television show or movie. (Check with your instructor first.) Make sure your examples clearly illustrate the types of conflict.

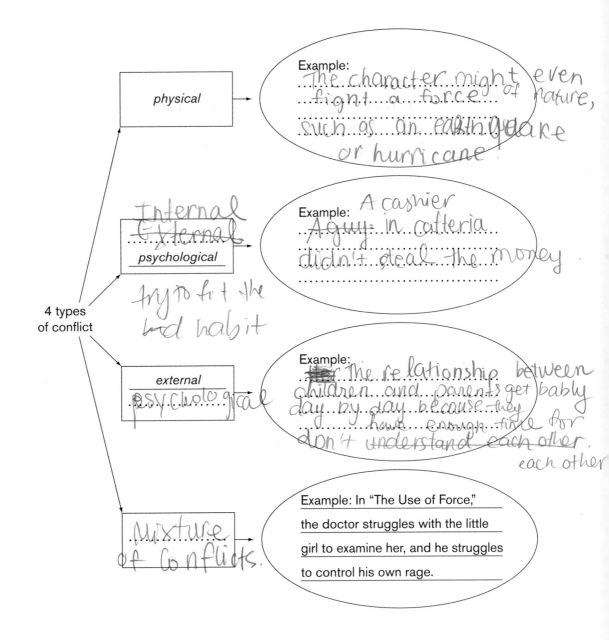

4 types of conflict

physical

Example: The character might even fight a force of nature, such as an earthquake or hurricane

~~Internal~~
~~External~~
psychological

Example: A cashier ~~A guy~~ in cafteria didn't steal the money

try to fit the ~~bad~~ habit

external
psychological

Example: The relationship between children and parents get bably day by day because they don't understand each other. don't have enough time for each other

Mixture of conflicts

Example: In "The Use of Force," the doctor struggles with the little girl to examine her, and he struggles to control his own rage.

% Correct _____

Appendix

Homework Lessons: *Word Analysis*

1 through 10

Word Lists

from *Vocabulary Previews*

"By Chapter" List of Words

Alphabetical List of Words

from *Homework Lessons*

Alphabetical List of Prefixes, Roots, Suffixes

Alphabetized List of New Words

Answer Keys

Chapters 1 through 10

Progress Charts

Pretests and Posttests

Chapter Reviews and Unit Tests

Timed Readings

Homework Lessons
Word Analysis

Homework Lessons

How to Use the Homework Lessons

The ten Homework Lessons in *Reading Faster and Understanding More* help you enlarge your vocabulary right away. They also teach you methods for expanding your vocabulary that you can continue to use for the rest of your life. These Homework Lessons are best studied in sequence outside of class. They will help you understand and remember the words in the Vocabulary Previews, which are before each chapter.

The first Homework Lesson gives you a dictionary review that will help you choose the best definition for the Words in Context. The second teaches a thorough flash card method that will help you remember the words. The last eight Homework Lessons will help you break down new words into their parts: roots, prefixes, and suffixes. This method is called "Word Attack."

The answers to all the Exercises are in the *Instructor's Manual*.

How to Use the Dictionary

You are probably thinking now that you already know how to use the dictionary. You already know how to look up a word because you know the alphabet. This means you can check for the correct spelling—if you have an idea of how the word starts. Also, you know how to find the meaning of a word. Spelling and meaning. That's enough, you may be thinking.

But you have only just begun to learn how to use the dictionary. Some words you look up may have up to fourteen different definitions listed. Why? Which one do you pick? Can you pronounce the word? Can you *use* the word?

There are at least ten other kinds of information (besides spelling and definition) that can be given about a word. How many can you think of? _____

_____

Examine the following entry *from the* Advanced Thorndike Barnhart Dictionary *(Scott, Foresman and Company), and look for other types of information.*

Pronunciation

front (frunt), *n.* **1**the first part; foremost part: *The title page is in the front of the book.* — Used in context **2**part that faces forward: *the front of a dress.* **3**the front face or part of a building. **4**thing fastened or worn on the front. **5**battlefront. **6**sphere of activity combining different groups in a political or economic battle: *the labor front.* **7**land facing a street, river, etc. **8**manner of looking or behaving: *a genial front.* **9**INFORMAL. an outward appearance of wealth, importance, etc.: *The newcomer put up an impressive front.*

Usage label — **10**INFORMAL. person or thing that serves as a cover for unlawful activities, for a pressure group, etc.: *The club was a front for illegal gambling.* **11**forehead. **12**face. **13**the dividing surface between two dissimilar air masses: *A cold front is moving toward this area from Canada.* **14**a call to a bellboy to come to the main part of the hotel lobby or to the desk. **15in front of**, in a place or position before (a person or thing); before.

—*adj.***1**of, on, in, or at the front. **2**(in phonetics) pronounced by raising the tongue against or near the forward part of the hard palate. The *e* of *be* and *bet* is a front vowel.

Three other parts of speech — —*v.t.***1**have the front toward; face: *Her house fronts the park.* **2**be in front of. **3**meet face to face; meet as an enemy; defy, oppose. —*v.i.***1**have the front in a certain direction: *Most houses front on the street.* **2**INFORMAL. Serve as a cover for a pressure group, an illegal activity, etc.

Etymology — [<Latin *frontem*, literally, forehead]

Entry

It is also important that you know the difference between the three major types of dictionaries. Do you know when to use each type?

the *unabridged* (or uncut) dictionary
the *abridged hardcover* dictionary
the *paperback* dictionary

The first type, which has approximately 500,000 *entries*, is usually too large. [An *entry* is an alphabetized word and all the information about it.] It is often in two volumes. And it is too expensive to be found in many homes. But unabridged dictionaries are usually available in libraries and most classrooms. The second type (about 150,000 entries) is found in most homes—or should be. But it is too heavy to take to class every day. It is the third type, the paperback dictionary (50,000 to 60,000 entries), that every college student needs. Plus, it is inexpensive enough and light enough to carry with you as another learning tool, like paper and pencils. (Don't confuse this dictionary with the pocketbook dictionary. With only 20,000 entries, it has only limited use but is better than no dictionary.)

It is worth your time to compare the three types of dictionaries so you will know which to consult for special problems. Examples: converting inches into millimeters or looking up *stet* on a list of "Proofreaders' Marks." (Both types of information are found in special charts in the larger dictionaries.)

Again, most students use the *paperback dictionary* for frequent reference. This exercise is designed to familiarize you with your paperback dictionary. (It should be a reputable, standard dictionary with at least 50,000 entries. Ask your instructor for a recommendation.)

Exercise

1. Give the complete title and publication date of your paperback dictionary.

   _____

2. How many entries are in your dictionary? (*Tip:* You do not have to count the words or pages. Look on the outside cover; the publisher wants you to see this number.) _____

3. What special sections or charts do you find in your dictionary? (*Tip:* Look before and after the alphabetized entries. Also look on the inside front and back covers.)

   _____

   _____

   _____

4. List the page numbers for the following.
   (a) the chart of abbreviations and symbols used within any dictionary entry _____
   (b) information about usage and other labels (example: *archaic* or *slang*) _____

5. How is the etymology (origin of a word) set apart from the rest of the entry? _____

6. What is the capital of Rhode Island? _____

7. What are the other verb forms (or tenses) for the following verbs?

   Example: **talk**   ___talked___   [have] talked   ___talking___

                                  [*past tense*]   [*past participle*]   [*present participle*]

   (a) **reward**   _____   _____   _____

   (b) **lie** (to recline)   _____   _____   _____

   [Clue: Your dictionary may not have the verb forms for *reward*. Why not? Why do you already know the forms for the regular verb *reward* and not for the irregular verb *lie*?]

8. List all the parts of speech for *cool*. Write out the whole word (not the abbreviation) for the part of speech. _____

9. Give the plural spelling of the following words.

   (a) elf   _____   (c) sister-in-law _____

   (b) thesis _____   (d) fox   _____

10. How many definitions are listed for *order*? _____

11. Give the complete etymology (origin) for the following words. Write out the whole word; do not use abbreviations or symbols.

    Example: serve <u>derived from Latin *servus,* slave</u>

    (a) stupid _____

    (b) draconian _____

12. What is the slang definition for *squeal*? _____

13. What is the definition for *factor* used in mathematics? _____
    _____

14. What do the following abbreviations stand for? (*Tip:* Do not look in the chart of abbreviations used in your dictionary.)

    (a) M.A. _____

    (b) ck   _____

15. (a) Give the definition of the suffix *-ic*. _____

    (b) Give the definition of the prefix *intra-*. _____

16. When you add suffixes to many words, you must double a final consonant, drop an *e*, or add an *i*. Your dictionary gives these inflectional changes. Look up the correct spelling for the following words and write the complete word (root plus suffix) in the blank. *Example:* grace + ious <u>gracious</u>

    (a) courage + ous _____   (c) refer + ed   _____

    (b) convey + ing _____   (d) acknowledge + ment _____

17. Look up the definitions for these commonly confused pairs of words.

    (a) affect _____   effect (*n.*) _____

    (b) imply _____   infer   _____

    Underline the correct word, enclosed in parentheses, in the following sentences.

    (c) She thought her parents' criticism would (*affect/effect*) her deeply, but their scolding was so mild that it had no (*affect/effect*) on her.

    (d) Mr. Biggley tried not to (*imply/infer*) that Susan was about to be fired, but she was able to (*imply/infer*) her future unemployment when her name plate was removed from her office door.

18. (a) Would the entry *McCoy* come before or after the entry *Machiavellian*?

    _____

    (b) Would the entry *ma* come before or after *McCoy* and *Machiavellian*?

    _____

19. Write all the pronunciation symbols and marks for the following words. (*Tip:* Make sure you copy the pronunciation perfectly. Every mark and symbol represents a sound.) Using the pronunciation key, prepare to pronounce the words in class. *Example: creme de menthe* (krem' də mänt')

    (a) ungulate _____

    (b) desuetude _____

    (c) satyriasis _____

    (d) phantasmagoria _____

20. List five different *types* of information (besides spelling and definitions) about a word that you can find your dictionary.

    _____

    _____   _____

    _____   _____

    Check the answers with your instructor.

How to Build a Vocabulary File

One of the most important factors that influence how fast we read and how well we understand is how many *vocabulary* words we know. Simply put, the more words we know, the better we will read. It's only logical that, if we pause a lot when we meet new words, we will read more slowly.

We actually have *four* vocabularies, one for each communication skill. Obviously, some words will overlap.

listening
reading } *passive*   **speaking**
writing } *active*

The first two, listening and reading, are more *passive*, or "receptive." Similar to a radio that receives a signal, you take in these words; you're receptive to them. But you don't transmit those words; you don't send them out. You will recognize many words in your class lectures or in your reading that you don't use yourself in your speaking and writing. For all of us, these "passive" vocabularies are much larger than our "active" vocabularies.

[In reality, the term "passive," used by many educators to describe your listening and reading vocabularies, doesn't tell the whole story. Your mind is obviously still active, but in a different way, even when you are in the "receiving" mode of listening and reading.]

Practice 1

(a) Which vocabulary is larger? _____ listening _____ reading

(b) Which skill came first? _____ listening _____ reading

(c) Which skill do you use the least? _____ listening _____ reading
_____ speaking _____ writing

Your *active*, or "expressive," vocabularies are made up of words you not only can receive but also sent out. You use them when you speak or write. You can form sentences with them. As you learn to pronounce and spell the words in your "receptive" vocabulary, you will start to use them actively; they will then move into your "expressive" vocabulary.

Practice 2

(a) Which vocabulary is smaller? _____ speaking _____ writing

(b) What do you have to know about a word you *say* that you don't have to know when you listen, read, or write? _____

(c) What do you have to know about a word you *write* that you don't have to know when you listen, read or speak? _____

The process of moving a word from your passive to your active vocabularies can be immediate. You can—and should—guess the meaning of many new words from their context, as you have found in the Vocabulary Previews. Sometimes, however, the process of starting to use a word takes years. The delay can happen because

- the word's meaning is complex or abstract
- you are not sure of the pronunciation or spelling
- the word seems to have different uses in different situations

In those cases, it is helpful to speed up the process of a word becoming part of your active vocabularies. After all, it seems a waste not to put forth a little more effort to utilize what you already know about a word you hear or read. You might as well add it to your speaking and writing vocabularies. The following method for making a *Vocabulary Card File* will help you

- learn how to pronounce a new word
- study its context
- note its part of speech
- see other forms of the word
- grasp the new word's various meanings

Directions: *Choose words you don't know from the Vocabulary Previews, words you would like to be able to use in speaking and writing. Start with five to ten each week. Prepare a separate 3 x 5 index card (lined on one side) for each word by looking up each word in the dictionary and following the outline shown here. Use a larger index card if you plan to share cards with a study group.*

Front (unlined side):

(a) In the upper right corner, identify the source of the word, if from this book.
(b) Clearly print the word you don't know in *large*, lowercase letters (unless it is a proper noun).
(c) Write the abbreviated part of speech.
(d) Write the pronunciation symbols in parentheses underneath the word itself.
(e) List other forms of the word and the part of speech for each form.

Example (from Vocabulary Preview, Chapter 2)

Ch. 2, #6

delusive
(adj.)

(di loō´ siv)

delude (v.) delusion (n.)

Back (lined side):

(a) Write the sentence in which you found the word. Put quotation marks around the sentence to show that you did not compose the sentence. (For words from the Vocabulary Previews, the sentence from the Exercise will give better context clues than the sentence from Words in Context.) You may shorten or paraphrase dictionary definitions to make them easier to study, but don't omit important information.

(b) Underline the vocabulary word in the sentence.

(c) Draw a line across the card or skip a line.

(d) List two or three definitions of the word, if more than one is given. If too many are given to fit onto the card, pick the most common definitions. Include the part of speech, if different from that of the vocabulary word.

(e) Place a checkmark in front of the definition that fits the way the word is used in the sentence.

Example

"Dwayne's conviction that he would be hired as president of the company was <u>delusive</u>; after all, he was a high school dropout."

1. Deceptive

2. False

3. Misleading

✓ 4. Unrealistic

Final Step: Use the cards as flash cards. Look at the word on the front and try to recall the definition(s) on the back. Form a study group and assign words from the next Vocabulary Preview. Lighten your homework load. Or divide the words with one other person. Meet regularly and use the cards for drills. To prepare for a test, review the cards at least three times each week. Experiment with using the words when you speak and when you write.

Let your card file grow. Add to it from textbooks in your other classes; it is a proven way to learn unfamiliar terms. Choose words you don't know from your personal reading: newspapers, magazines, novels, technical manuals. Review the words from time to time. Make this method a lifetime learning tool for increasing your vocabulary. Learning new words doesn't have to end when this class, or your formal education, ends.

Exercise

Choose any two words that are hard for you from the Vocabulary Preview, Chapter 2. Make sample flash cards (front and back) in the empty boxes below. Continue to make five to ten flash cards from each Vocabulary Preview. If you are in a study group, use larger flash cards for easier viewing.

FIRST CARD:

front

back

SECOND CARD:

front

***

back

***

About Word Attack

Word Attack is one more way that a reader can unlock the meanings of words. You may learn a word through its use in context, you may use a dictionary, or you may consciously analyze the word. If English is your native language, you already practice word analysis unconsciously. For example, you know that the last word "unconsciously," in the previous sentence is the "way you practice." Why do you know this? Because of the little two-letter ending -*ly*. You probably also know that the two-letter beginning -*un* means *not*. The whole word then means "without being conscious of doing it."

In this way, one English word can stand for several words or for a whole phrase. If you can consciously learn how these word parts work and memorize some uncommon parts as well as common ones, you can unlock even more words, especially in more difficult and technical reading.

Practice 1   The previous sentence is repeated below. Underline any word beginnings and endings that can be removed from the words in the sentence. The first one has been done to give you a model.

If you can conscious<u>ly</u> learn how these word parts work and memorize some uncommmon parts as well as common ones, you can unlock even more words, especially in more difficult and technical reading.

The three major parts of an English word are called the *root*, *prefix*, and *suffix*. The root is discussed first because it is the only essential part of the word. It is the part of the word that is left after you remove the beginnings and endings. A word consists of *at least* a root. *We will* italicize *the* words *in this sentence that are root* words only. Do you see any beginnings or endings on those italicized words that can be removed and still leave a basic word? (Your answer should be no.)

But if you can remove a part, one that you have seen attached to many other words, and still have a basic word remaining, then that letter or part is probably a *prefix* or *suffix*. Can you do this to the words "removed," "attached," and "words"? If you took off a part from the beginning of the word, the part is called a *prefix*. If you took off a part from the end, it is called a *suffix*.

To remember the order of these three possible word parts in a word, read the word from left to right as usual → and think Prefix-Root-Suffix, or PRS.

Look at the table of contents again and notice how many Homework Lessons are devoted to roots, prefixes and suffixes.

While 80 roots, 40 prefixes, and 49 suffixes may sound like a lot of word parts to memorize, you know many of them already. If you do not, your vocabulary is gravely hampered because these 169 parts are basic to the English language and therefore extremely important. As you advance through your studies, you will learn dozens more, formally through learning lists like these, and informally through your reading and general vocabulary growth.

About Roots

We begin our word attack with a list of twenty common root words that English has borrowed from two ancient languages, Latin and Greek. You will see these roots in many English words, often combined with prefixes and suffixes. Note that a borrowed root does not always make a familiar English word by itself. "Cent" and "cult" are whole words, but "cogni" and "cor" are not. Also note that the root is usually a stressed syllable in a word.

Directions: *First, learn each root with its original meaning. Next, review the common examples of the root. Then, look up the "new word" in your dictionary, and write its definition on the blank lines.*

ROOT	MEANING	EXAMPLES	NEW WORD AND DEFINITION
1. (a)**equi**	equal, even	equate equivalent	**equivocal:** _____ _____
2. **anima**	breath, spirit, mind	animal inanimate	**magnanimous:** _____ _____
3. **ann, enn***	year	bicentennial biennial	**annuity:** _____ _____
4. **anthropo**	man	anthropology philanthropy	**misanthropic:** _____ _____
5. **astro***	star	astronomical astrology	**astral:** _____ _____
6. **aud, audit***	to hear	audiotape audiofrequency	**audiophile:** _____ _____
7. **auto***	self	automation autopilot	**autistic:** _____ _____
8. **bellum**	war	rebellious belligerent	**bellicose:** _____ _____
9. **bene***	good, well	beneficial benefactor	**benign:** _____ _____
10. **bio***	life	autobiography bionic	**biodegrade:** _____ _____
11. **cap, cept**	to take	capture captivate	**capacious:** _____ _____

---

*Also presented in *Reading Faster and Understanding More, Book One* and included here for review.

ROOT	MEANING	EXAMPLES	NEW WORD AND DEFINITION
12. **capit***	head	caption capitalization	**decapitation:** _____ _____
13. **cede, ceed**	to yield, to go	concede accessory	**concession:** _____ _____
14. **cent**	hundred	centennial percentage	**centipede:** _____ _____
15. **chron***	time	synchronize chronology	**anachronistic:** _____ _____
16. **civ***	citizen	civvies civilization	**civility:** _____ _____
17. **cogni**	to know	recognize incognito	**connoisseur:** _____ _____
18. **corpus**	body	corp corpse	**corpulent:** _____ _____
19. **crat, cracy***	rule	democratic aristocracy	**bureaucrat:** _____ _____
20. **cred, credit***	to believe	credibility creditor	**credence:** _____ _____

Exercise, Homework Lesson 3

Complete the following sentences by choosing words from the box. Use context clues to help you choose the appropriate word.

magnanimous	**annuity**	**astral**	**decapitation**	**corpulent**
biodegrade	**benign**	**civility**	**connoisseur**	**autistic**

1. Wanda had to cut out French fries and cupcakes for lunch because she was beginning to get _____.
2. Franklin became a(n) _____ of French wine after visiting French wineries and reading about the history of wine making in France.
3. Most people today are so sensitive about polluting the environment that they buy products that will _____.

_____

*Also presented in Reading Faster and Understanding More, Book One and included here for review.

4. The coroner listed _____ as the cause of death for the young couple when their convertible sports car slammed into the back end of the tractor-trailer.

5. It is wise to invest at least 10 percent of your annual income in a tax-sheltered _____.

6. I was relieved to hear that my tumor was _____ instead of being cancerous.

7. A battery of psychiatrists tried to draw out the _____ child, but he remained withdrawn and self-absorbed.

8. The woman wished the rude young man behind the counter would show her more_____.

9. In a(n) _____ decision, the city council voted to donate all of the money for a bicycle lane through the city.

10. A(n) _____ object flew down from the sky and blinded the young boy.

To complete the following sentences, choose one of the three words below the sentence. Write the correct word on the blank line in each sentence, and write the letter of the answer on the blank to the left. Again, use context clues to help you choose the appropriate word.

_____ 11. Jesse spends all his extra time listening to music and all his extra money on the best high-quality, high-fidelity equipment; he is truly a(n) _____.
(a) bureaucrat (b) autistic (c) audiophile

_____ 12. Attila and his Huns, never accused of being peacemakers, were known for their _____ tendencies.
(a) benign (b) bellicose (c) autistic

_____ 13. When Billy told his wife he was late because a truckful of chickens rammed into his car, she didn't want to believe him; but, when he started pulling chicken feathers out of his pockets, she had to give his story some _____.
(a) credence (b) concession (c) connoisseur

_____ 14. John negotiated for years with the IRS agent over the tax deductions he had taken, but the agent stubbornly refused to make even one _____.
(a) creditor (b) concession (c) annuity

_____ 15. When Fran moved to a larger apartment, she discovered that she didn't have enough furniture to fill the _____ rooms.
(a) capacious (b) bionic (c) magnanimous

_____ 16. You would think a(n) _____ could travel faster with what seems like a hundred little legs.
(a) animal   (b) audiophile   (c) centipede

_____ 17. The other students were charmed by Pamela's _____ writing instruments; one day she might use a sharpened goose feather dipped in ink, and another day she might use a futuristic, laser device that beamed the answers onto the page.
(a) decapitated   (b) anachronistic   (c) benign

_____ 18. After the divorce, all Hester wanted to do was officially change back to her maiden name of Rodman, but she had to fill out too many forms and talk to too many inflexible _____.
(a) audiophiles   (b) connoisseurs   (c) bureaucrats

_____ 19. Allison could not decide if she wanted to go to the prom with Eric or wait for a better offer, so she gave him a(n) _____ answer.
(a) equivocal   (b) bellicose   (c) anachronistic

_____ 20. The character Scrooge, in Dickens' _A Christmas Carol_, worked his employees for long hours with little pay, but his refusal to give them the day off for Christmas was his most _____ policy of all.
(a) magnanimous   (b) capacious   (c) misanthropic

Check your answers with your instructor, and record your score below.

% Correct _____

Word Attack—Roots

Directions: *First, learn each root with its original meaning. Next, review the common examples of the root. Then, look up the "new word" in your dictionary, and write its definition on the blank lines.*

ROOT	MEANING	EXAMPLES	NEW WORD AND DEFINITION
1. **cult**	to care for	culture cultivate	occult: _____ _____
2. **cycle**	wheel, circle	unicycle recycle	cyclical: _____ _____
3. **dem**	people	democracy demographic	pandemic: _____ _____
4. **dent**	tooth	dental dentin	dentifrice: _____ _____
5. **derm**	skin	dermatologist hypodermic	pachyderm: _____ _____
6. **dic, dict***	to say, to speak	indicate verdict	abdicate: _____ _____
7. **duc, duct**	to lead	educate conduct	conducive: _____ _____
8. **fac, fact***	to make	facile factor	facsimile: _____ _____
9. **fin***	end, to complete	finale refine	infinity: _____ _____
10. **gen, gene***	birth, origin	gender genocide	engender: _____ _____
11. **geo**	earth	geography geophysics	geothermal: _____ _____
12. **gram***	to write	grammatical grammarian	epigram: _____ _____
13. **graph***	to write	graffiti photograph	holograph: _____ _____

---

*Also presented in *Reading Faster and Understanding More, Book One,* and included here for review.

ROOT	MEANING	EXAMPLES	NEW WORD AND DEFINITION
14. **hetero**	other	heterosexual heterogeneous	**heterodox:** _____ _____
15. **homo***	same	homogenize homonym	**homophobia:** _____ _____
16. **hydra**	water	hydrant hydroelectric	**dehydrated:** _____ _____
17. **jac, ject***	to throw	ejaculate eject	**dejected:** _____ _____
18. **log, logo***	word, study	dermatology mineralogy	**etymology:** _____ _____
19. **loqui, locut**	talk	ventriloquist loquacious	**elocution:** _____ _____
20. **luc, lus**	light	illustrate illuminate	**elucidate:** _____ _____

Exercise, Homework Lesson 4

Complete the following sentences by choosing words from the box. Use context clues to help you choose the appropriate word.

dejected	occult	epigrams	etymology	elocution
elucidate	pachyderms	engender	heterodox	facsimile

1. The minister captures his congregation's attention by quoting
   _____, like the Arabic proverb, "Trust in Allah, but tie up
   your camel."
2. Little Lucy loved the monkeys at the zoo, but she was frightened by the
   larger _____, the elephant and the rhinoceros.
3. The advertising agency had a brainstorming session to
   _____ some clever new ideas for advertisements.
4. Anthony was fascinated with the _____, researching all
   aspects of the supernatural on the Internet.
5. A few die-hard English teachers insist on proper _____,
   refusing to acknowledge slang or improper pronunciation during class discussions.

---

*Also presented in _Reading Faster and Understanding More, Book One_, and included here for review.

6. The _____ of his signature on the check looked so genuine that even the check's owner could not detect it as a copy.

7. Jack woke up on a rainy Sunday morning feeling _____ and continued feeling gloomy until the sun started to shine.

8. Although Dave's parents stayed with their orthodox, or traditional, religion, their son's views were more _____.

9. The tutor's clear explanation helped to _____ a difficult point in the trigonometry lesson.

10. Charlotte mistakenly told her study group the origin of the root *homo* in *Homo sapiens* is Greek, and means "same"; but, when she checked its _____ in her dictionary, she discovered its origin is modern scientific Latin, and means "man."

To complete the following sentences, choose one of the three words below the sentence. Write the correct word on the blank line in each sentence, and write the letter of the answer on the blank to the left.

_____ 11. When Mark discovered his mother on the porch with his gay friends, he was fearful that her _____ and other prejudices would soon became obvious to everyone.
(a) epigrams   (b) pachyderms   (c) homophobia

_____ 12. Partly because of their concern for the environment, partly because of high heating bills, the Konopkas built their own _____ house, sunk deep into the earth.
(a) geothermal   (b) conducive   (c) colloquial

_____ 13. The fear of polio was so widespread, so _____, in the 1950s, that parents wouldn't let their children swim in public swimming pools.
(a) cyclical   (b) loquacious   (c) pandemic

_____ 14. As the museum's curator, I was required to examine the _____ very carefully so that I could determine its authenticity.
(a) heterodox   (b) holograph   (c) epigram

_____ 15. "Actually, my dear, her interest in marriage is rather _____; it comes and goes," purred the lady from behind her fan.
(a) infinite   (b) cyclical   (c) elucidating

_____ 16. Amelia managed to land her plane in a clearing in the jungle; but after a few days with no toiletries, her teeth became so coated, that what she desired above all was some_____.
(a) dentifrice   (b) culture   (c) geography

_____ 17. After playing three sets of tennis in the hot sun, without drinking any water, Ken felt so _____ he thought he would faint.
(a) dehydrated   (b) dejected   (c) cultivated

_____ 18. When Jennifer parachuted from the plane, she felt as if she were floating into _____, as if her descent would never end.
(a) finale   (b) infinity   (c) facsimile

_____ 19. Edward VII of England shocked all the world in 1936 with his romantic sacrifice when he _____ his throne to marry the woman he loved.
(a) engendered   (b) cultivated   (c) abdicated

_____ 20. The television and the radio were blaring; the telephone and the doorbell were ringing; five people were arguing loudly—the room was not _____ to studying.
(a) pandemic   (b) indicative   (c) conducive

Check your answers with your instructor, and record your score below.

% Correct _____

Word Attack—Roots

Directions: *First, learn each root with its original meaning. Next, review the common examples of the root. Then, look up the "new word" in your dictionary, and write its definition on the blank lines.*

ROOT	MEANING	EXAMPLES	NEW WORD AND DEFINITION
1. **mania**	madness, derangement	maniac nymphomaniac	**pyromaniac:** _____ _____
2. **manus**	hand	manual manipulate	**manacle:** _____ _____
3. **metr***	measure	perimeter barometer	**parameter:** _____ _____
4. **micro**	small	microscope microbe	**microfiche:** _____ _____
5. **mit, miss***	to send	transmit mission	**demise:** _____ _____
6. **mono**	one	monotone monogamy	**monopolize:** _____ _____
7. **mor**	dead	mortal morgue	**immortality:** _____ _____
8. **ocul**	eye	binocular oculist	**monocle:** _____ _____
9. **path***	feeling, suffering	psychopath empathy	**apathy:** _____ _____
10. **ped**	foot (also child)	pedestrian pediatrics	**expedite:** _____ _____
11. **pel, puls**	drive	propeller expel	**expulsion:** _____ _____
12. **phil, philo***	to love	philharmonic philosophic	**pedophile:** _____ _____
13. **phobia***	fear	claustrophobia agoraphobia	**acrophobia:** _____ _____

*Also presented in *Reading Faster and Understanding More, Book One*, and included here for review.

ROOT	MEANING	EXAMPLES	NEW WORD AND DEFINITION
14. **phon***	sound	symphony phonetics	**cacophony:** _____ _____
15. **photo***	light	photogenic photosynthesis	**photophobic:** _____ _____
16. **pod**	foot	tripod arthropod	**podiatrist:** _____ _____
17. **poly***	many	polygraph polyunsaturated	**polysyllabic:** _____ _____
18. **pon, pos**	to place	position transpose	**depose:** _____ _____
19. **popul***	people	populate populous	***vox populi:*** _____ _____
20. **port***	to carry	deported portfolio	**rapport:** _____ _____

Exercise, Homework Lesson 5

Complete the following sentences by choosing words from the box. Use context clues to help you choose the appropriate word.

> **demise   parameters   apathetic   pedophile   expedite**
> **expulsion   immortality   manacled   pyromaniac   monocle**

1. Being a(n) _____, Mr. Johnson was obsessed with children and spent most of his extra time fantasizing about them.

2. The _____ was caught in the act of setting a brush fire near town; plus, he was suspected of being responsible for the last two forest fires.

3. In order to _____ completion of the important project before the deadline, many employees chose to work over the weekend.

4. Randy's _____ from class upset him; he wished he could convince the instructor to reinstate him in the class.

5. The unexplained _____ of several patients who had been taking the new drug resulted in their survivors suing the drug company.

---

*Also presented in Reading Faster and Understanding More, Book One, and included here for review.

---

6. Instead of wearing the usual eyeglasses, the legendary British actor, Charles Laughton, often wore a(n) _____.

7. Ponce de Leon searched for the Fountain of Youth because he wanted _____; he never wanted to get old and die.

8. The college football team had lost so many games that its fans had become _____ and no longer bothered to attend the games.

9. The prisoner was so tightly _____ that his wrists and ankles began to go numb.

10. In order to test the _____ of his job, the intern boldly refused the artwork for the new campaign and ordered the art department to come up with something better.

To complete the following sentences, choose one of the three words or phrases below the sentence. Write the correct word on the blank line in each sentence, and write the letter of the answer on the blank to the left.

_____ 11. After trying for years to _____ all of his wife's time, George finally gave up and made some friends of his own.
(a) depose   (b) monopolize   (c) export

_____ 12. Instead of keeping stacks of old newspapers and magazines, libraries today save space by putting the information on _____ or entering the information into a computer database.
(a) microscopes   (b) microphone   (c) microfiche

_____ 13. Stephen refused to go above the second floor because of his
_____.
(a) acrophobia   (b) agoraphobia   (c) pyromania

_____ 14. The _____ of the student cafeteria was enough to send the teacher back to the quiet and solitude of her office.
(a) cacophony   (b) symphony   (c) apathy

_____ 15. Ken and Cory had developed a good _____; they felt they could talk to each other about almost anything.
(a) deport   (b) transport   (c) rapport

_____ 16. The long word "supercallifragilisticexpialidocious," sung by Julie Andrews in *Mary Poppins*, is a good example of a
_____ word.
(a) polytechnical   (b) polysyllabic   (c) polygamist's

_____ 17. When his bunions and ingrown toenails finally caused him to limp, he made an appointment with a _____.
(a) podiatrist   (b) pyromaniac   (c) pedophile

_____ 18. The Special Prosecutor never again ignored the
_____ when deciding whether or not to continue an investigation into the president's personal matters.
(a) microfiche   (b) podiatrist   (c) *vox populi*

_____ 19. After the Watergate scandal, President Nixon resigned before he could be _____ from office.

(a) exposed   (b) deposed   (c) transposed

_____ 20. Because he refused to go outside during the day and sat in the dark with the curtains closed, we concluded that he was either a depressed vampire or that he was _____.

(a) apathetic   (b) unphotogenic   (c) photophobic

Check your answers with your instructor, and record your score below.

% Correct   _____

Word Attack—Roots

Directions: *First, learn each root with its original meaning. Next, review the common examples of the root. Then, look up the "new word" in your dictionary, and write its definition on the blank lines.*

ROOT	MEANING	EXAMPLES	NEW WORD AND DEFINITION
1. **psych***	mind	psychopath psychological	**psychosomatic:** _____ _____
2. **rupt**	to break	disrupt eruption	**corruptible:** _____ _____
3. **scrib, script***	to write	inscribe transcribe	**nondescript:** _____ _____
4. **sect**	to cut	sector bisect	**vivisection:** _____ _____
5. **sens, sent***	to feel	insensitive sentimentality	**sentient:** _____ _____
6. **spec, spect***	to look at	spectrum spectator	**circumspect:** _____ _____
7. **spir**	to breathe	inspire conspire	**aspiration:** _____ _____
8. **tain, ten**	to hold	retain retention	**tenacious:** _____ _____
9. **tele***	distant	telescope teletype	**telekinesis:** _____ _____
10. **tempor***	time	temporal contemplate	**contretemps:** _____ _____
11. **tend, tens**	to stretch	distend extension	**tensile:** _____ _____
12. **terra**	earth	terrestrial *terra firma*	**inter:** _____ _____
13. **the**	god	atheist theology	**polytheism:** _____ _____

---

*Also presented in *Reading Faster and Understanding More, Book One*, and included here for review.

ROOT	MEANING	EXAMPLES	NEW WORD AND DEFINITION
14. **therm***	heat	thermal thermodynamics	**diathermy:** _____ _____
15. **vene, vent**	to come	convent circumvent	**convene:** _____ _____
16. **vers, vert**	to turn	adversary avert	**vertigo:** _____ _____
17. **vid, vis***	to see	vista audiovisual	**providence:** _____ _____
18. **viv, vit***	to live, life	vivacious revitalize	**convivial:** _____ _____
19. **voc, vocat***	to call	vocalize avocation	**invocation:** _____ _____
20. **volens**	wishing, willing	benevolence malevolence	**volition:** _____ _____

Exercise, Homework Lesson 6

Complete the following sentences by choosing words from the box. Use context clues to help you choose the appropriate word.

nondescript	vertigo	tenacious	psychosomatic	diathermy
telekinesis	convene	tensile	contretemps	corruptible

1. Despite the difficulty she had getting into medical school, Maria was _____ in her efforts to become a doctor; she overcome every barrier to succeed.

2. Not knowing he was committing a _____, Walter slurped water from the finger bowl; he believed he was being polite by drinking what he thought was rather bland soup.

3. Knowing that the police chief was _____, the drug dealer gave him a bribe.

4. The doctor treated Gary's skin disease by using _____, since all ointments applied to the surface of his skin had failed.

---

*Also presented in Reading Faster and Understanding More, Book One, and included here for review.

5. Unable to overcome her _____, Michele had to refuse the invitation to join her friends for a hot-air balloon ride.

6. Most paper is unsuitable for making clothing because it lacks _____ strength and tears with any movement.

7. Harper was so ordinary looking and boring, so _____, that none of his acquaintances could describe him.

8. The members of the steering committee will _____ at 9:30 A.M. to discuss plans for the upcoming year.

9. Hannah was convinced that she had a brain tumor and heart failure; but, after her doctor assured everybody that she was perfectly healthy, her family realized Hannah's complaints had been _____.

10. The child displayed her ability to use _____ by moving her tricycle through the air with the power of her mind.

To complete the following sentences, choose one of the three words or phrases below the sentence. Write the correct word on the blank line in each sentence, and write the letter of the answer on the blank to the left.

_____ 11. An animal-rights group objected to the _____ of the live laboratory rat, but they had no objection to a dead rat being cut up.
(a) vivisection   (b) dissection   (c) circumspection

_____ 12. The mourners walked in a solemn procession from the church to the cemetery to witness their loved one being _____.
(a) convened   (b) interred   (c) on *terra firma*

_____ 13. At the end of the church service, the minister gave a(n) _____, or a prayer calling for God's help and protection in the coming week.
(a) invocation   (b) aspiration   (c) eruption

_____ 14. Maria, influenced by her interest in pagan cultures, gave up her belief in only one God and dedicated her life to _____.
(a) diathermy   (b) telekinesis   (c) polytheism

_____ 15. Much of the controversy over abortion stems from the debate as to when an embryo or fetus becomes a _____ being.
(a) tensile   (b) corruptible   (c) sentient

_____ 16. In many early pagan cultures, human sacrifice was considered necessary and self-sacrifice noble. It was not uncommon for many people to offer their lives to the gods of their own _____; they didn't have to be forced.
(a) aspiration   (b) volition   (c) invocation

_____ 17. Alicia didn't dwell on her present problems; instead, she concentrated on her future goals and accomplishments, or her

_____.

(a) aspirations (b) vertigo (c) contretemps

_____ 18. Barbara invited only _____ people to her birthday party, careful not to repeat last year's party fiasco with several hostile, unfriendly guests.

(a) terrestrial (b) convivial (c) psychosomatic

_____ 19. The detective was _____ in his investigation, not wanting to upset the powerful people involved until he had a stronger case.

(a) tenacious (b) circumspect (c) corrupt

_____ 20. The young woman felt it was more _____ than good planning that helped them to survive their first year of marriage.

(a) vertigo (b) diathermy (c) providence

Check your answers with your instructor, and record your score below.

% Correct _____

Word Attack — Prefixes

About Prefixes

In Homework Lesson 3, you discovered the idea of word parts. You also learned some common root words that English has borrowed from Greek and Latin.

Another clue that helps you unlock the meaning of new words is the word part called a "prefix." A prefix is a letter or group of letters that goes before the root. A prefix adds to, modifies, or reverses the meaning of the root.

The word "prefix" is itself an example of a word made up of a root plus a prefix, or a P-R combination: *pre + fix* = prefix.

Other common P-R examples that you will recognize are

pre + *view* = preview
re + *read* = reread
in + *sane* = insane

Notice how the prefix either adds to or changes the meaning of the root in these examples and in the examples and new words on the chart below.

Directions: *First, learn each prefix with its original meaning. Just as in root words, the original meaning of each prefix helps you understand the English word. (Note: Prefixes are seldom usable English words by themselves. That's why they are listed here with hyphens.) Next, review the examples using the prefixes. Then, look up the "new word" in your dictionary, and write its definition on the blank lines.*

PREFIX	MEANING	EXAMPLES	NEW WORD AND DEFINITION
1. **ab-**	away from, down	abdicate abduct	**abscond:** _____ _____
2. **ad-**	to, toward	advocate adverse	**adjacent:** _____ _____
3. **ambi-, amphi-**	on both sides, around	amphitheater ambidextrous	**ambivalent:** _____ _____
4. **arch-**	chief, principal	archangel architect	**archetype:** _____ _____
5. **bi-**	two	bifocal bilingual	**binary:** _____ _____
6. **circum-**	around	circuit circumspect	**circumlocution:** _____ _____
7. **con-, com-**	with, together	congregate companion	**conjunction:** _____ _____
8. **extra-**	outside, beyond	extramarital extradite	**extraneous:** _____ _____

PREFIX	MEANING	EXAMPLES	NEW WORD AND DEFINITION
9. **inter-**	among, between	interject international	**intercede:** _____ _____
10. **mal-**	bad, wrong	malfunction malpractice	**malady:** _____ _____
11. **in- (im-, il-, ir-,)** (in- may also mean "inside")*	not, opposite of	inarticulate impeccable illegitimate irrational	**intractable:** _____ _____
12. **a-***	not, without	asexual apathy	**asymmetrical:** _____ _____
13. **dis-*** (dis- may also mean "apart")	not	dissimilar discontent	**disinclined:** _____ _____
14. **un-***	not	unrestrained unaccountable	**unfathomable:** _____ _____
15. **non-***	not	nonaddictive nonprofit	**nontoxic:** _____ _____
16. **in-*** (in-, may also mean "not")*	inside, within	ingest intoxicate	**incarceration:** _____ _____
17. **intra-***	inside, within	introverted intrastate	**intrauterine:** _____ _____
18. **e-, ex-***	out, away from	emigrate excise	**egress:** _____ _____
19. **de-***	away, down	depress descend	**degrade:** _____ _____
20. **dis-***	apart	disperse dissect	**disembodied:** _____ _____

---

*Also presented in _Reading Faster and Understanding More, Book One_, and included here for review.

Exercise, Homework Lesson 7

Complete the following sentences by choosing words from the box. Use context clues to help you choose the appropriate word.

binary	circumlocution	archetype	ambivalent	nontoxic
asymmetrical	incarceration	extraneous	interceded	degrade

1. Although the right and left sides of our bodies may look equally proportioned, careful measuring shows they are actually _____.

2. Professor Parks said there were too many _____, or unnecessary, ideas in my essay. He suggested that I delete one-third of them.

3. A(n) _____ star is composed of two parts.

4. In a mean-spirited attempt to _____ his wife, the man made a clumsy pass at the waitress as his wife returned to the table.

5. George searched for the _____, or original model, of the plane so he could make an authentic looking replica for the museum.

6. After her long _____ for bank robbery was over, she made use of her freedom by living a productive, law-abiding life.

7. In order to protect the children in her care, the nursery school director ordered only _____ crayons and paints.

8. My feelings about snakes are _____. On the one hand, I admire their resourcefulness and beauty; but, on the other hand, I fear them.

9. Her brother had always _____ on her behalf, getting her out of trouble countless times.

10. If you ask my Aunt Sarah for help, she won't turn you down directly, but will give you a great deal of sweet _____.

To complete the following sentences, choose one of the three words or phrases below the sentence. Write the correct word on the blank line in each sentence, and write the letter of the answer on the blank to the left.

_____ 11. The king was forced to _____ with the crown jewels after he was replaced.
(a) abscond (b) egress (c) disembody

_____ 12. In the delivery room, the doctor chose to use a(n) _____ device to monitor the fetus' vital statistics as the mother was obviously in distress.
(a) nontoxic (b) binary (c) intrauterine

_____ 13. At Wacky World's Haunted House of Horrors, Susan thought she heard a(n) _____ voice seeming to come from nowhere.

(a) disembodied   (b) intractable   (c) disinclined

_____ 14. As the two buildings were _____, they shared a water line as well as a sewer pipe.

(a) intractable   (b) unfathomable   (c) adjacent

_____ 15. The killer's motives were _____. He came from a normal, happy, middle-class family without any obvious, deep-seated problems.

(a) extraneous   (b) degrading   (c) unfathomable

_____ 16. Shelley's son wanted her to consent to piercing his nose, but she was _____ to change her mind.

(a) ambivalent   (b) disinclined   (c) binary

_____ 17. The _____ youth was an enormous challenge for the new teacher.

(a) intractable   (b) extraneous   (c) archetype

_____ 18. The young girl wanted to say she had a mysterious _____; her mumps were too ordinary for her tastes.

(a) circumlocution   (b) malady   (c) incarceration

_____ 19. In _____ with her other debts, Cecelia decided that a car payment was not a good idea.

(a) conjunction   (b) apathy   (c) egress

_____ 20. Because of its unusual form of _____, the trap-door spider has been widely studied.

(a) incarceration   (b) circumlocution   (c) egress

Check your answers with your instructor, and record your score below.

% Correct _____

Word Attack — Prefixes

Directions: First, learn this list of prefixes with their original meanings. Next, review the examples using the prefixes. Then, look up the "new word" in your dictionary, and write its definition on the blank lines.

PREFIX	MEANING	EXAMPLES	NEW WORD AND DEFINITION
1. **mis-**	wrong, ill	mispronounce misunderstand	**misnomer:** _____ _____
2. **multi-**	many	multitude multimillionaire	**multifaceted:** _____ _____
3. **peri-**	around	periphery perimeter	**peripatetic:** _____ _____
4. **pro-** (pro- may also mean "for")	before, forward	proficient proactive	**prologue:** _____ _____
5. **re-**	again, back	recede revitalize	**reinvigorate:** _____ _____
6. **retro-**	back	retrospect retroactive	**retrogress:** _____ _____
7. **semi-**	half	semicolon semiconscious	**semiannually:** _____ _____
8. **syn-, sym-**	together	synchronize synthesize	**symbiosis:** _____ _____
9. **trans-**	across	transpire translate	**transcend:** _____ _____
10. **tri-**	three	tripod trilateral	**triumvirate:** _____ _____
11. **pro-*** (pro- may also mean "before")	for, in favor of	progressive pro-revolution	**propaganda:** _____ _____
12. **anti-***	against	antibiotic anticlimactic	**antithesis:** _____ _____
13. **contra-*** **counter-***	against	contradict counterpoint	**contraband:** _____ _____

*Also presented in *Reading Faster and Understanding More, Book One*, and included here for review.

PREFIX	MEANING	EXAMPLES	NEW WORD AND DEFINITION
14. **post-***	after	posterity postdoctoral	**posthumous:** _____ _____
15. **pre-***	before	preclude predetermined	**precedent:** _____ _____
16. **ante-***	before	antebellum antechamber	**antediluvian:** _____ _____
17. **sub-***	under	subordinate subsequent	**subjugate:** _____ _____
18. **hypo-***	under	hypoglycemia hypothetical	**hypothermia:** _____ _____
19. **hyper-***	above, beyond	hyperventilate hypertension	**hyperbole:** _____ _____
20. **super-***	above, upon	supernatural superimpose	**superfluous:** _____ _____

Exercise, Homework Lesson 8

Complete the following sentences by choosing words from the box. Use context clues to help you choose the appropriate word.

reinvigorate	hypothermia	subjugate	multifaceted	posthumous
propaganda	antithesis	prologue	peripatetic	antediluvian

1. The diamond ring was small but _____. Therefore it reflected light from every surface.
2. Unfortunately, he was the _____ of everything she was looking for in a husband.
3. Let's skip the _____ and get to the heart of this romantic tale.
4. I don't see the point of granting someone a _____ degree. You can't exactly use it on your résumé if you are dead.
5. The quickest way to _____ myself after a long, tough day at work is to exercise.

---

*Also presented in *Reading Faster and Understanding More, Book One*, and included here for review.

6. Due to negative government _____ the visitors did not receive a very warm welcome from the people of Haiti.

7. Jimmy was rushed to the hospital, for it was clear that he was suffering from _____ after falling into the icy lake.

8. Professor Jamison felt that the aging dean's _____ ideas were holding back the progressive Women's Studies Program at the college.

9. A product of an earlier time, the veteran teacher still felt the need to _____ the children in her care in order to maintain perfect order in the classroom.

10. America's Secretary of State is usually called _____ because of his constant traveling.

To complete the following sentences, choose one of the three words below the sentence. Write the correct word on the blank line in each sentence, and write the letter of the answer on the blank to the left.

_____ 11. Alice's income from her part-time job as a waitress seemed _____ to her friends, who knew that her salary as a lawyer was more than adequate.
(a) triumvirate   (b) superfluous   (c) multifaceted

_____ 12. Many self-employed business people prefer to pay their taxes _____ to avoid having to pay one lump sum in April.
(a) semiannually   (b) posthumously   (c) transcendentally

_____ 13. A type of folk tale, called a "Jack tale," is traditionally full of _____ meant to amuse and amaze rather than inform.
(a) symbiosis   (b) prologue   (c) hyperbole

_____ 14. The child managed to _____ all hopes and expectations, impressing even the doctors with her complete recovery.
(a) subjugate   (b) transcend   (c) retrogress

_____ 15. The voters in the small, newly independent country decided to elect a _____ instead of the traditional, one-man type of leadership.
(a) antithesis   (b) antediluvian   (c) triumvirate

_____ 16. Cathy felt it was a _____ to call her husband her "mate," as it had been many years since they had shared a bed and had never produced any children.
(a) symbiosis   (b) precedent   (c) misnomer

_____ 17. The judge felt that to free this young man would set a legal _____ that could be abused later.
(a) precedent   (b) triumvirate   (c) peripatetic

_____ 18. An unlikely _____ developed between the two roommates who came from such different backgrounds.

(a) triumvirate   (b) hyperbole   (c) symbiosis

_____ 19. The Border Patrol intercepted the truck carrying _____ and arrested the driver.

(a) contraband   (b) propaganda   (c) antediluvian

_____ 20. Any time life got too messy, Frank would _____ to an earlier stage in his recovery, blaming anyone and everything for his frustrations.

(a) reinvigorate   (b) retrogress   (c) transcend

Check your answers with your instructor, and record your score below.

% Correct _____

Word Attack—Suffixes

About Noun Suffixes

Homework Lesson 7 explained the P or Prefix part of a word. You now know that a word may be only a root (for example, the eleven words preceding the parenthesis). Or the root word may have a *prefix* at the beginning, as in the words "*pre*fix," "*re*read," and "*pre*ceding." Or it may have a *suffix* at the end, as in the words "end*s*" and "end*ing*." As you can see, a *suffix* is a single letter or group of letters that comes after the root, forming an R-S combination.

Our English language has many more suffixes than prefixes. Also, many have the same meaning. In some cases it takes years of listening, reading, and writing to know which one of several suffixes, all with the same meaning, is the correct suffix for your word. Do we call a talkative person "word*y*," "word*ish*," "word*ic*," "word*ive*," or "word*al*"? Those suffixes all mean "having the quality of."

However, some classification of English suffixes by meaning is possible, and often helpful. If nothing else, you will begin to notice suffixes and their effect on words to which they are attached. The most important reason for learning suffixes is that they give you flexibility in using words you already know. And, since adding a suffix will often change the part of speech of a word, their study will give you some insight into the structure of our language.

We'll start with suffixes that generally indicate that a word is a noun.

Five Tests for Nouns

By "noun" we mean a thing—a person, a place, an idea, a quality, an object of some sort. If you are not sure whether a word is being used as a noun, you can apply five tests.

1. Put *a*, *an*, or *the* before it (a *bone*, an *hour*, the *thought*).
2. Put an *-s* on it for a plural (more than one) (*bones*, *hours*, *thoughts*).
3. Precede it with a descriptive word (dry *bones*, wee *hours*, deep *thoughts*).
4. Make it the subject of a sentence (His *bones* are buried in the yard).
5. Make it the object of a preposition (There's dust around those *bones*).

If the word sounds right and makes sense in these tests, then it is a noun. For example, try the five tests out on the word "if." 1. an *if* 2. the *ifs* 3. a bright *if* 4. Her *if* is plain to see. 5. with *if*, beside *if*. Does "if" pass these tests for a noun? _____

Practice

Now try the five tests with the word "love." Can "love" be used as a noun? _____

1. _____
2. _____
3. _____
4. _____
5. _____

Love, of course, is a root word; it does not have a suffix—yet. But if we were to add a suffix to *love* to make it a noun, what would we use? Try the preceding five tests with the words "love-ly," "lov-ing," "love-liness." Which ending is a noun suffix? _____ Does that word fit most of the five conditions? _____ Can *love* also be used as a verb, as in "He *loves* her"? _____

Because there are so many suffixes, we have grouped those with similar meanings together. *Note:* Some noun suffixes, unfortunately, are also used as adjective suffixes. An example is *-ent*: He is my *dependent*—noun. He is a very *dependent* person—adjective.

Directions: *First, learn this list of common noun suffixes, with their meanings. Next, review the examples of words using these suffixes. Notice how the suffixes affect the meaning of the words in the examples. Look up the "new word" in your dictionary, and write its definition on the blank lines.*

SUFFIX	MEANING	EXAMPLES	NEW WORD AND DEFINITION
1. **-s -es**	simple plural	judgments, reflexes	**complexes:** _____ _____
2. **-ette** **-ie, -y** **-let** **-ling** **-ule**	little	novelette, sermonette Annie, lassie, piggy booklet, streamlet duckling, princeling globule, granule	**nodule:** _____ _____
3. **-ism***	state of, doctrine	Communism capitalism	**despotism:** _____ _____
4. **-ese** **-er** **-ian**	inhabitant of	Japanese, Chinese southerner Bostonian	**agrarian:** _____ _____
5. **-cide**	killing	matricide, suicide homicide, genocide	**patricide:** _____ _____
6. **-dom**	place, condition, rank	Christendom, boredom kingdom, wisdom	**martyrdom:** _____ _____
7. **-itis**	inflammation, disease	tonsillitis bronchitis	**neuritis:** _____ _____
8. **-ee***	one who receives an action	appointee addressee	**lessee:** _____ _____
9. **-er*** **-ar*** **-or***	one who, a thing that	teacher beggar, liar protector, instructor	**lessor:** _____ _____

*Also presented in *Reading Faster and Understanding More, Book One*, and included here for review.

SUFFIX	MEANING	EXAMPLES	NEW WORD AND DEFINITION
10. **-an, -ian***	one who	pediatrician, technician	**charlatan:** _____ _____
11. **-ist, -tist***	one who	violinist, artist	**egotist:** _____ _____
12. **-ant, -ent***	one who	attendant, resident	**appellant:** _____ _____
13. **-eer, -ier**	one who	auctioneer, bombardier	**glazier:** _____ _____
14. **-ster**	one who	gangster, youngster	**spinster:** _____ _____
15. **-ess**	one who, female	authoress, stewardess	**tigress:** _____ _____
16. **-acy**	state of	privacy, accuracy	**advocacy:** _____ _____
17. **-ance, -ence***	state of, quality of	performance competence	**protuberance:** _____ _____
18. **-tude, -lude***	state of, quality of	altitude interlude	**fortitude:** _____ _____
19. **-ion, -tion* -sion***	state of, quality of	fusion, relaxation revulsion	**deflation:** _____ _____
20. **-ity, -ty***	state of, quality of	publicity certainty	**novelty:** _____ _____
21. **-ment***	state of, quality of	enlargement disappointment	**enlightenment:** _____ _____
22. **-ness***	state of, quality of	courteousness foolishness	**hardiness:** _____ _____
23. **-ship, -hood***	state of, quality of	courtship childhood	**hardship:** _____ _____
24. **-ary, -ery,* -ory***	a place for	dictionary, monastery depository	**sanctuary:** _____ _____
25. **-arium, -orium**	a place for	aquarium auditorium	**solarium:** _____ _____

---

*Also presented in _Reading Faster and Understanding More, Book One,_ and included here for review.

Exercise, Homework Lesson 9

Decide from the context of each sentence which noun suffix must be added to the word or word part in parentheses. Then write the entire word in the blank, changing the spelling if necessary.

Example: The little (lass) _____lassie_____ took her dainty (handkerchief) _____hankie_____ and wiped off her (pig's) _____piggy's_____ little (feet) _____feetsies_____.

Use suffixes meaning "little."

1. In the chase scene of this (novel) _____, Susan, our little heroine, holds her (dog) _____ tightly, and daintily steps over the (stream) _____, taking care not to frighten the (duck) _____, or get a (glob) _____ of water on her tiny velvet slippers.

Use suffixes indicating "inhabitants of."

2. The (New York) _____ calmly took a bite out of the big apple as his (Peking) _____ dog gave his regards to Broadway and the astonished (Boston) _____ looked the other way.

Use a suffix indicating the female gender.

3. The famous (actor) _____ on the plane little suspected that the (steward) _____ was not only an (heir) _____ but a (prince) _____ too.

Use suffixes meaning "one who."

4. "Oh my (protect) _____ and (defend) _____," the (drama) _____ wrote, "I surely would have been a (gone) _____ without your help!"

5. Against my express wishes, that (prank) _____, (gang) _____, and (rough) _____, my brother-in-law, Freddy, turned my new Cadillac into a "low-rider."

6. The letter indicated that I would receive, as the (pay) _____, the yearly sum of $1,000 from my (guard) _____, as long as I remained a (ten) _____ of the old house.

7. She was not (climb) _____ enough to venture higher without the help of a (mountain) _____.

Use suffixes meaning "state" of "quality of."

8. In (recognize) _____ of your (encourage)
   _____ and (assist) _____ during my
   times of (solitary) _____ and (depend)
   _____, I offer my (grateful) _____, (loyal)
   _____, and (friend) _____.

9. For the sake of (private) _____ and (accurate)
   _____, I strongly suggest that you submit a written state-
   ment to the press instead of allowing an interview.

10. Having just turned twenty-one, the youth celebrated his transition from
    (child) _____ to (man) _____ by a little
    (relax) _____ at the local bar.

*To complete the following sentences, choose one of the three words below the sen-
tence. Write the correct word on the longer blank line, and write the letter of the
answer on the blank line to the left.*

_____ 11. Because he hated his father so much, he committed
          _____ and went to jail.
          (a) despotism   (b) martyrdom   (c) patricide

_____ 12. She bought an apartment house and became the
          _____ for many of her acquaintances who needed
          to rent an apartment.
          (a) lessee   (b) lessor   (c) agrarian

_____ 13. Instead of seeing a real doctor who could treat his cancer, he con-
          sulted a _____ who took his money and gave him
          bottles of colored water.
          (a) charlatan   (b) spinster   (c) egotist

_____ 14. The early settlers of America suffered one _____
          after another.
          (a) hardship   (b) hardiness   (c) nodule

_____ 15. The governor's public _____ for protection of ani-
          mals prevented many animals in his state from being killed for
          research.
          (a) fortitude   (b) advocacy   (c) complexes

_____ 16. Her calling him a conceited ignoramus in front of his friends result-
          ed in a _____ of his ego.
          (a) egotist   (b) protuberance   (c) deflation

_____ 17. Before large cities and modern technology, we lived in a mostly
          _____ society, growing our own food.
          (a) patricide   (b) agrarian   (c) despotism

_____ 18. His mother complained so often of her sacrifices for her children that we began to suspect that she enjoyed her own

_____.

(a) martyrdom   (b) neuritis   (c) complexes

_____ 19. Always a sun-worshipper, Janet's favorite room in her house is her

_____.

(a) sanctuary   (b) novelty   (c) solarium

_____ 20. Agnes carefully examined the small lump, or _____, on her neck.

(a) enlightenment   (b) nodule   (c) neuritis

Check the answers with your instructor, and record your score below.

% Correct   _____

Word Attack—Suffixes

About Verb Suffixes

What do we mean by a *verb*? A verb is a word or words that show action or existence. (*Is* and *show* in the preceding sentence are verbs.) Along with the noun subject, the verb makes the skeleton, the basic part of a sentence. For example, in these basic sentences, the subject is underlined once and the verb twice.

God is. The people were. Jody waited. He had been waiting.

In Homework Lesson 9, you learned five tests for a noun. To test a word to see if it's a verb, you can apply these two tests.

1. Put *he*, *she*, or *it* before the word and add an *-s* to the word.
   - He *walks*. She *walks*. It *walks*.

2. Change the time (or tense) to past, continuing present, and future.
   - He *walked*. (past)
   - He *is walking*. (continuing present)
   - He *will walk*. (future)

Let's try the tests out on the word "cow":

1. He *cows*. She *cows*. It *cows*.
2. He *cowed*. He *is cowing*. He *will cow*.

Do you think the word "cow" is usually a verb? _____

Practice 1

Now try the two tests on the word "act."

1. _____

_____

2. _____

_____

Can the word "act" be used as a verb? _____

Like the test word "love" in Homework Lesson 9, "act" is a root word. And also like *love*, we can add suffixes to act and still have a verb. Extra practice: What noun suffixes can you add to *act*? _____
(Check Homework Lesson 9 if you have forgotten.)

Practice 2

Try the tests for a verb on the word "activate."

1. _____

2. _____

Is *activate* a verb? _____

About Adjective and Adverb Suffixes

This last group of suffixes is used to show that a word is being used as either an adjective or adverb. Again, we should review what is meant by an adjective and an adverb. They are words that modify (describe) other words. An adjective describes a noun or pronoun; an adverb describes a verb, adjective, or another adverb. An adverb indicates how, when, where, why, or to what degree.

As with the verbs, we can take a skeleton sentence and add an adjective and an adverb like this:

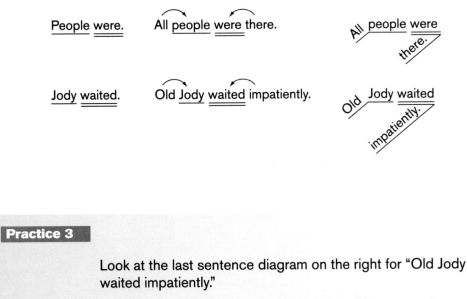

Practice 3

Look at the last sentence diagram on the right for "Old Jody waited impatiently."

1. Does the adjective *old* in that sentence have a prefix or suffix?
   _____

2. Is *old* a root word? _____

3. Does the adverb *impatiently* have a prefix or suffix? _____

4. Does *impatiently* have a root? _____

If you saw that *old* is a root word without a prefix or suffix, and that *im-* is the prefix for *impatiently* and *-ly* is the suffix, you have kept on top of the word analysis exercises.

Do you remember from Homework Lesson 9 the problem some students face when they don't know whether to describe a person as word*y*, word*ish*, word*al*, word*ic*, or word*ive*? These are all possible adjective endings describing a noun, and English has so many it is easy to be confused. Sometimes the only way to make the choice is to read and listen until "the *ear* knows." As with the noun suffixes in Homework Lesson 9, as many as possible are grouped together by similar meaning.

Luckily, the adverb ending in English is usually *-ly*; so you can learn that one easily and quickly.

Stop and underline carefully the adverb endings that have been obviously and carefully and pointedly added in this sentence.

Verb Suffixes

English has few verb suffixes other than the regular - *s*, *-ed*, and *-ing* (works, work*ed*, work*ing*) and sometimes *-en* and *-t* (writt*en*, burn*t*). These endings are so much a part of words that many people don't think of them as suffixes at all. Knowing them gives you flexibility with words you already know, because verbs with these endings are usually made from nouns and adjectives. You do need them to communicate clearly. In our short list of verb suffixes, we present four more.

Directions: *In addition to the regular verb suffixes of -s, -ed, and -ing, learn this short list of suffixes. Notice how the meaning affects the way the sample words can be used. Use the dictionary to look up the "new word," and write its definition on the blank lines.*

SUFFIX	MEANING	EXAMPLES	NEW WORD AND DEFINITION
1. **-ate***	to make, cause to be	eliminate salivate	**marinate:** _____ _____
2. **-en***	to make, cause to be	fasten lengthen	**embolden:** _____ _____
3. **-fy***	to make, cause to be	intensify testify	**nullify:** _____ _____
4. **-ize***	to make, cause to be	sympathize fertilize	**jeopardize:** _____ _____

Adjective Suffixes

Directions: *Review this list of adjective suffixes (and one adverb suffix) and their meanings. Next, notice how the suffix affects the way you use the examples. Then, look up the "new word" in your dictionary, and write its meaning on the blank lines.*

SUFFIX	MEANING	EXAMPLES	NEW WORD AND DEFINITION
1. **-er***	comparative (of two)	calmer haughtier	**wrier:** _(wry + er)_ _____ _____
2. **-est***	superlative (of more than two)	naughtiest smartest	**lithest:** _(lithe + est)_ _____ _____

*Also presented in *Reading Faster and Understanding More, Book One*, and included here for review.

SUFFIX	MEANING	EXAMPLES	NEW WORD AND DEFINITION
3. **-able, -ible***	able to be	durable reliable	**inedible:** _____ _____
4. **-oid**	in the form of	humanoid paranoid	**android:** _____ _____
5. **-esque**	having the nature of	picturesque burlesque	**statuesque:** _____ _____
6. **-ic***	having the nature of	historic graphic	**acerbic:** _____ _____
7. **-ish***	having the nature of	devilish gibberish	**skittish:** _____ _____
8. **-ose, -ous**	having the nature of	verbose generous	**morose:** _____ _____
9. **-tious, -cious***	having the nature of	repetitious malicious	**auspicious:** _____ _____
10. **-ive, -ative***	having the nature of	festive talkative	**formative:** _____ _____
11. **-ant, -ent***	having the nature of	extravagant deviant	**complacent:** _____ _____
12. **-ac, -an**	having the nature of	cardiac American	**insomniac:** _____ _____
13. **-al**	having the nature of	sentimental horizontal	**menial:** _____ _____
14. **-ar**	having the nature of	circular particular	**lunar:** _____ _____
15. **-some**	having the nature of	wearisome loathsome	**winsome:** _____ _____
16. **-ful***	full of	graceful fanciful	**fretful:** _____ _____
17. **-less***	without, free of	worthless penniless	**peerless:** _____ _____
18. **-ward**	direction	homeward backward	**wayward:** _____ _____

*Also presented in *Reading Faster and Understanding More, Book One*, and included here for review.

SUFFIX	MEANING	EXAMPLES	NEW WORD AND DEFINITION
19. **-y, -ly***	having the nature of	worthy lonely	**humanly:** _____ _____
Adverb Suffix			
20. **-ly***	in a certain manner	abruptly solemnly	**incorrigibly:** _____ _____

[Note: While most -ly endings indicate an adverb, a few words ending in -ly are adjectives: elderly, homely, brotherly, friendly, lively, leisurely, lovely, kindly.]

Exercise, Homework Lesson 10

Verb Suffixes

Directions: *Decide from the context what verb suffix must be added to the word in parentheses. Then write the entire word in the blank, changing the spelling when necessary. Note: Keep the verb tense consistent within each sentence. Many verbs can be either present or past tense.*

Example: James (fertile) ____fertilized____ his dry, barren land before he (plant) ____planted____ his crops.

1. Christopher Columbus probably never understood that murdering the native population might (jeopardy) _____ his position in history.

2. The seamstress could (length) _____ the skirt and (fast) _____ the loose buckles, but she could never make the outfit look the same on Mrs. Johnson as it did on the models in the magazine.

3. Each week of the semester, the work would (intense) _____, and Joe would stay out later and later to avoid the inevitable, all of which did not help to (strength) _____ his resolve to study.

4. Dan decided to (marinade) _____ the steaks in barbecue sauce, which caused his dogs to (saliva) _____ in anticipation.

5. England's attempts to (colony) _____ were seen as acts of aggression by the rest of the world, serving to (null) _____ their efforts.

---

*Also presented in *Reading Faster and Understanding More, Book One,* and included here for review.

Adjective Suffixes

Directions: *Choose the best adjective suffix for the word in parentheses and write the entire word in the blank, changing the spelling if necessary.*

Example: an (admire) ___admirable___ *act*

6. his (devil) _____ charms

7. a (picture) _____ village

8. the (paranoia) _____ schizophrenic

9. the last (lunar) _____ eclipse

10. a (loathe) _____ duty

11. the (calm) _____ of the two women

12. the (form) _____ years

13. a (grace) _____ beauty

14. the (naughty) _____ of them all

15. an (auspice) _____ occasion

Adverb Suffixes

Directions: *Attach the adverb suffix to the word in parentheses and write the entire word in the blank. In some cases, the word in parentheses is a noun and must first be given an adjective suffix before the adverb suffix can be added. Change the spelling when necessary.*

Example: to write (fancy) ___fancifully___

16. is (physical) _____ fit

17. inquire (full of purpose) _____

18. kisses (loving) _____

19. is (hypnotic) _____ charming

20. was (impossible) _____ complicated

To complete the following sentences, choose one of the words below the sentence. Write the correct word on the longer blank line, and write the letter of the answer on the blank to the left.

_____ 21. Morris did not like to argue; he was _____ about most suggestions.
(a) wayward   (b) peerless   (c) complacent

_____ 22. Because of his _____ condition, Bill would telephone his friends, waking them up night after night.
(a) skittish   (b) insomniac   (c) menial

_____ 23. After a few drinks, Jill would listen to old love songs, think about her ex-boyfriend, and become _____.
(a) morose   (b) auspicious   (c) statuesque

_____ 24. When John realized his bank account was empty, he began to
_____ all the checks he had written.

(a) nullify   (b) jeopardize   (c) embolden

_____ 25. No matter what Angela did to punish little Lucy, her daughter
remained the most _____ naughty child in day
care.

(a) humanly   (b) wryly   (c) incorrigibly

Check the answers with your instructor and record your score below.

% Correct _____

Word Lists

from *Vocabulary Previews*

"By Chapter" List of Words

Alphabetical List of Words

from *Homework Lessons*

Alphabetical List of Prefixes, Roots, and

Suffixes

Alphabetical List of New Words

"By Chapter" List of Words from *Vocabulary Previews*

Vocabulary	Chapter	Vocabulary	Chapter	Vocabulary	Chapter
stricken	1	unequivocal	2	consolation	4
rigorous	1	immune	2	trauma	4
calisthenics	1	resolution	2	tenuous	4
lynch	1	distraught	2	perusal	4
disparaged	1	caveats	2	filial	4
celibate	1	grappled	2	heathen	4
uterus	1	perspective	2	pediatrician	4
fetus	1	rationalized	2	permissive	4
evanescent	1	dissipated	2	immediate	5
quipsters	1	panacea	2	carbon monoxide	5
melancholy	1	proliferation	3	freaked	5
suit of mail	1	chastise	3	quest	5
lance	1	dubious	3	frugal	5
lathe	1	repertoire	3	rhinoplastic	5
transom	1	spunky	3	transcendental	5
averred	1	mired	3	suspending	5
cad	1	implacable	3	chill	5
peerage	1	eke	3	tranquil	5
gusto	1	persona	3	fawn	5
guffawing	1	haphazardly	3	grovel	5
taxing	1	balked	3	desultory	5
cashier	1	touted	3	catalyst	5
insatiable	1	bulk	3	slumbering	5
luster	1	soliciting	3	obnoxious	5
chintzy	1	ironic	3	futile	5
scruffy	1	scenarios	3	mediocrity	5
sinister	1	canine	3	flagrantly	5
sardonic	1	frivolity	3	placards	5
intrigues	1	tack	3	inscribed	5
incredulous	1	smitten	3	protractor	5
acupuncture	2	calamity	3	dogma	6
cellulite	2	scrutiny	3	contemporaries	6
charred	2	solicitation	3	fixity	6
hemorrhoids	2	cherished	3	herald	6
carcinogens	2	crest	3	heritability	6
delusive	2	fashioned	3	musings	6
transient	2	registry	3	era	6
cynical	2	sapling	3	protégé	6
expounded	2	affix	3	fossils	6
propagation	2	initial	3	surmised	6
monogamy	2	complimentary	3	writhing	6
diversity	2	ethnic	4	flailing	6
hiatus	2	elective	4	exuberant	6
duration	2	affinity	4	beatitudes	6
infatuation	2	luxuriate	4	prowess	6
trauma	2	transcended	4	trifling	6
anonymous	2	ill	4	desolate	6
recount	2	facetious	4	gaucho	6
embarked	2	demeanor	4	tenet	6
correlation	2	incarnate	4	motley	6
vented	2	spliced	4	withering	6
depicted	2	prankster	4	paltry	6
profound	2	degradation	4	psychosomatic	6

Vocabulary	Chapter	Vocabulary	Chapter	Vocabulary	Chapter
facetiously	6	lax	8	fare	9
fray	6	contemporary	8	dweeby	9
diversified	7	intervened	8	dynamic	9
elite	7	purview	8	idiocy	10
stems	7	accord	8	operatives	10
coup	7	casualties	8	membrane	10
authentic	7	massacre	8	mandrake	10
gubernatorial	7	balkanized	8	cleft	10
launching	7	Goths	8	thou	10
diabolical	7	parody	8	befell	10
melodrama	7	anonymity	8	fair	10
banality	7	decipher	8	pilgrimage	10
subversion	7	diminish	8	ere	10
influx	7	sentimentality	8	Braille	10
anarchic	7	multiculturalism	8	putter	10
iniquity	7	communal	8	noblesse oblige	10
unrequited	7	conformist	8	emaciated	10
charismatic	7	impersonality	8	solar plexus	10
fledgling	7	solitude	8	dereliction	10
prohibition	7	parochial	8	lurching	10
caste	7	theological	8	smoldering	10
reprehensible	7	tribalism	8	parody	10
conscripted	7	oppressively	9	improvisation	10
perpetuates	7	insufferable	9	burbling	10
reverberated	7	mere	9	roiling	10
servitude	7	bleak	9	hunkered	10
cloning	8	unnerved	9	pathetic	10
draconian	8	empathy	9	gothic	10
barbarity	8	furor	9	troll	10
white-supremacist	8	harassment	9	embossing	10
felon	8	unicorn	9	livid	10
refute	8	cropping	9	overt	10
dispatch	8	gloat	9	invective	10
prolific	8	subduing	9	molten	10
fodder	8	hazing	9	bunker	10
advocates	8	roustabouts	9	smote	10
alleged	8	belittled	9	martyr	10
cant	8	dusky	9	glowered	10
bridles	8	quid pro quo	9	gawked	10
inculcating	8	heterosexual	9	flourish	10

Alphabetical List of Words from *Vocabulary Previews*

Vocabulary	Chapter	Vocabulary	Chapter	Vocabulary	Chapter
accord	8	coup	7	fodder	8
acupuncture	2	crest	3	fossils	6
advocates	8	cropping	9	fray	6
affinity	4	cynical	2	freaked	5
affix	3	decipher	8	frivolity	3
alleged	8	degradation	4	frugal	5
anarchic	7	delusive	2	furor	9
anonymity	8	demeanor	4	futile	5
anonymous	2	depicted	2	gaucho	6
authentic	7	dereliction	10	gawked	10
averred	1	desolate	6	gloat	9
balkanized	8	desultory	5	glowered	10
balked	3	diabolical	7	gothic	10
banality	7	diminish	8	Goths	8
barbarity	8	disparaged	1	grappled	2
beatitudes	6	dispatch	8	grovel	5
befell	10	dissipated	2	gubernatorial	7
belittled	9	distraught	2	guffawing	1
bleak	9	diversified	7	gusto	1
Braille	10	diversity	2	haphazardly	3
bridles	8	dogma	6	harassment	9
bulk	3	draconian	8	hazing	9
bunker	10	dubious	3	heathen	4
burbling	10	duration	2	hemorrhoids	2
cad	1	dusky	9	herald	6
calamity	3	dweeby	9	heritability	6
calisthenics	1	dynamic	9	heterosexual	9
canine	3	eke	3	hiatus	2
cant	8	elective	4	hunkered	10
carbon monoxide	5	elite	7	idiocy	10
carcinogens	2	emaciated	10	ill	4
cashier	1	embarked	2	immediate	5
caste	7	embossing	10	immune	2
casualties	8	empathy	9	impersonality	8
catalyst	5	era	6	implacable	3
caveats	2	ere	10	improvisation	10
celibate	1	ethnic	4	incarnate	4
cellulite	2	evanescent	1	incredulous	1
charismatic	7	expounded	2	inculcating	8
charred	2	exuberant	6	infatuation	2
chastise	3	facetious	4	influx	7
cherished	3	facetiously	6	iniquity	7
chill	5	fair	10	initial	3
chintzy	1	fare	9	insatiable	1
cleft	10	fashioned	3	inscribed	5
cloning	8	fawn	5	insufferable	9
communal	8	felon	8	intervened	8
complimentary	3	fetus	1	intrigues	1
conformist	8	filial	4	invective	10
conscripted	7	fixity	6	ironic	3
consolation	4	flagrantly	5	lance	1
contemporaries	6	flailing	6	lathe	1
contemporary	8	fledgling	7	launching	7
correlation	2	flourish	10	lax	8

Vocabulary	Chapter	Vocabulary	Chapter	Vocabulary	Chapter
livid	10	prankster	4	solar plexus	10
lurching	10	profound	2	solicitation	3
luster	1	prohibition	7	soliciting	3
luxuriate	4	proliferation	3	solitude	8
lynch	1	prolific	8	spliced	4
mandrake	10	propagation	2	spunky	3
martyr	10	protégé	6	stems	7
massacre	8	protractor	5	stricken	1
mediocrity	5	prowess	6	subduing	9
melancholy	1	psychosomatic	6	subversion	7
melodrama	7	purview	8	suit of mail	1
membrane	10	putter	10	surmised	6
mere	9	quest	5	suspending	5
mired	3	quid pro quo	9	tack	3
molten	10	quipsters	1	taxing	1
monogamy	2	rationalized	2	tenet	6
motley	6	recount	2	tenuous	4
multiculturalism	8	refute	8	theological	8
musings	6	registry	3	thou	10
noblesse oblige	10	repertoire	3	touted	3
obnoxious	5	reprehensible	7	transcendental	5
operatives	10	resolution	2	tranquil	5
oppressively	9	reverberated	7	transcended	4
overt	10	rhinoplastic	5	transient	2
paltry	6	rigorous	1	transom	1
panacea	2	roiling	10	traumas	2
parochial	8	roustabouts	9	trauma	4
parody	8	sapling	3	tribalism	8
parody	10	sardonic	1	trifling	6
pathetic	10	scenarios	3	troll	10
pediatrician	4	scruffy	1	unequivocal	2
peerage	1	scrutiny	3	unicorn	9
permissive	4	sentimentality	8	unnerved	9
perpetuates	7	servitude	7	unrequited	7
persona	3	sinister	1	uterus	1
perspective	2	slumbering	5	vented	2
perusal	4	smitten	3	white-supremacist	8
pilgrimage	10	smoldering	10	withering	6
placards	5	smote	10	writhing	6

Alphabetical List of Roots, Prefixes, and Suffixes

The following is an alphabetical list of word parts studied in the Homework Lessons 3 through 10.

Roots

root word	meaning	root word	meaning
1. (a)equis	equal, even	41. mania	madness, derangement
2. anima	breath, spirit, mind	42. manus	hand
3. ann, enn*	year	43. metr*	measure
4. anthropo	man	44. micro	small
5. astro*	star	45. mit, miss*	to send
6. aud, audit*	to hear	46. mono	one
7. auto*	self	47. mor	dead
8. bellum	war	48. ocul	eye
9. bene*	good, well	49. path*	feeling, suffering
10. bio*	life	50. ped	foot (also child)
11. cap, cept	to take	51. pel, puls	drive
12. capit*	head	52. phil, philo*	to love
13. cede, ceed	to yield, to go	53. phobia*	fear
14. cent	hundred	54. phon*	sound
15. chron*	time	55. photo*	light
16. civ*	citizen	56. pod	foot
17. cogni	to know	57. poly*	many
18. cor	heart	58. pon, pos	to place
19. crat, cracy*	rule	59. popul*	people
20. cred, credit*	to believe	60. port*	to carry
21. cult	to care for	61. psych*	mind
22. cycle	wheel, circle	62. rupt	to break
23. dem	people	63. scrib, script*	to write
24. dent	tooth	64. sect	to cut
25. derm	skin	65. sens, sent*	to feel
26. dic, dict*	to say, to speak	66. spec, spect*	to look at
27. duc, duct	to lead	67. spir	to breathe
28. fac, fact*	to make	68. tain, ten	to hold
29. fin*	end, to complete	69. tele*	distant
30. gen, gene*	birth, origin	70. tempor*	time
31. geo*	earth	71. tend, tens	to stretch
32. gram*	to write	72. terra	earth
33. graph*	to write	73. the	god
34. hetero	other	74. therm*	heat
35. homo*	same	75. vene, vent	to come
36. hydra	water	76. vers, vert	to turn
37. jac, ject*	to throw	77. vid, vis*	to see
38. log, logo*	word, study	78. viv, vit*	to live, life
39. loqui, locut	talk	79. voc, vocat*	to call
40. luc, lus	light	80. volens	wishing, willing

---

*Also presented in *Reading Faster and Understanding More, Book One*, and included here for review.

Prefixes

prefix	meaning	prefix	meaning
1. a-*	not, without	21. inter-	among, between
2. ab-	away from, down	22. intra-*	inside, within
3. ad-	to, toward	23. mal-	bad, wrong
4. ambi-, amphi-	on both sides, around	24. mis-	wrong, ill
5. ante-*	before	25. multi-	many
6. anti-*	against	26. non-*	not
7. arch-	chief, principal	27. peri-	around
8. bi-	two	28. post-*	after
9. circum-	around	29. pre-*	before
10. con-, com-	with, together	30. pro-*	for, in favor of
11. contra-, counter-*	against	31. pro-	before, forward
12. de-*	away, down	32. re-	again, back
13. dis-*	not, without	33. retro-	back
14. dis-*	apart	34. semi-	half
15. e-, ex-*	out, away from	35. sub-*	under
16. extra-	outside, beyond	36. super-*	above, upon
17. hyper-*	above, beyond	37. syn-, sym-	together
18. hypo-*	under	38. trans-	across
19. in-*	inside, within	39. tri-	three
20. in- (im-, il-, ir-)*	not, opposite of	40. un-*	not

Suffixes

suffix	part of speech	meaning
1. -able, -ible*	adj.	able to be
2. -ac, -an	adj.	having the nature of
3. -acy	n.	state of
4. -an, -ian*	n.	one who
5. -ance, -ence*	n.	state of, quality of
6. -ant, -ent*	n.	one who
7. -ant, -ent*	adj.	having the nature of
8. -al, -ar*	adj.	having the nature of
9. -ar*	adj.	having the nature of
10. -arium, -orium	n.	a place for
11. -ary, -ery, -ory*	n.	a place for
12. -ate*	v.	to make, cause to be
13. -cide	n.	killing
14. -dom	n.	place, condition, rank
15. -ee*	n.	one who receives an action
16. -eer, -ier	n.	one who
17. -en*	v.	to make, cause to be
18. -er*	adj.	comparative (of two)
19. -er, -ar, -or*	n.	one who, a thing that
20. -ese, -er, -ian	n.	inhabitant of
21. -esque	adj.	having the nature of
22. -ess	n.	one who, female

*Also presented in *Reading Faster and Understanding More, Book One*, and included here for review.

suffix	part of speech	meaning
23. -est*	adj.	superlative (of more than two)
24. -ette (-ie, -y, -let, -ling, -ule)	n.	little noun
25. -ful*	adj.	full of
26. -fy*	v.	to make, cause to be
27. -ic*	adj.	having the nature of
28. -ish*	adj.	having the nature of
29. -ion, -tion, -sion*	n.	state of, quality of
30. -ism*	n.	state of, doctrine
31. -ist, -tist*	n.	one who
32. -itis	n.	inflammation, disease
33. -ive, -ative*	adj.	having the nature of
34. -ity, -ty*	n.	state of, quality of
35. -ize*	v.	to make, cause to be
36. -less*	adj.	without, free of
37. -ly*	adv.	in a certain manner
38. -ment*	n.	state of, quality of
39. -ness*	n.	state of, quality of
40. -oid	adj.	in the form of
41. -ose, -ous	adj.	having the nature of
42. -s, -es*	n.	plural of noun
43. -ship, -hood*	n.	state of, quality of
44. -some	adj.	having the nature of
45. -ster	n.	one who
46. -tious, -cious*	adj.	having the nature of
47. -tude, -lude*	n.	state of, quality of
48. -ward	adj.	in the direction of
49. -y, -ly*	adj.	having the nature of

---

*Also presented in *Reading Faster and Understanding More, Book One*, and included here for review.

Alphabetical List of New Words from *Homework Lessons*

Vocabulary	Lesson	Vocabulary	Lesson	Vocabulary	Lesson
abdicate	4	depose	5	monopolize	5
abscond	7	diathermy	6	morose	10
acerbic	10	disembodied	7	multifaceted	8
acrophobia	5	disinclined	7	neuritis	9
adjacent	7	despotism	9	nodule	9
advocacy	9	egotist	9	nondescript	6
agrarian	9	egress	7	nontoxic	7
ambivalent	7	elocution	3	novelty	9
anachronistic	3	elucidate	4	nullify	10
android	10	embolden	10	pachyderm	4
annuity	3	engender	4	pandemic	4
antediluvian	8	enlightenment	9	parameter	5
antithesis	8	epigram	4	pedophile	5
apathy	5	equivocal	3	peerless	10
appellant	9	etymology	4	peripatetic	8
archetype	7	expedite	5	photophobic	5
aspiration	6	expulsion	5	podiatrist	5
astral	3	extraneous	7	polysyllabic	5
asymmetrical	7	facsimile	4	polytheism	6
audiophile	3	fortitude	9	posthumous	8
auspicious	10	formative	10	precedence	8
autistic	3	fretful	10	prologue	8
bellicose	3	geothermal	4	propaganda	8
benign	3	glazier	9	protuberance	9
binary	7	hardiness	9	providence	6
biodegrade	3	hardship	9	psychosomatic	6
bureaucrat	3	heterodox	4	pyromaniac	5
cacophony	5	homonym	4	rapport	5
capacious	3	hyperbole	8	reinvigorate	8
centipede	3	hypocrisy	8	retrogress	8
charlatan	9	immortality	5	sanctuary	9
circumlocution	7	incarceration	7	semiannually	8
circumspect	6	incorrigibly	10	sentient	6
civility	3	inedible	9	skittish	10
colloquial	4	infinity	4	solarium	9
complacent	10	insomniac	10	spinster	9
complexes	9	inter	6	statuesque	10
concession	3	intercede	7	stenographer	4
conducive	4	intractable	7	subjugate	8
conjunction	7	intrauterine	7	superfluous	8
connoisseur	3	invocation	6	symbiosis	8
contretemps	6	jeopardize	10	telekinesis	6
convene	6	lessee	9	tenacious	6
convivial	6	lessor	9	tensile	6
corpulent	3	lithest	10	tigress	9
corruptible	6	lunar	10	transcend	8
credence	3	magnanimous	3	triumvirate	8
cultivate	4	malady	7	unfathomable	7
cyclical	4	manacle	5	vertigo	6
decapitation	3	marinate	10	vivisection	6
deflation	9	martyrdom	9	volition	6
degrade	7	menial	10	vox populi	5
dehydrated	4	microfiche	5	wayward	10
dejected	4	misanthropic	3	winsome	10
demise	5	misnomer	8	worthy	10
dentifrice	4	monocle	5	wrier	10

Answer Keys

for Chapters 1 through 10

Answer Key for Chapter 1

Practice 1

classroom [or] teacher [or] student [or] desk
trunk [or] branch [or] leaf [or] roots
corpse [or] coffin [or] tears [or] grave

Practice 2

fruit

Practice 3

automobile [or] vehicle [or] car [or] truck

Practice 4

Rosa Parks and Civil Rights
[or] Rosa Parks' Role in the Civil Rights Movement

Practice 5

High Fiber Diet and Colon Cancer
[or] The Effect of a High-Fiber Diet on Colon Cancer

Practice 6

1. M T   4. M T
2. T M   5. T M
3. T M

Practice 7

Noise pollution has become a serious problem in America.
[or] Loud noises are damaging America's eardrums.

Practice 8

Rosa Parks, a Trigger for the Civil Rights Movement
Rosa Parks, in 1955, was an unintentional trigger for the Civil Rights movement.

Exercise 1A: Paragraph

1. (b)
2. (c)
3.

	Roosevelt	Elders
differences:	wealthy background	poor background
	shy	outspoken
	famous by chance	worked toward high positions

Exercise 1B: Paragraph

1. The Courage and Compassion of Eleanor Roosevelt. [or] Eleanor Roosevelt, a Great First Lady
2. (b)
3.

negative experiences	*positive acts*
miserable childhood	rigorous calisthenics and cold showers
dead child	cared for poor
unfaithful husband with polio	supported civil rights
disapproving press	worked for women's and human rights

Exercise 1C: Paragraph

1. Jocelyn Elders, a Controversial Surgeon General
2. Jocelyn Elders, the first female Surgeon General, was outspoken and controversial.

3. drew fire, spoke mind, called for resignation, outspoken opinions, bluntly, shocked, added fuel to fire, continued to speak mind
   Examples:
   suggested study to legalize drugs
   scolded lawmakers for rejecting cigarette tax
   accused abortion foes of being part of "celibate, male-dominated church..."
   told others they loved fetuses in someone else's uterus
   spoke out on masturbation for safe sex

Exercise 1F: Timed Reading

1. (b)
2. (b)
3. (a)
4. He suggested the arguments are thin and insubstantial.
5. (d)

Exercise 1G: Timed Reading

1. (b)
2. (a)
3. (b)
4. (c)
5. (a)
6. (b)
7. (c)
8. (c)
9. that he was secure enough to be kidded about his importance
10. Kennedy used humor not only for amusing people but also for relieving the tension of serious issues.

Answer Key for Chapter 2

Practice 1

Yes
First sentence
Yes [the last sentence]

Practice 2

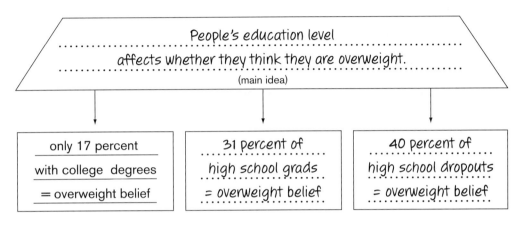

Practice 3

(c)

Practice 4

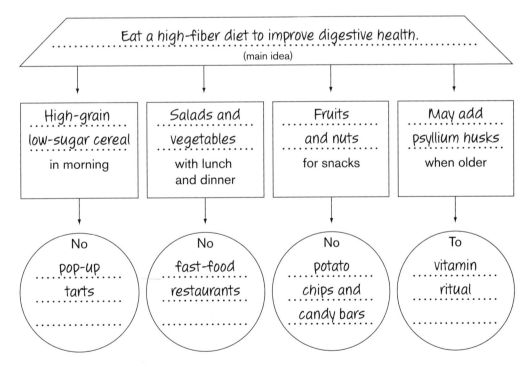

Practice 5

Sentence 5
Self-hypnosis is beneficial in many ways, both mentally and physically.

Practice 6

oak tree

Practice 7

Harry's hot temper causes him to overreact.

Practice 8

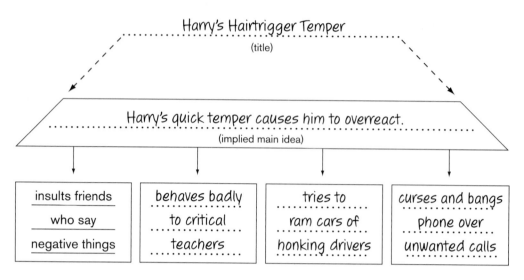

Exercise 2A: Paragraph

1. (c)
2. Yes, #3 [Sentences #1 and #2 are introductory; sentences #4–#15 are examples supporting topic sentence #3. Sentence #16 is general enough, but the examples are not about money.]
3. More Americans (two out of five) are turning to alternative cures for illnesses and other problems.
4. [any 4 examples in each column]

problem or illness	*alternative treatment*
back problems	chiropractors or acupuncturists
arthritic joints	glucosamine
colds	echinacea
lack of alertness	ginkgo
lack of energy	ginseng
memory loss	kava
depression	St.-John's-Wort and SAM-e
cellulite	cellasine

Exercise 2B: Paragraph

1. Benefits of Chili Peppers
2. Yes, #4 [Sentences #1 and #2 are introductory; #3 tells what chili peppers do *not* do; #5–8 give supporting causes; and #9 and #10 are related points.]
3. (a)
4. [any 4 details—less important details are indented]
   Adds vitamins A and C to diet
      [but no fat and few calories]
   Improves digestion
      [caused by increased salivation and stimulation of stomach activity]
   Capsaicin, helping to burn 25% more calories a day
      [caused by prevention of some toxins in liver turning into carcinogens]
   [related detail] Possible benefits removed by decreasing pepper's hotness

Exercise 2C: Paragraph

1. Breathing and Relaxation [or] The Effects of Breathing on Your Tension Level
2. Yes, #2 [Sentence #1 is introductory, and all other sentences support #2.]
3. Your breathing affects how relaxed or how tense you are.
4. <u>shallow and ragged, like panting—from chest or throat</u>
   <u>holding breath or exhaling quicker than inhaling</u>
   <u>breathe to a rhythm and check breath</u>

Practice (p. 71)

Answers will vary. Check with Instructor.

Exercise 2F: Timed Reading

1. hormones
2. (b)
3. (b)
4. violent, insane, delusive, transient, required to swear, abnormal, exhausting
5. (d)

Exercise 2G: Timed Reading

1. (b)
2. (a)
3. father telling boy about divorce and blaming kids [or]
   girl sexually abused by grandfather [or]
   woman unable to tell parents she is gay [or]
   young man's grief over dead dog [or]
   three people coping with parents' divorces
4. (a)
5. (b)
6. fourth
7. Without judgment, write (objectively and subjectively) about what bothers you the most.
8. Try to write for fifteen minutes a day in a special, quiet place.
9. Write only for yourself and expect to feel sad at first.
10. The author recommends that we write regularly in a journal to heal ourselves from emotional traumas.

Answer Key for Chapter 3

Practice 1

The better the fitness level in a group, the more time is spent jogging and the less time spent walking.

Practice 2

early years [closely connected is "marked by wealth"]

Practice 3

Time sequence in Model Paragraph 1 involves events (what happened), and *process* in Model Paragraph 2 involves steps (how to do something).

Practice 4

(a) three solutions
(b) more parking spaces
    students riding buses or bikes
    open parking

Practice 5

fruit	vegetables	herbs
oranges	*potatoes*	thyme
apples	onions	dill
strawberries	beans	basil
pears	squash	cilantro

Practice 6

(a) Four
(b) Four

Exercise 3A: Paragraph

1. (b)
2. Yes, #3 [Sentence #2 is close, but not negative enough to cover all the negative examples that follow.]
3. Some changes, due to progress in the twentieth century, seem to have made our lives worse.
4.

signs of progress	transitions and key words
more gadgets	*one doubtful sign*
increased use of polls	another dubious improvement
more junk mail	finally, one of the most alarming changes

5. (c)
   some signs of progress

Exercise 3B: Paragraph

1. Tips for Traveling with Kids
2. yes, #3
3. (a)
4. Prepare well before the trip.   [transition: *first*]
   Get children involved in travel route.   [transition: *second*]
   Hold back some books and games for last part of trip.   [transition: *finally*]
5. (a) some creative suggestions [or the transitions *first, second, finally*]
   (b) before the trip; from the beginning; last endless stretch of time

Exercise 3C: Paragraph

1. Why Women Read Historical Romances
2. #5 and #16 [or #17 or #18]

3. A lot of today's women are reading historical romances because excitement and romance are missing in their lives.

4. larger-than-life characters   dramatic action   exotic settings
     handsome, brave heroes   pirates   southern plantations
     spunky, pretty heroines   kidnapping   sultans' harems
                               [or close calls]   [or kings' courts]

5. *addition* and *classification*
   three characteristics [or] three attractions

Exercise 3F: Timed Reading

1. (c)
2. (b)
3. (a)
4. *time sequence* and *process*
5. The author hates self-service gas stations because they remind her of what she hates most about farm life and city life. [See sentence #7 in the first paragraph for thesis.]

   [or] The author hates self-service gas stations because of the smell, the manual labor, and the directions.

Exercise 3G: Timed Reading

1. (d)
2. Ashley; he was named by the author's daughter who admired the character Ashley Wilkes in *Gone With the Wind*.

3 & 4. calls asking for money [or]

     call from a lawn service [or]

     call from an electronic security service [or see article for other examples]

5. (b)
6. (a)
7. It upset one caller who had just talked to the author's son pretending to be Ashley; the caller thought the boy had died.
8. (c)
9. (c)
10. The ridiculous phone calls and junk mail, for the purpose of selling to a dog, make a negative commentary about the time and resources wasted.

Answer Key for Chapter 4

Practice 1

then, however, of course, so [Remember, no transitions in quotation marks]

Practice 2

(a) rural Louisiana vs. Manhattan penthouse [or]
   Grand Ol' Opry vs. Metropolitan Opera
(b) many similar paths

Practice 3

They both guide you, or help you anticipate, what is next, whether in a paragraph or on a dangerous road.

Practice 4

college students who are recent high school graduates vs. older college students

Practice 5

didn't hear alarm *caused by* watching TV too late [or]
no parking space *caused by* too many students with cars [or]
missed bus *caused by* oversleeping and not getting to bus stop on time [or]
also missed bus *caused by* bus being late

Practice 6

(a) *addition*
(b) several unpleasant results

Practice 7

(a) flatboat down Mississippi River during thunderstorm
   backpacking through African jungle
   trying to climb Mount Everest during snowstorm
(b) *contrast*

Practice 8

smell—mildew, cold pizza, metallic like blood
touch—damp floor, icy feet
sound—rats fighting

Practice 9

The more familiar traits of an experienced cook are compared to the less familiar traits of an inexperienced reader.

Exercise 4A: Paragraph

1. (d)
2. 3 [prejudice against black people, against Mexicans, against Irish]
3. [compared to] understanding our ancestors and where we came from helps us understand
   our own differences

   [compared to] dark, secret hatred and prejudice toward people who are different
4. Yet

   Irish considered low-class a century ago vs. an Irishman elected president and his family
   called American royalty

Exercise 4B: Paragraph

1. The author wants both to be a part of other groups and also to enjoy being African-American.
2. even so, so, but, but [The *and's* connect words, but not ideas.]

3. (b)

4. Bach vs. James Brown   sushi vs. fried catfish

Exercise 4C: Paragraph

1. Yes, #1

2. The Spanish language connects the author to her cultural center.

3. Sometimes, then

4. (d)

Exercise 4F: Timed Reading

1. (a)

2. His father chooses the most dangerous looking horse and rides him skillfully.

3. that he was a champion horseback rider in the Polish Army [or]
   that he had been a motorcycle rider, a prankster, and the leader of his gang [or]
   that he trained and took care of the commandant's horses at Auschwitz

4. major pattern: *time sequence* [or] *contrast*
   minor pattern: *description* [or] *process* [or] *cause* [or] *effect*

5. The author discovers that his father is more heroic and tragic than he had thought.

Exercise 4G: Timed Reading

1. (b)

2. (a)

3. (b)

4. She says that maybe John is not Sophie's father.

5. (c)

6. (b)

7. [to the narrator] Sophie's Chinese side, considered positive by the narrator
   [to the Shea family] Sophie's Chinese side, considered negative by the Sheas

8. When the narrator suggests that John is not Sophie's father, it stops (or wrecks) the endless cycle (like that of a toy train) of speculation about Sophie's brown skin.

9. Sophie's Chinese heritage vs. Sophie's Irish-American heritage [or] the narrator's Chinese heritage vs. the Shea's Irish-American heritage

10. The narrator-grandmother struggles against her daughter and the Sheas to protect Sophie's Chinese heritage.

Answer Key for Chapter 5

Practice 1

tennis = <u>first</u> level; racquet = <u>second</u> level; handle = <u>third</u> level

Practice 2

(a) however, these three types, second, more severe, most severe and least common
(b) *addition* and *classification*
(c) three different types
(d) *description; effect* [or] *contrast*

Practice 3

Tension headache; Migraine headache; Cluster headache

Practices 4, 5, and 6

Model outlines are in the ***Instructor's Manual.***

Exercise 5A: Paragraph

1. #1
2. number of benefits
3. (b) *contrast*   (d) *addition*
   (c) *example*   (e) *example*
4. See instructor for model *mapping outline,* which is in the ***Instructor's Manual***.

Exercise 5B: Paragraph

The model *topic outline* is in the ***Instructor's Manual***.

Exercise 5C: Paragraph

The model *sentence outline* is in the ***Instructor's Manual***.

Exercise 5F: Timed Reading

1. The author's friend tried three unsuccessful projects in her search for total beauty.
2. (a) *addition*   (b) *contrast*   (c) *process* [or] *description*
3–10. See model *mapping outline* below.

mapping outline:

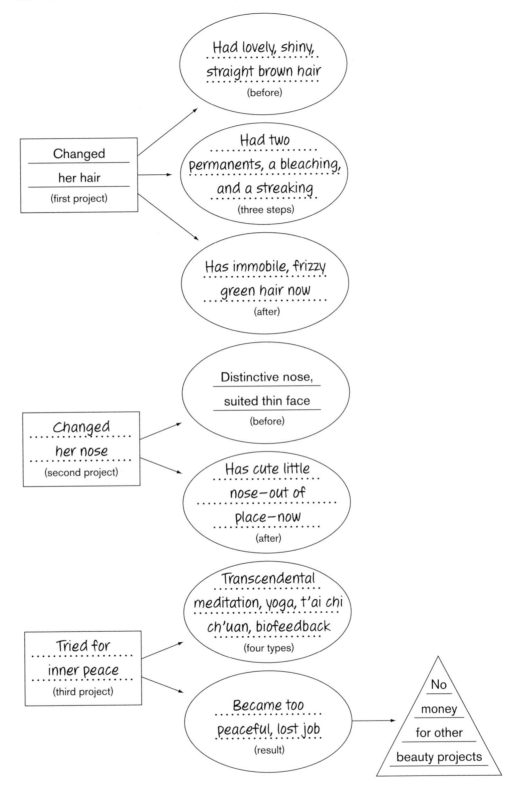

Exercise 5G: Timed Reading

1. (b)

2. *process*

3–20. See model (combination) outline below.

Introduction:

A. Be polite and thoughtful to teachers.

B. Be not only responsible but anticipate how you might contribute to the class.

I. What kind of student are you?

    A. Would you be an unprepared bluffer?

    Try to get the class off the subject to hide ignorance.

    B. Would you be the fluttering magpie?

    Interrupt a lot without thinking or repeat what has already been covered.

    C. Would you be the sensitive hopeful?

    Are prepared but afraid to speak up because of what others might think.

    D. Would you be the accomplished leader?

    Ideal: well-prepared on basics and already thought of relevant answers.

II. How do you develop confidence in your abilities?

    A. Go to class with your assignments prepared.

    Ask yourself three questions:

    Am I pleased with what I have done?

    Will my work satisfy the teacher?

    Will my work be judged the best paper in the class?

    B. Go to class with the proper tools.

    Take your text, notebook, pen or sharpened pencil, etc., to show your interest in the class.

    C. Follow instructions.

    Record your assignments in an organized way, and follow general instructions on format.

Answer Key for Chapter 6

Exercise 6A: Paragraph

1. In 1753, Georges-Louis Leclerc de Buffon suggested a theory on creation that was slightly different from the church's position.
2. The church's position on creation vs. Buffon's theory about creation
3.   (front of card)

Georges-Louis Leclerc de Buffon (1707–1788)

4.   (back of card)

His theory: Inferior animals were caused by imperfections in the Creator's ideal.

Exercise 6B: Paragraph

1. Around 1763, Erasmus Darwin (Charles' grandfather), a physician and an amateur naturalist, wrote about the relationships among animals.
2. (a) Competition among animals helped form the species.
    (b) The environment brought about changes in species.
    (c) These changes were inherited by offspring.

Exercise 6C: Paragraph

1. Sentence #2
2. In France, around mid- and late-eighteenth century, Jean Baptiste de Lemarck theorized that humans had arisen from other species.
3. (d)
4.

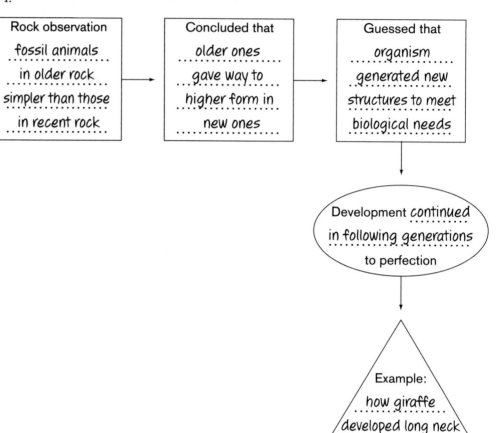

Exercise 6F: Timed Reading

model study outline:

A Brief History and the Enchanted Isles

Introduction:

A. As a young man, Darwin was strong, adventurous, and curious—especially about nature.
B. His father, an upper-class British physician, expected his son to be a failure.
C. Darwin failed in his studies of theology and medicine.

I. What is important about Darwin's voyage on the *Beagle*?

A. In 1831, he was offered free passage as a naturalist's companion on a survey ship to South America.
B. He was seasick and uncomfortable during the 5-year voyage.
C. He made the most of his time on shore: taking notes and collecting strange things.

II. How did the field of biology begin?

A. Before the 18th century, science was limited to inanimate subjects.
B. Most scientists then believed life was created in its present form and had not changed.
   1. Example: Carl von Linne (1707–1778) devised a system of classification for all living things.

C. A few departures from the theory, "fixity of species," influenced Darwin:
  1. Georges-Louis Leclerc de Buffon (1707–1788) believed <u>lesser animals were imperfections in the Creator's ideal.</u>
  2. <u>Erasmus Darwin (1731–1802), Charles' grandfather, wrote about the importance of competition, the effects of the environment on changes in species, and the heritability of these changes.</u>
  3. <u>Jean Baptiste de Lamarck (1744–1829) also speculated on changeability and heritability.</u>
     a. He suggested that <u>humans had arisen from other species but believed in the old "scale of nature," with humans at the top.</u>
     b. He guessed that <u>there was some "force of life" causing an organism to generate new structures that continued to change and pass on those changes to offspring.</u>
        (1). Example: <u>The giraffe got its long neck by stretching to reach the top tree branches.</u>
D. Nineteenth-century society mostly stuck with the theory of each form arisen from special creation.

PERCENTAGE CHART	number of errors	0	1	2	3	4	5	6	7	8	9	10	11	12	13	14	15
	percent correct	100	94	87	80	74	67	60	54	47	40	34	27	20	14	7	0

Answer Key for Chapter 7

Practice 1

(a) Unlike ordinary soap operas with characters as victims, *Por Estas Calles* has ambitious, greedy, and violent characters.

(b) Don Chepe and Lucha = ambitious; [or] Dr. Valerio = ambitious and greedy; [or] Natalio Vega = violent; [or] Mauro = devilish drug dealer

(c) but; then; and; finally

Practice 2

(a) & (b) See model below. [Other examples could be underlined.]

This is the typical day of a relatively typical soul in today's diversified world. I wake up to the sound of my Japanese clock radio, put on a T-shirt sent me by an uncle in Nigeria and walk out into the street, past the German cars, to my office. Around me are English-language students from Korea, Switzerland and Argentina—all on this Spanish-named road in this Mediterranean-style town. On TV, I find, the news is in Mandarin; today's baseball game is being broadcast in Korean. For lunch I can walk to a sushi bar, a tandoori palace, a Thai café, or the newest burrito joint (run by an old Japanese lady). Who am I, I sometimes wonder, the son of Indian parents and a British citizen who spends much of his time in Japan (and is therefore—what else?—an American permanent resident)? And where am I?

Practice 3

(a) A Return to Phonics in Schools

(b) Rising Prices of Textbooks

(c) Child Porn on World Wide Web

Practice 4

(a) Lifting Weights While You Watch Television [or] Increase in Personal Trainers

(b) The Younger the Driver, the Quicker the Trigger [or] Ramming Cars Seen as Teenage Revenge

Exercise 7A: Scanning

1. P. Sutch
2. Credit in English R or qualification by testing and assessment
3. MCS-#219
4. Tuesday and Thursday
5. (a) if you got a C or better in a prerequisite course at another college;
   (b) if you can prove you have met the prerequisite at another college; or
   (c) if you can substitute SAT scores.

Exercise 7B: Scanning

1. You may get a letter grade of A through F.
2. when the number of absences is more than the number of units assigned to the course
3. You may be dropped from the roster and your place given to another student.
4. 60
5. Yes [but only with instructor/dean approval and under extenuating circumstances]

Exercise 7C: Skimming and Scanning

2. people	15. dog, fleas	27. arms	34. manager	41. mothers, hands
5. men	20. flies	28. kids	35. fist	44. feet
9. farmer	21. teenagers	30. waitress	37. customers	46. band
11. wife	23. Son, Monster	31. boy	38. cashiers	48. hands
13. horse	24. clerk	33. waitress	39. children	49. hearts

Exercise 7D: Skimming and Scanning

4. coyote	16. eyes	25. wings	34. hand	44. fangs, throat
6. paw	17. foot	27. girl	37. eyes	46. body
11. rat	19. eyes, victim	29. hand	41. throat	47. doctor
12. doctor	22. child	30. eyelid	42. lips	49. cheeks
15. arm	24. vultures	32. bird	43. teeth	50. Vampira

Exercise 7G: Timed Reading

1. *Por Estas Calles* [or] *Along These Streets*
2. (c)
3. It breaks with tradition and attempts more important topics.
4. (a)
5. The soap opera *Por Estas Calles* is popular with most of Venezuela because, in addition to keeping the usual melodrama, it tackles social and political issues.
6. more than two-thirds
7. They were both involved in scandals.
8. They are not the usual soap opera victims.
9. The USIA reports that the show has no bite: it spends more time on traditional soap opera drama than on social justice.
10. (b)

Exercise 7H: Timed Reading

1. (c)
2. to free children held in slavery
3. (b)
4. (a)
5. Satyarthi and the International Labor Organization are trying to end forced child labor, more than 200 million children, which is increasing because of modern technology.
6. Promise: $100 a month for two hours of work—with education.
   Reality: pennies a day for working 4 A.M. till late evening—working, eating, sleeping in a locked room
7. (a)
8. 300 million
9. It would ban importation into the United States of any goods produced by children under 15.
10. (a)

swer Key for Chapter 8

Practice 1

(a) to persuade
(b) to inform
(c) to entertain

Practice 2

Answers will vary. [Remember, your facts don't have to be true.] Check with your instructor.

Practice 3

Only (a) is a fact; (b) is an obvious opinion; (c) sounds good but can't be proved true or false.

Practice 4

(a) Author Anne Fadiman's father helped start America's Book-of-the-Month Club; this influenced his daughter to love books all her life.
(b) The Texas school board once banned *The Tropic of Cancer* from its school libraries because it is a dirty book, unsuitable for young minds.
(c) The Stanford 9 test scores in 1999 show a big plunge in reading scores, but not in math, between the eighth and ninth grades, proving that students like math more than they like reading.
(d) Eleanor Roosevelt once made this statement about decreased funding for black children: "How stupid we are: We're all going to go ahead together, or we're all going to go down together."

Practice 5

(B) 1. to inform [Secondary purpose, expressed by Ms. Herman, is to *persuade* students to stay in school.]
2. More high school graduates are attending college, but are then dropping out even though education affects income.
3. (a) yes; yes [at the publication of this book]; yes
   (b) yes; [the Labor Department and Labor Secretary Herman]
4. Support is only (b) fair because the paragraph could use some statistics contrasting income for high school graduates vs. income for college graduates.

[Note: The answers to the following Exercises are subjective: that is, influenced by the authors' opinions about a controversial topic.]

Exercise 8A: Paragraph

1. to persuade [by informing]
2. Violence against children, committed by people with illegal guns, increased at the end of the twentieth century.
3. (a) yes; yes; yes [*Newsweek* is a reputable national magazine.]
   (b) yes [although no statistics or examples are given for violence committed by people legally owning guns]
4. *for* because all the examples given support the angle of *illegally* owned guns causing the violence

Exercise 8B: Paragraph

1. to persuade
2. Access to handguns is not the reason for violence.
3. (a) no [none given for gun-control laws and the murder rate in other states]
   (b) no, matter of opinion, based on your position on gun control
   (c) Not mentioned is how easy it is to go over state lines and purchase guns in Virginia. Also not mentioned are higher unemployment and high crime rates in general in the District of Columbia.
4. *against*

432   *Answer Keys*

Exercise 8C: Paragraph

1. to persuade
2. Children's access to guns should be severely restricted.
3. (a) opinion
   (b) 1 [only the first sentence—and part of the sentence about Andrew Golden]
   (c) yes [*The Wall Street Journal* is a reputable, nationally known newspaper. The fact that Kellerman is a child psychologist gives him more reliability than his being a novelist.]
   (d) Your answer to this will be influenced by whether you agree with the author.
4. (a) poor, because the author gives only two examples as support, although those two may be convincing enough.

Exercise 8F: Timed Reading

1. (b)
2. (b)
3. (a)
4. (b)
5. The author believes that teaching children the difference between right and wrong is the answer to school violence—not more gun-control laws.

Exercise 8G: Timed Reading

1. (b)
2. (c)
3. (a)
4. (c)
5. separate bedrooms [or] separate floors and basements [or] their own televisions and computers
6. The character Huck Finn is portrayed in a positive way—as an adventurer who runs away from his small town where he is being pressured to conform and "speak regular." Today's nonconformist teen is portrayed in a negative way—as a troubled loner in an impersonal world—seeking to belong, even if it is to a group of other outsiders.
7. (a)
8. (b)
9. The fact that a million poor families want their children in a private or parochial school is bad news for public schools.
10. The author believes that the recent school violence is a symptom of an impersonal world—with public schools as the unmentioned victim.

Answer Key for Chapter 9

Practice 1

(a) There have been some problems with gun-related violence.

(b) The parents don't trust either their daughter or her friend. [or] The parents believe the friend's neighborhood is unsafe.

(c) The student can't afford the textbook. [or] The student is an irresponsible procrastinator.

Practice 2

(a) obese   negative
(b) tramp   negative
(c) my ball and chain   negative
(d) steed   positive

Practice 3

(a) inconclusive
(b) firm
(c) low-income
(d) empty

Practice 4

(a) 2.

(b) dull, dark, soundless, autumn [when things die], clouds, oppressively low, alone, dreary, shades of the evening, melancholy, insufferable gloom, mere house, simple landscape, bleak, vacant eyelike, rank, decayed, utter depression, iciness, sinking, sickening, unredeemed dreariness

(c) He dreads going there. [or] He is afraid of it.

(d) Something really bad has happened there.

(e) Murder has been committed there and is about to occur again. [or] The house is haunted by the ghosts of mutilated children.

Exercise 9A: Paragraph

1. women's most frequently expressed complaint vs. men's most frequently expressed complaint

2. (b)

3. (b)

4. #1 and #6 Men and woman have different expectations, and both misunderstand each other—as if they were from different planets.

Exercise 9B: Paragraph

1. The woman whom he called "dear" must have accused him of being "politically incorrect."

2. (b); (b)

3. (b)

4. (c) [Sentence #5 is a good example of *verbal irony*. The role reversal, with women calling him "dear" and his pretending to be sexually harassed, is *situational irony*.]

5. The author reverses roles and exaggerates being a victim of sexual harassment in order to make a point about a criticism he considers petty.

Exercise 9C: Paragraph

1. [author] (a); [audience] (a)

2. "gals" [in sentence #6]

3. (a) No [consider the source: an obviously made-up name and a fictitious publication];

   (b) date rape, sexual blackmail for grades or jobs or raises, sexual humiliation, the large number of women afraid to complain about sexual harassment

4. The author is warning men that women are taking financial advantage of the court ruling on sexual harassment.

Exercise 9D: Phrases

livid with fear repeated four times; *singed his finger* repeated three times

Exercise 9E: Phrases

tract of land repeated four times; *curries favor* repeated two times

Exercise 9F: Timed Reading

1. (c)
2. (b)
3. (b)
4. unfriendly eye; turned her back; looked at him coldly; excited [about putting him in the booby-hatch]; gloat in her eye
5. The narrator, with a little wit, was able to turn a potentially bad situation to his own advantage. [or] A man who sees something magical is called crazy by his wife, but the tables are turned so that she looks crazy instead.

Exercise 9G: Timed Reading

1. an oil rig, offshore Louisiana
2. (b)
3. demanding sex in exchange for a job
4. (a)
5. (a)
6. (b)
7. "Harassment" implies use of sexual power over an unwilling victim; whereas, "hazing" implies a voluntary initiation into a group (as in a college fraternity).
8. (a)
9. The implication is that, if men or women do not fit the traditional gender role, they are punished for it or pressured to adapt to the role.
10. Oncale's case, involving all heterosexual males, reinforces the idea that sexual harassment is about power, not about sexual attraction.

Answer Key for Chapter 10

Practice 1

(a) physical

(b) external psychological

(c) internal psychological

(d) mixture (external psychological and physical)

Practice 2

[Remember, there is no one correct theme. There are only possible themes.]

(a) For some people, it can be more important to be right than to be alive.

(b) The survival instinct is stronger than the need to triumph over someone.

(c) The survival instinct overrules the complexities of a relationship, but compromise can still be possible at the last minute.

Exercise 10A: Passage (from a short story)

1. between the doctor and the girl—his forcibly trying to examine her throat and her physically resisting.

2. his struggle with the disease to protect the girl and society

3. his struggle with his own irrational rage at the girl

4. (c)

Readers tend to be more forgiving of people who admit their flaws—as the narrator-doctor does.

Exercise 10B: Poem

1. All these tasks are all impossible.

2. to find a woman who is both faithful and beautiful

3. Although he wants to go next door and see the faithful, beautiful woman, by the time he gets there, she will have been unfaithful with two or three men.

4. (b)

Exercise 10C: Passage (from a novel)

1. (a) She struggles with the inconvenience caused by the lightbulb being out and the difficulty of changing it.

   (b) She wants James to change the lightbulb right away; he wants to postpone changing it.

   (c) She is frustrated by having so much to do and feeling that nobody is helping—all made worse by the unchanged lightbulb.

2. do it by braille, unseen screws, arm started to fall off, neck got stiff, dead flies glued to sticky dust

3. (a) [She thinks he *should* leap up and change the lightbulb.]

4. (b) [If (a) were the correct answer, there would be no conflict, thus no story.]

Exercise 10D: Phrases

bears in mind repeated five times; *the right station* repeated four times

Exercise 10E: Phrases

copes with life repeated three times; *a slow drawl* repeated three times

Exercise 10F: Timed Reading

1. (c)

2. fix motors [or] putter with his car [or] take apart lawn mower [or] outdoor things like hauling things out [or] huge projects

3. (a)

4. He wants to make a big show of doing a small task—and perhaps show her she is making a big deal over an insignificant thing.

5. that night
6. (a)
7. (d)
8. The words *ruins of her room* implies that Rosie is the slob she is accusing James of being.
9. (a)
10. The seemingly petty conflict over the lightbulb is representative of some deeper conflicts between men and women.

Credits

Progress Charts

Pretests and Posttests

Chapter Reviews and Unit Tests

Timed Readings